THE YEW TREE

THE YEW TREE

A THOUSAND WHISPERS

Biography of a Species

by Hal Hartzell, Jr.

HULOGOSI
Eugene, Oregon

Also by Hal Hartzell, Jr.

Birth of a Cooperative

Special thanks to the Furthur Foundation and the Oregon Natural
Resources Council for a grant in aid of publication

Cover photograph by the Reverend David Partridge

Book design by Alan Trist

LIBRARY OF CONGRESS CATALOGING-IN-PUBLICATION DATA
Hartzell, Hal. 1946–
The yew tree : a thousand whispers : the biography of a species
by Hal Hartzell, Jr.
Includes bibliographical references and index.
ISBN 0-938493-13-2 (cloth) — ISBN 0-938493-14-0 (pbk.)
1. Yew. 2. Yew—Folklore. 3. Yew—Utilization. 4. Taxus.
I. Title.
QK494.5.T25H37 1991
585'.2—dc20   LC 91–24673

Printed in the U.S.A.

HULOGOSI, P.O. BOX 1188, EUGENE, OREGON 97440

TABLE OF CONTENTS

LIST OF ILLUSTRATIONS

LIST OF PHOTOGRAPHS

*Photograph of an engraving of a drawing by Alfred Agate, in Wilkes, *Narrative*; courtesy of Special Collections, University of Washington Libraries.

To J. L. S.
her basket of roses and her poems

FOREWORD

I never realized what a yew tree was until 1974 when I saw hundreds of them cut and left on units where we were piling slash in the Tiller Ranger District of the Umpqua National Forest. We carried a few out to the road one at a time – six people to a log. We loaded them onto several pickups, filled the crummy and the school bus kitchen. That summer we built an agricultural building that stands on 24 stout yew poles. It was sometime after that I realized that yew trees had actually been in my life every summer since 1948 when as a child I made my first trip to the family summer home at Fish Lake. I remember the old road into the cabin being dark and long and, except for the car scraping over an occasional rock and although we were excited children, a hushed reverence fell as we crept through the dark woods with moss strewn yew trees lurking under a full old-growth canopy. This early memory still lives in my mind each time I return to those yew woods. Today, I'm worried about those trees.

Since 1974 the yew tree has captivated my consciousness. There aren't many left and big ones are a remarkable sight to behold; each has its own shape, more like a gnarled hardwood tree than a straight evergreen. A good sized tree is 50 to 75 feet tall and two or three feet in diameter. A three foot diameter tree is probably 600 years old, representing a life which extends back to the time when Native American people relied on the yew.

Yew trees have mottled brown-purple-gray and blood red bark which is usually home to various lichens and mosses that carpet the upper side of the stout limbs and hang like wisps of smoke from the branches. Yew trees provide owls with a vantage point, beneath the canopy, over the forest floor; its foliage is a preferred browse of deer, elk and moose; its berries attractive to birds and small mammals. For millennia in the Pacific Northwest the yew tree provided critical tools: salmon spears, whale harpoons, bows to hunt deer and elk, camass digging sticks and stout pry bars to harvest chitons and mussels from the rocks at low tide, as well as medicines, tonics and poison.

Since 1974 I have planted over half a million trees in seven Northwest states. I have seen up close the effect that clear cuts, herbicides, slash piles and burning have had on units. The industrial forest is not wild forest but a tamed monoculture where 'bad' species are killed and 'good' species planted. Unfortunately for the yew, and now it seems for us too, the policies of clear cut, slash and burn have decimated the Pacific yew population. The ancient forest resource base is simply gone, used up. It amazes me how those responsible for these policies have managed to shift the blame for the loss of jobs in the timber industry onto spotted owls, Pacific salmon, marbled murrelets and environmentalists. Jobs were lost when 90 percent of the resource base was clear cut with no thought of a sustainable yield program in mind. Granted these decisions provided the timber to fuel the Northwest economy for a century, but now it's time for a change. To blame creatures who face extinction because of our short-sighted destruction of their native habitat is immoral.

In 1976 those of us who walked across those burned-out units were still wondering why yew logs were being cut, piled and burned with the rest of the debris from the clear cut operation. A friend of mine, also a treeplanter at the time, decided to run for the office of County Commissioner – imagine that, a treeplanter right off the unit, running for office. The season was over – there wasn't too much for treeplanters to do in the summertime – so many of us decided to help in the campaign. It was great fun. We didn't have much money, so when it came to campaign buttons, which cost 75 cents a piece, we had to have an alternative. One of the issues in the campaign was the continued destruction of the resource base, so we took the yew as a symbol of waste in the woods. We sliced off miniature rounds on a table saw, an eighth of an inch thick from limbs taken from yew trees that had been cut and left on logging units. It was a long summer and we made about 10,000 yew buttons. My friend won.

In 1982 he ran for governor of Oregon. He came in third in a field of eight in the Democratic primary but the issue of destruction of the resource base was raised all over Oregon and another 25,000 yew buttons were given away, again as symbols of waste. In order to raise money to pay off an enormous (for us) campaign debt, my friend and I wrote a book about the myth, legend, lore, historical and poetical associations of the yew tree. In that book there were two sentences about the wonder drug taxol. What started out to be a two month project slowly turned into a year's effort, which was finished off in a fire look-out tower in, of all places, Tiller, in September of 1983. We published 500 copies, sold them all in three months and payed off a good part of the debt. I was surprised that it sold that quickly, but not that it didn't have any impact to speak of on the status of the yew tree. They were still cut and burned on the units.

In 1987 the National Cancer Institute (NCI) put out a call to the Forest Service for 60,000 pounds of dried Pacific yew bark to be used to make taxol, an experimental anti-cancer compound. My friend and I became alarmed, because the yew is thin-skinned, yielding only five pounds of bark from a large tree.

In December 1989 I decided to rewrite the original yew book and add to it more mythical and poetical allusions, as well as historical, geographical and botanical information and an update on taxol, which seemed to be causing quite a stir. The book would have been finished six months later had not NCI officials announced in June 1990 that much more bark was needed to produce taxol, because it was proving to be the most promising anti-cancer drug discovered to date. They talked of another 60,000 pounds; environmentalists began to stir – six months later the demand had risen twelve fold to 750,000 pounds, and the issue soared into the national media. The two sentences about taxol in the '83 *Yew* book grew into three chapters.

Today, six months later, reports are that the 750,000 pounds was only a minimal goal and that a million or more pounds of bark are wanted now on an annual basis. On June 19, 1991 Bristol-Myers Squibb announced that, although it was investigating extracting taxol with other methods and from other sources, it wanted open access to yew bark until 1998. Federal agencies, the Forest Service, the Bureau of Land Management and the National Cancer Institute have created new procedures to help Bristol-Myers Squibb obtain all the bark they want, and recently granted them exclusive rights to all yew trees on federal lands at no cost. In return Bristol-Myers Squibb will pay for the harvest and the cost of an inventory and tracking program to find out how many Pacific yews remain and where they are in what is left of the Northwest forest. Six new bark-stripping and collection plants have been set up in Oregon, Washington, and Idaho; others are contemplated in Montana and British Columbia, obvioualy to get as much bark as they can, as quickly as possible.

At the moment nobody knows how many yew trees are left out there, but the best guess from the USDA Pacific Northwest Research Station is that there are probably less than four million yew trees left with any size to them in what remains of the old-growth forest on federal lands. Only thirty-five percent of the Pacific yew population is five inches in diameter or larger. The rest are saplings or shrubs with little bark on them. A ten-inch diameter tree, twelve feet tall would yield about five pounds of dried bark; a five-inch tree, about two. It takes sixty pounds of dried bark to produce enough taxol for one patient's treatment, that's twelve ten-inch trees or thirty five-inch trees or some combination thereof. One million people die of cancer every year in the United States and if taxol is as promising as doctors seem to think, many of these cancer patients could be treated with taxol. A million treatments of taxol would require 2,000 kilograms of taxol or 60,000,000 pounds of Pacific yew bark or the equivalent of 12,000,000 yew trees ten inches or larger in diameter. There is no way that bark can be the answer.

The story of the yew is incredible in several regards. The tree itself has a unique combination of traits among trees. It is poisonous. Individual trees are either male or female. It's an evergreen with pliable, workable hardwood. It has always been a most prized wood for tools, weapons and other critical implements. Because of its utility it became a subject of myth and legend and a maker of history. Because of its use for weapons and poisons and its extreme longevity, the yew tree became associated with death and the afterlife for Greeks, Romans, Celtic Druids and Christians alike. Indeed some living yew trees in English churchyards are thought to be three to four thousand years old and the yew is incorporated into many churchyard tales. One of them is that the yew sends its roots into the throats of the buried dead, retrieves their untold secrets and transforms them into whispers to be blown loose from the foliage in the wind.

This book is a chorus of voices raised or words penned about the yew tree in human history, a clear record that our ancestors in the northern hemisphere revered the yew above all other trees in the forest. It is the product of hundreds of minds over thousands of years in witness to the yew tree and all its former glory. Today voices are raised once again as the yew is vitally threatened. I would like to express my appreciation to all persons whose candid points of view appear in this book, from those long dead to those whose voices are still raised on the question of the yew. I have tried to give everyone, especially those key players, a collective fabric from which to hang their individual perceptions of the yew and the taxol situation. I hope that all our efforts to solve the dilemma are not in vain.

The structure of this book is simple like a tree. The theme of the book is like the trunk; each of the six sections are main branches, each of the chapters within are secondary branches, the internal headings are branchlets, each word a whisper. Without the trimming and pruning of chief gardeners Steve Van Strum and Alan Trist and the care of artists Sidney Rust, Bob DeVine, Jim Ulrich and Jim Carpenter, this tree, this book would not live.

In the spring of 1991, I took a break from writing to work a stewardship (guaranteed survival) treeplanting contract in, once again, Tiller. One chilly morning after the crew went over the hill I was burning trash bags and warming up when a breeze came by and caught the wisps of ash in an updraft. I followed their flight which led to a huge yew tree – the only one on the unit, and I hadn't noticed it before. The ashes were falling on the foliage. At that moment I thought of Eliot's *Ash Wednesday* and the whispers being blown from tree to tree and I realized that, indeed, it *was* Ash Wednesday. From somewhere the yew was talking to me.

It occurred to me recently while surrounded by these whispers that the yew tree is an indicator species. Like a canary in the mine it measures the health of the ambient environment of the ancient forests and the species that inhabit it as well as our own well being as a species on this planet. The yew's dilemma is our own. We have a long way to go and little time.

Eugene, Oregon, July 27, 1991

Who knows what the future might bring – certainly changes in the taxol/bark situation. Perhaps an updated version will be in order some day. I would welcome more yew-lore from any source. I can be reached c/o the publishers.

PART 1

OLD WORLD YEW

Well coude he dresse his takel yewmanly;
His arrowes drouped not with fethers lowe,
And in hande he bare a mighty bowe.

– Geoffrey Chaucer

CHAPTER ONE

MYTHIC QUALITIES

IMAGE

TREES have always been important to the spiritual as well as the physical aspects of our lives. None more than the yew. When humans followed the retreating glaciers north and across what was to become the northern temperate zone, they found that the yew also had survived the scouring Ice Age. Archaeological data show that the poisonous, tough, evergreen, long-lived and slow-burning yew played a part in the very beginning of Homo sapiens' consciousness about tools, plant-remedies, fire, language and spirit.

I have seen yew trees thirty-feet in girth, gnarled, red trunks and peeling bark, limbs twisted like frozen lightning with feathery branchlets full of dark green leaves supporting gold anthers or scarlet berries. The entire tree is poisonous except for the fleshy red aril or 'berry' surrounding the seed. Some of these trees sprouted prior to or coeval with the coming of Christ. The Fortingall Yew, situated in a chuchyard at the entrance to Glen Lyon, Perthshire, is deemed to be the oldest living, according to a commemorative plaque hanging in a nearby church.

> This celebrated yew tree has grown here for many centuries; just how many no one can say with total accuracy. Distinguished botanists however are agreed that this specimen of the primeval forest must be 3,000 years old, as old as the time of Solomon; and it is believed to be the most ancient piece of vegetation in Europe.[1]

It measured 52 feet in circumference in 1769, but by the middle of the 19th century, according to John Selby:

> ...considerable spoilations have evidently been committed on the tree since 1769; large arms have been removed, and masses of the trunk itself carried off by the country-people, with the view of forming quechs, or drinking cups, and other relics which visitors were in the habit of demanding.[2]

Village boys were also blamed, according to J.H. Wilkes:

> In 1825, the limbs had fallen away from each other, no doubt due to the fact that for 200 years it had been subjected to vandalistic treatment by the village boys who lit their Beltane fires between the separated parts. About the middle of the 19th century the local authorities were compelled to build a wall for its protection.[3]

THE FORTINGALL YEW, 3,000 YEARS OLD, 52 FEET IN GIRTH

The tree had grown to a circumference of 56 feet 6 inches in circumference by 1870.[4] I was fortunate to see it in 1983. The trunk is riven into two distinct halves, but the foliage grows back together twelve to fifteen feet above ground level, like two pieces of ancient driftwood sprouting green enmeshed at the top. It was the custom for funeral processions to pass through the living arch formed by the tree. It looked at the same time to be very lively although incredibly ancient. On another placard in the stone church a local legend recounts the birth of Pontius Pilate nearby in a Roman camp, who as the legend goes, suckled at his mother's breast beneath its sacred boughs. The tree would have been 1,000 years old then. In an adjacent field across the road are two triangles composed of three huge round stones. The fields and rolling hills stretch for miles and no other large round rocks appear. Perhaps they mark an old pagan site.

One tree now gone was even larger than the Fortingall Yew. John Evelyn reported in 1664 that it stood in the churchyard of St. Mary Blessed Virgin in Brabourne, Kent. He said that it was 58 feet 6 inches in girth,[5] which would have made it well over 3,000 years old then.

THE CLASSICAL RECORD

Since the commencement of civilization man has known of the yew's poisonous nature and of its special quality as wood for weapons, its superiority for bows. These physical qualities eventually brought death to become an inherent component of the yew's mythic image. Man has used sprigs of yew in funeral ceremonies, wreaths were woven of it in honor of Hecate, crone aspect of the Great Goddess, whose dominion was death. The myth and legend surrounding the yew convey to us a sense of awe at the tree which man has held through many ages.

I have tried to walk softly over the path of the yew tree's story so as not to frighten away a fragile concept, the mythic and poetic image of a tree growing organically within a body of literature. To this end, I felt the need to examine separate aspects of the total image taken out of time, to place each allusion to the yew with others that are similar to it, rather than to set out a less fluid, more strictly chronological order. The whole mythic image of the yew grew from simple aspects like its physical qualities and appearance into more complex associations with death and the grave, to even more numinous concepts of an afterlife and immortality.

An early Greek writer, Theophrastus (371–287 B.C.) in his *Inquiry into Plants*, describes the tree:

> The yew has also but one kind, is straightgrowing, grows readily, and is like the silver fir, except that it is not so tall and is more branched... and they say that if beasts of burden eat of the leaves they die while ruminants take no hurt. Even some men eat the fruit, which is sweet and harmless.[6]

Many allusions occur to the simple existence of the yew tree. Virgil (70–19 B.C.), wrote in *Georgics,* 'the baleful yew to northern blasts assigns,' refering to its natural range which is the northern temperate zones, or in Virgil's case, Gaul.

Pliny The Elder (23–79 A.D.) described it to be like a pine:

> ...but that it is not so greene; more slender also and smaller, unpleasant and fearfulle to look upon, as a cursed tree, without any liquid substance at all; and of these trees it alone beareth berries.[7]

Dioscurides, a Greek doctor with the Roman army during Nero's reign (54–68 A.D.), made an account of 600 plants and their medicinal properties. Of the yew he wrote:

> It is a tree resembling the fir as regards the leaves and the size. It grows in Italy and in Narvonia of Spain. If the birds eat the fruit of the yew growing in Italy they suffocate; the men who taste the yew fruit suffer from diarrhea; the yew growing in Narvonia has such a power that those who sit or sleep under its shade suffer harm or in many cases they may even die![8]

CELTIC ALLUSIONS

Celtic legends also note the yew tree's corporal existence and place it in the wild where strange inhabitants frequent the deeply shaded forest floor, among them, the 'Nightmare', one of the last minions of Hecate, according to poet Robert Graves:

> Her nests, when one comes across them in dreams, lodged in rock-clefts or the branches of enormous hollow yews, are built of carefully chosen twigs, lined with white horse-hair and the plumage of prophetic birds and littered with the jaw-bones and entrails of poets.[9]

Another legendary denizen of the deep forest was poor Suibne, who at one time had been a poet-king. Unfortunately, Suibne incurred the wrath of an Irish ollave or arch-druid, who turned him into a madman, condemning him to live:

> like the wild things: feeding on sloes, holly-berries, watercress, brooklime, acorns; sleeping in yew trees and rocky clefts of ivy-clad cliffs, and even in hawthorn and bramble bushes.[10]

On one occasion Suibne was joined on his perch in a tree (possibly a yew?) by a hag, (possibly a nightmare) or some similar emanation of Hecate, whereupon his poetic nature led him to babble a floral catalogue of his wild kingdom. Of the yew, he said:

> Yew tree, yew tree, true to your kind
> In churchyard you are found.[11]

SUIBNE AT ONE TIME HAD BEEN A POET KING

Suibne's placement of the yew indicates that it was commonly found in churchyards. In Ireland today it survives chiefly in churchyards.

LONGEVITY

A folk-saying from Robert Graves calculates the longevity of the yew, after the tradition of Nennius' *Seven Ages*.

> The lives of three wattles, the life of a hound;
> The lives of three steeds, the life of a man;
> The lives of three men, the life of an eagle;
> The lives of three eagles, the life of a yew;
> The life of a yew, the length of a ridge;
> Seven ridges from Creation to Doom.[12]

If a wattle, a contraption of wooden stakes bound together and interlaced with twigs and branches, lasts for four years, then by this account the life of a yew would extend 972 years; the length of an Age, 6,804. It is known that some individual yews live much longer than this, although this mystically derived average may be about right for the species. One more recent English chronicler compared living yew trees to oak.

"THOSE ANCIENT BRITONS, WHOM JULIUS CAESAR BEHELD."

If the Oak tree, as some say, in a few specially long-lived instances saw Roman legions, what sights might not the Methuselah among Yews have feasted his eyes upon? Perhaps the forefathers of those ancient Britons, whom Julius Caesar beheld, and described as smeared in the dye of woad, clad in the tawny skins of wild beasts, with streaming locks and flying moustachios, disconcerting by feats of horsemanship the old hands of his cohorts.[13]

A tale that gives and takes from the yew's association with longevity, begins with the Great Flood. One Fintann, a descendant of flood survivors and himself of great age, was asked to attest to certain disputed facts involving the origins of Ireland. Fintann, surrounded by scores of his own descendants, gave this account before the court of Diarmuid MacCarroll at Tara, in the 6th century:

> I passed one day through a wood in West Munster: I brought home with me a red berry of the yew tree, which I planted in the garden of my mansion, and it grew there until it was as tall as a man. I then took it out of the garden and planted it in the green lawn of my mansion; and it grew in the centre of that lawn until an hundred champions could fit under the foliage, and find shelter there from wind, and rain, and cold, and heat. I remained so, and my yew remained so, spending our time alike, until at last it ceased to put forth leaves, from old age. When, afterwards, I thought of turning it to some profit, I cut it from its stem, and made from it seven vats, seven keeves, seven stans, seven churns, seven pitchers, seven milans and seven medars, with hoops for all. I remained still with my yew vessels, until their hoops all fell off from decay and old age. After this I re-made them, but could only get a keeve out of the vat, and a stan out of the keeve, a mug out of the stan, a cilorn out of the mug, a milan out of the cilorn, and a medar out of the milan – and I leave it to Almighty God that I do not know where their dust is now, after their dissolution with me, from decay.[14]

UTILITY

We see in this tale, besides allegations of mythical longevity, testimony to its greatest boon to civilization, a crucial utility, without peer for the manufacture of durable utensils and weapons. Considered a 'chieftain tree', it was protected under ancient Breton law and penalties were prescribed for disfiguring yew wood furniture, carvings, lintels or doors.[15]

Another use indicative of its strength is related in a folk legend from Herefordshire:

> Marden Church in former times stood close to the river, and by some mischance one of its bells had been allowed to fall into it. It was immediately seized by a mermaid who carried it to the bottom and held it fast, so that any number of horses could not move it. According to some, the people of Marden were told by a wise man how to recover it; others said that the bell itself gave instructions from the bottom of the river. At any rate, a team of white freemartins [sterile female cows] was to be attached to the bell with yokes made of yew wood and bands of 'wittern', and it was to be drawn up in silence. The instructions were followed and the bell hoisted to the bank, with the mermaid asleep inside it. But in his excitement, one of the drivers called out:
>
> > In spite of all the devils in hell,
> > Now we'll land Marden's great bell.
>
> This woke the mermaid, who darted back into the water again, taking the bell with her and crying:
>
> > If it had not been
> > For your wittern bands
> > And you yew tree pin,
> > I'd have had your twelve free-martins in.[16]

Greek, Roman and European archers made their strongest bows of yew wood. The scientific name for yew is *Taxus*, the latin word for yew, derived from the Greek word, *taxos*, hauntingly similar to their word for bow, *toxon*. From this was derived their word for poisonous, *toxikon*, because in battle or in the hunt primitive warriors tipped their arrows with yew poison and shot them with short but powerful yew bows.[17] The earliest reference I have found relating to yew bows is Pope's translation of Homer's *Iliad*, which recounts certain escapades from the 9th century B.C.

> Raging with grief, great Menelaus burns,
> And, fraught with vengeance, to the victor turns

That shook the ponderous lance, in act to throw
And this stood adverse with the bended bow
Atrides, watchful of the wary foe,
Pierced with his lance the hand that grasp'd the bow,
And nail'd it to the yew.[18]

More recently, near the time of Christ, Virgil wrote in *Georgics*:

...the tougher yew
Receives the bending figure of a bow.[19]

And in the *Aeneid* as well:

....and from her quiver chose with speed
The winged shaft predestined for the deed:
Then to the stubborn yew her strength applied,
Till the far-distant horns approach'd on either side.[20]

One can only wonder at the vast number of yew staves that were turned into weapons by Greek heroes and Roman legions. During the 'dark ages' in Europe the bow was used for hunting small game but it was not considered to be a noble instrument for use in personal battle or war, for which the sword was the ethical weapon of honor. This attitude had changed by the time William the Conqueror defeated the Saxons in 1066. The Saxon King Harold was slain with an arrow through the eye, shot by a Norman with a yew wood bow. Thousands of other Europeans met a similar demise during the middle ages as we will see in an ensuing chapter.

ROBIN HOOD

Geoffrey Chaucer, well acquainted with English affairs of state, knew full well wherein England's military might was founded. He described an archer's equipment in *Prologue to the Canterbury Tales*:

He was clade in cote and hode of grene,
A shefe of peacock arrowes bright and shene
Under his belt he bare full thriftely.
Well coude he dresse his takel yewmanly;
His arrowes drouped not with fethers lowe,
And in hande he bare a mighty bowe.[21]

'Yewmanly', well reflects the archer's association with the tree and England has had a history full of archers who were especially proficient with the longbow. Most famous of all yeoman was outlaw Robin Hood, who dwelt in Sherwood Forest with his merry band. Robin's prowess as an archer was of great renown. It is said that King Richard 'Lion-Heart', when returned to his throne after years of crusading, rewarded Robin's loyal resistance against the usurpations of Richard's brother John, by making him 'Chief Yemen' of the English forests.[22]

Much later in the course of English literature, Lord Tennyson portrays Robin in a play, *Foresters*, along with Prince John and his co-conspirator, the Sheriff of Nottingham. In one scene, the Prince and Sheriff were out looking for Robin, when suddenly he appeared before them in the guise of an old crone, suspiciously armed with a longbow. The Sheriff asked what an old woman was doing with such a bow and Robin replied that it was to shoot nightingales.

> SHERIFF: This is no bow to hit nightingales; this is a true woodsman's bow of the best yew wood to slay the deer. Look my lord, there goes one in the moonlight. Shoot!
> PRINCE JOHN: (Shoots) Missed! There goes another. Shoot Sheriff!
> SHERIFF: (Shoots) Missed!
> ROBIN: And here comes another. Why an old woman can shoot closer than you two.[23]

Of course Robin Hood hits his mark, whereupon the Sheriff and Prince John attempt to capture him. At the very last moment, Friar Tuck appears with his battle stave (probably also made of yew) and rescues Robin. Indicative of Tennyson's poetic sensibility, the action unfolds in the moonlight and Robin is disguised as an old crone. Both moon and yew are sacred to Hecate and archer guilds in those days were commonly associated with a pagan pantheon rather than Christianity.

In other tales, Robin's death and subsequent interment were physically as well as symbolically embodied in the yew. According to legend, just before he died his last requests were:

> And sett my bright sword at my head,
> Mine arrowes at my feete,
> And lay my yew bow by my side,[24]

"AND IN HANDE HE BARE A MIGHTY BOWE"

And with his last breath:

> ..the dying man asked for his good yew bow and arrows. 'Bury me where this arrow falls,' he entreated; then, fitting an arrow to the string, he shot. The missile fell at the foot of a yew which might have yielded such a bow as he held in his unconscious

grasp. A sigh, and Robin Hood was a memory. The mortal part of him they buried, as he had bidden, under the yew.[25]

Tales of Robin Hood exemplify the attraction the yew tree has held for the English for millenia. Because of the preeminence of English archers, often against great odds, the yew became a symbol for English determination. Once again I marvel at the number of yew wood bow staves it must have taken to arm entire armies for centuries.

THERE IS A YEW TREE IN DOVERIDGE, DERBYSHIRE, REPORTED TO BE 1,400 YEARS OLD, UNDER WHICH ROBIN AND MAID MARION WERE BETROTHED.[26]

WILLIAM TELL

Legends from other countries also indicate great demand for yew wood. One Swiss legend bears resemblance to Robin Hood and although there probably never was an individual Robin, there was only one William Tell. To this day the yew is called 'William's Tree', in Switzerland and according to Dallimore the tale goes like this:

The Swiss were oppressed by their rulers, the Austrians, and on one occasion in 1307, when the Austrian ruler wished to show himself to be all-powerful over his subjects, he placed his hat upon a staff in Altfort marketplace and ordered all the Swiss to bow down to it. When it came to Tell's turn, he refused to obey such a ridiculous order, and as a result was condemned to death. He had, however, attained great renown as a marksman, and the Austrian duke, wishing for an exhibition of his skill, ordered him to divide an apple with an arrow, shot from considerable distance, the apple being placed on the head of Tell's son. The feat was performed without accident, but it marked a new era in the history of Switzerland, for it was the signal for a general uprising by means of which the Swiss were enabled to throw off the foreign yoke.[27]

LETHAL REPUTATION

Besides its use for weapons of war, another fatal characteristic of the yew propelled it even further toward mystical associations with death and the afterworld. Juice or oil extracted from crushed leaves, bark or seeds made a deadly poison. In the 2nd century B.C. Nicander, Greek didactic poet, wrote about venomous plants and animals and their antidotes. Of the yew he said:

> Shun the poysonous Yew, the which on Oeata grows,
> Like to the Firre, it causes bitter death,
> Unlesse besides they use pure wine that flowes
> From empty'd cups, thou drunke, when as thy breath
> Begins to fade, and passage of thy life grows straight![28]

Virgil refers to this lethal quality in *Georgics,* admonishing bee-keepers to keep their hives away from 'where the yew, their poisonous neighbor grows.'[29] Pliny thought yew berries to be mortal poison and that people who drank wine that was stored in yew wood casks would die.[30] Plutarch (46–120 A.D.) recorded that the yew was deadly when in flower and that to sleep in its shade was certain death.[31] Because it was so closely associated by its physical properties with death, the yew tree's sacred image was also related to death.

CHAPTER TWO

SACRED CONNECTIONS

THE TRIPLE GODDESS

 S the image grew more involved, the yew took on a sense of sanctity; certain individual trees came to be particularly venerated; mystical and religious associations developed linking the yew to death, graves, an afterlife and to the Great Goddess – sometimes called the Triple Goddess because her maiden, matron and crone aspects correspond to the waxing, full and waning moon and her tripartite role as giver of birth, sustainer of life and presider over the dead. Her authority eventually waned when her consorts on earth, sun-kings and priestly attendants forsook her. New deities, male and female, began to usurp her once singular power. By the time of Hesiod, writing in the 8th century B.C., the Goddess had been fragmented into a myriad of deities, Hera, Persephone, Artemis, Demeter and Hecate among them.

In the 2nd century A.D. Pausanius wrote about a yew tree found on Mount Ithome by Epaminondas, a great Theban commander of the 3rd century B.C., who found a tin scroll upon which were inscribed the mysteries of the Great Goddess. The scroll was buried in a bronze urn, between a yew and a myrtle.[1]

In the 2nd century B.C., Greeks held the yew sacred to Hecate, who represented the crone/waning moon/death aspect of the Great Goddess in their pantheon. It was Hecate who zealously watched over the maiden Persephone during her annual six-month sojurn in Hades. It was Hecate who held dominion over the land of the dead. Since Greek times Hecate could be invoked for assistance in rites of black magic, and summoned at places where three roads met. Yew wreaths were placed by priests and priestesses around the necks of black bulls when they were sacrificed to Hecate.[2] Eventually she became 'a queen of ghosts and magic, haunting cross-roads and attended by hell-hounds.'[3] Retaining vestiges of her once tripartite self she often appears with three heads: lion, dog and horse.[4] The Greeks also 'believed it to be the tree of the netherworld from which the furies carved their torches.'[5] By Shakespeare's time, as in *Macbeth*, Hecate had become a queen of witches.

GREEKS HELD THE YEW SACRED TO HECATE

CELTIC TOTEM TREE

The yew was sacred to Greeks and Romans, who worshipped their gods and goddesses in great cities; it was sacred to Celts who worshipped theirs in sylvan sanctuaries.

> The Celts made their sacred places in dark groves, the trees being hung with offerings or with the heads of victims. Human sacrifices were hung or impaled on trees, e.g. by the warriors of Boudicca. These, like the offerings still placed by the folk on sacred trees, were attached to them because the trees were the abode of spirits or divinities who in many cases had power over vegetation.[6]

Accordingly, Celts learned the practice of 'veneration of trees growing beside burial mounds or megalithic monuments' from an earlier cult; 'the tree embodied the ghost of the person buried under it.'[7]

Furthermore, in the vegetation rites of ancient cultures, the sun-king lived in splendor for a season to be sacrificed when the harvest was done to make room for the new king. Eventually the terms of office for a king extended beyond a single season to seven years or until bad harvests needed to be atoned for. In Celtic culture, kings and chiefs were inaugurated beneath the branches of sacred trees, were 'representatives of the spirit of vegetation embodied in the tree.' As terms of office were extended to sun-kings so were the lives of certain sacred trees spared and a surrogate sent to face axe and fire.[8]

Caesar (102–44 B.C.) recounts, in his *Gallic Wars*, the death of Cativolcus, king of the Eburones, who poisoned himself with yew juice[9] after some disgrace, perhaps a great battle lost to the Romans. Eburones took their name from their totem tree, the yew. Ritual suicide by the king is thus intimately related to the tree.

> A whole series of names of peoples and places contains the word 'eburos', the yew, the most sacred of all trees, and all must be connected. There were Eburones between the Main and Rhine, Eburovices at Evreux, and Eburobriga in Yonne (Aurolles)...The Eburovices were Aulerci or Belgae associated with them, or else Brythons who had remained in the midst of the Belgae.[10]

Roman Emperor Claudius (41–54 A.D.) advised the Roman Senate that yew juice was the best antidote for viper bite.[11] As emperor in such dangerous times, it is likely that Claudius had a keen interest in and knowledge of poisons. Although Julius Caesar's small army had landed in England and marched inland some ways, they left quickly when winter storms were wreaking havoc on their ships. It was the legions of Claudius who conquered Britain and it was Claudius who recognized Druids, the Celtic spiritual leaders and advisors to kings, to be his chief adversaries in persistently urging Gauls on the continent and Britons to rebel against Roman rule. Druids ran a college on the Isle of Angelsea, where initiates from all over Europe were trained in Druid arts. Claudius feared Druids and did his best to eradicate their mystical, political and social power from his far-flung empire.

FUNERAL RITES

As had Greeks and Romans, Druids associated yew trees with death and an afterlife. They believed, like Christians, that death was the key to immortality and so the yew tree comes to connect with an afterlife; a stunning paradox for the yew, tree of death, to come to represent eternal life, but its slow growth and great longevity, its red berries and evergreen branches in the dead of winter were shining facets of the transformation.

Virgil listed it in his description of Dido's self-immolation:

> The fatal pile they rear
> Within the secret court, exposed in air.
> The cloven Holms and Pines are heaped on high.
> And garlands in the hollow spaces lie.
> Sad Cypress, Vervain, Yew, compose the wreath
> And every baleful flower denoting death.[12]

According to Ovid (43 B.C.–18 A.D.), living yew trees marked the entrance to Hell.

> Dismal yew shades the declining way that, through labyrinths of shade and horror, leads to Tartarus; languid Styx exhaling continual clouds.[13]

YEW TREES MARKED THE ENTRANCE TO HELL

VOTIVE OBJECTS

Another special use for yew wood was for carved votive objects. Archaeological sites in Britain, Switzerland and France associated with springs or wells have yielded large deposits of well-preserved wooden objects. According to Stuart Piggot:

> In Gaul, there are those from a shaft at Montbouy near Orleans, others from Essarois (Cote-d'Or), and the astonishing collection of nearly 200 wooden sculptures from what must have been a Celtic sanctuary at the source of the River Seine, including human and animal representions as well as those of internal organs, these last presumably votive or associated with divination in a manner recalling Etruscan practices. Pre-Roman Celtic religious sculpture in wood may have been far more abundant than we have thought in the past.[14]

More recently 5,000 wood figures have been found around the spring of Les Roches, Chamalieres (Auvgerne), thought to be from early Gallo-Roman times.[15]

Yew wood, ideal for that purpose, was the most durable and rot-resistant wood in the European forests. It was already considered to be holy and was associated with gods. More practically, it is also a very heavy wood and sinks, which, assuming people didn't want their votive

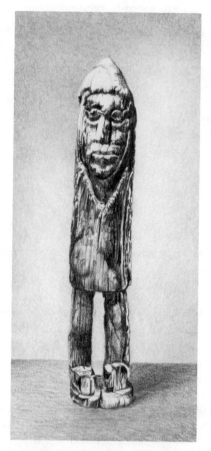

YEW WOOD VOTIVE FIGURINE

body part floating around on top of the well, was a desirable quality. The red, tight-grained wood was easily carved and polished. It is with little leap of imagination I posit that some, if not most, of these wooden articles were carved of yew.

CELTIC FOLKLORE

In what Celtic folklore has come through to us today, tales of the British Isles seem to hold the strongest tradition with the yew, or the best recorded.

The Irish Druids attributed special virtues to the hazel, rowan and yew, the wood of which was used in magical ceremonies described in Irish texts...the wood of all these trees is still believed to be efficacious against fairies and witches.[16]

The Irish 'bile' is a holy tree which sometimes grows near sacred springs or forts. They were tribal totems and in time of war one tribe would try to destroy the bile of another. One such sacred Irish yew tree was described as 'a firm strong god,' and 'spell of knowledge.' It symbolized connections between the tree and ogham runes, a form of writing or carving letters or words on wooden rods.[17]

Irish folklore is wrought through with yew tree legends, some of which will be recounted in following chapters. Here is a tale of the beautiful Fiongalla:

> ...the 'fair-cheeked one' lived in the far south-western corner of Ireland, where legend says that she was held in enchantment by the powerful druid Amerach from Ulster, who grew no older as years passed. She made Fiongalla vow never to sleep with a man until one brought magical yew berries, holly boughs and marigolds from the earthly seat of power. Amerach lost her power over Fiongalla when a hero named Feargal actually managed to perform the almost-impossible task.[18]

Another Irish legend establishes a more specific connection between yew trees and graves, reminiscent of Celtic cults who thought spirits of the dead were embodied in trees:

> Yew stakes driven through the bodies of Naisi and Deirdre to keep them apart, became yew trees the tops of which embraced over Armagh Cathedral. A yew sprang from the grave of Baile MacBuain, and an apple-tree from that of his lover Aillinn, and the top of each had the form of their heads...Writing tablets, made from each of the trees when they were cut down, sprang together and could not be separated...The identification of tree and ghost is here complete.[19]

The legend *Eochardh Airemh* attests to the fact that the yew was the most powerful sacred tree of Ireland and that the Irish Druids made their 'wands of divination' from it.[20]

ENGLISH FOLKLORE

In England, folk tales and local legends retain ancient beliefs and burial rites involved with yew. In Somerset:

> Our forefathers were particularly careful in preserving this funeral tree, whose branches it was said were used for mourners to carry in solemn procession to the grave and afterwards to deposit therein under the bodies of their departing friends. The branches thus cut off from their native stock, which was to shoot forth again at the return of spring, were beautifully emblematical of the resurrection of the body, as, by reason of their perpetual verdure, they were of the immortality of the soul.[21]

From the Lake District, one elder recalled:

> ...that a small table with a white cloth was placed outside the door of the deceased on the day of the funeral. It held a vase or basin with sprigs of box or yew in it. Mourners took a sprig to drop on to the coffin after it had been lowered into the grave.[22]

In some shires of England it was considered a very ill omen if yew boughs or sprigs were brought into the house. In Suffolk:

> ...if yew was brought into the house...on Christmas Eve...with the other evergreens for decoration it was believed that there would be a death in the family by the end of the year – a belief possibly arising out of the tree's associations.[23]

But in Derbyshire, under extenuating circumstances, yew could be brought indoors.

> In decorating the leaded panes of the cottage windows, care was taken that in a row of panes one at least should have a sprig of variegated holly, and also that some of the diamond panes should have slips of yew and box. The yew had on no account to be picked from a churchyard (possibly because of its associations with death), and the box had to be obtained from the garden. The assumption is that this would have brought bad luck if the custom had been broken.[24]

Because of its somber qualities and religious associations, the yew gave rise to many folk-tales and superstitions. For instance, how the town of Halifax got its name:

A certain amorous clergyman fell in love with a pretty maid who refused his addresses. Maddened by her refusal, he cut off her head, which being hung upon a Yew tree till it was quite decayed, the tree was reputed as sacred, not only whilst the virgin's head hung on it, but as long as the tree itself lasted; to which the people went in pilgrimage, plucking and bearing away branches of it as a holy relique, whilst there remained any of the trunk; persuading themselves that those small veins and filaments resembling hairs were the hairs of the virgin. But what is stranger, the resort to this place, then called Houton, a despicable village, occasioned the building of the now famous town of Halifax in Yorkshire, the name of which imports 'holy hair'.[25]

And in Herefordshire:

To dream of yew presages the death of some old person which will be of benefit to the dreamer.[26]

And in the north of England:

...it was used in a variant of dowsing to find lost property; the seeker held a yew branch in front of him, which led him to the goods and turned in his hand when he was by them.[27]

And in the Lake District:

Another old man of the same district used to cut yew into weird shapes to give the pieces to his friends, claiming that these would protect them from the six evils.[28]

According to Reverend J.G. Collins, legends are still being created. One yew tree reported by Vaughn Cornish and John Lowe to be in excess of 28 feet in circumference, resides in the churchyard of St. James in Stedham, near Midhurst, West Sussex.

This tree is dated by experts, Dr. David Bellamy et al, as being 2,500 years old: I doubt this but it is certainly well over 1,000 years and is regarded as the second oldest yew in England. Again, I have seen other yews which also would claim this.

There is a story told by the school children that if you run around the tree 100 times, then you will be sucked into the middle! This is a story of recent years since none of the older residents of Stedham have heard it.[29]

THE GODALMING YEW

SCOTTISH FOLKLORE

In Scotland during a major border dispute, several clans were gathered beneath a venerable yew to discuss a proposed treaty with the British. One of the clans sold out, making their own false treaty. The Battle of Culloden ensued, with disastrous consequences for the Scots. Since then the yew tree came to be known as the Traitor's Tree in Scotland.

The magical yew also granted speakers a way to cut through the normal bounds of propriety established to maintain order among the close-knit clans.

It is an idea in the north of Scotland that a person, when grasping a branch of churchyard yew in his left hand, may speak to any one he pleases, but however loud he may call, the person spoken to will not be able to hear what is said, though the words will be audible to all around...a man who wished to prejudice the clan against their chief without receiving punishment for his rashness, approached the chief when all his clan were around him, and bowing profoundly as if to show his devotion, with the branch of yew in his hand, spoke in the most insulting and defiant manner for all around to hear. The result of this strange experiment may easily be conceived.[30]

EUROPEAN FOLKLORE

I sent out queries about other European customs as regards the yew tree and got back scanty though tantalizing information. Some of it demonstrates the universality of the yew tree's image in Europe. In the Province of Brabant in Belgium, for instance, there are several yew trees with legendary significance. One yew planted in 1578 commemorates the double beheading of Count d'Edgmont and Count de Hornes; another whose branches cover a 30 meter diameter is thought to be over 800 years old. Another, Caesar's Tree, thought to be over 1,000 years old, thrives in downtown Lo-Reninge.[31] Apparently Caesar is said to have tethered his horse to this tree, although it is only 10 feet in circumference and probably not much over 600 years old.

In Sweden it's called the 'death tree' and according to Kristina Lindell:

> The most interesting piece of information is that the 'evergreen tree' at the heathen temple of Old Uppsala may have been a yew. There is also a semicircle of very old yew trees at Osterslav, north of the city of Kristianstad, which may date back to heathen times.[32]

In Switzerland the yew tree is referred to as 'William's tree' and remains a symbol of sorrow, or nostalgia for the olden days around Christmas time. It also symbolizes long life.[33]

In Germany the yew tree retains strong associations with death and the afterlife in various tales. Many places and villages are named after the precious yew, although the tree is becoming scarce in Germany. Large stands of yew are very rare, but it is grown often in parks and cemeteries. One old tree called the Balderswang Eibe is said by some to be over 3,000 years old. Another old tree is the Hintersteiner Eibe which has a diameter of one meter and an age of about 2,000 years.[34]

In Germany, Sweden, Norway, Yugoslavia and Russia people hang sprigs of yew tied up with ribbons around the house at Christmas time, and sprigs were also used in place of palm on Palm Sunday. They use evergreen plants including yew for wreaths to lay on the coffin. They call it the death tree because it is found amongst the graves in churchyards and cemeteries and because of the poison in the tree. In some areas they put out strings of lights in the cemetery on All Souls Day and on this occasion they use yew twigs to decorate.

The Germans also used the yew for folk remedies. Yew pitch mixed with unwashed butter and chewed up served as an antidote for tuberculosis.[35] It is often called the forbidden tree because it was used for abortions. In some areas yew sprigs taken from a churchyard yew are touched against the statue of St. Valentine and a tea is made from them to be used against the 'falling disease'.

Some folk stories attribute deaths directly to the yew. In one some boys supposedly had to spend the night in a place called the Devil's Ravine. In order to prove that they had been there, they had to cut a little piece out of an old sacred yew tree. They all died three days later of the fever.[36] In 1577, Hieronymous Bosch mentioned yew in his herb book, admonishing that to sleep beneath a blossoming yew tree's shadow was to risk death.[37]

There were also beneficial aspects of the yew. It was used to get rid of trolls or giants; crossed yew twigs put in front of their holes or in front of a stable they wanted to rob or across a path that they might use would drive them away.[38]

There was a German Tree Alphabet similar to that of Ireland; accordingly, a German rune 'ihwaz' represented the yew. Because of the scarcity of the tree, a decree was issued in 1571 forbidding yew to be cut for charcoal production.[39]

In the Icelandic saga, *The Elder Edda,* Grimnir, who is the shape-changer Odin, says:

> Ull yonder in Yew-Dale
> Has made himself a mansion:
> Elf-Home for Frey in the old days
> The Gods gave us a tooth-fee.[40]

In Norse and Germanic mythology the yew tree was known as Uller's Tree. Uller was the archer god, son of Thor.

YEW AND THE ALPHABET

Originally in Greece and then later in Germany and Ireland, the yew itself came to figure as an element of the alphabet. According to Graves, the alphabet came from early pre-Pelasgian Greece and was at one time 'a religious secret held by the priestesses of the moon.' The alphabet was also 'closely linked with the calendar and its letters were represented not by written characters, but by twigs cut from different trees typical of the years' sequent months.'[41]

The ancient Irish alphabet, like that used by the Gallic Druids of whom Caesar wrote, might not at first be written down, and all its letters were named after trees. It was called the Beth-Luis-Nion...and its canon corresponded with the Pelasgian and the Latin alphabets, namely thirteen consonants and five vowels...

Each vowel represented a quarterly station of the year: O (gorse) the Spring Equinox; U (heather) the Summer Solstice; E (poplar) the Autumn Equinox; A (fir or palm) the birth-tree and I (yew) the death shared the Winter Solstice between them. This order of trees is implicit in Greek and Latin myth and the sacral tradition of all Europe and, mutatis mundi, Syria and Asia Minor...

I place the station of the yew on the last day of the year, the eve of the Winter Solstice. Ailm (A) the Silver-Fir of Birth and Idho (I) the Yew of Death are sisters: they stand next to each other in the circle of the year and their foliage is almost identical. Fir is to Yew as silver is to lead. The medieval alchemists, following ancient tradition, reckoned silver to the Moon as presiding over birth, and lead to Saturn as presiding over death; and extracted both metals from the same mixed ore.[42]

THE OGHAM SCRIPT

Druids, like the members of so many other primal cultures, strove to keep secret the names of their gods, hence writing down letters was forbidden. The trained and secretive Druids used the alphabet to communicate the mysteries of the various deities to each other only. They developed a secret finger-language and eventually an ogham or runic script. The alphabet was not to be profaned by the uninitiated because the Druids believed that, should an enemy learn the names of their tribal gods and be able to pronounce them, that enemy would gain control over them.

Druids were able to converse with each other in silence. The inner right hand was the keyboard upon which all of the letters of the alphabet were located. With the left hand they signalled the individual letters of the words by touching the place on the right hand that corresponded to the intended letter. The place of the yew, or Idho (I), was at the base of the Mercury finger (little finger) at the line that separates it from the palm. And as Robert Graves put it:

> The connection of Mercury finger with the yew is made by Mercury's conducting of souls to the place presided over by the death-goddess, Hecate, alias his mother, Maia, to whom the yew was sacred.[43]

The ability of Druids to communicate in silence with each other would have appeared magical to any person who witnessed it. The alphabet, which enabled them to communicate the mysteries of the Goddess, was the epitome of power. It took an initiate twenty years of arduous study to acquire essentially the entire repertoire of the culture. According to Graves the Druid or ollave:

> ...in ancient Ireland had to be master of one-hundred-fifty Oghams, or verbal ciphers, which allowed him to converse with his fellow-poets over the heads of unlearned bystanders; to be able to repeat at a moment's notice any one of three-hundred-fifty long traditional histories and romances, together with the incidental poems they contained, with appropriate harp accompaniment; to have memorized an immense number of other poems of different sorts; to be learned in philosophy; to be a doctor of civil law; to understand the history of modern, middle and ancient Irish with the derivations and changes of meaning of

every word; to be skilled in music, augury, divination, medicine, mathematics, geography, universal history, astronomy, rhetoric and foreign languages; and to be able to extemporize in fifty or more complicated metres.[44]

Each Druid was a repository of the old ways and passed on the knowledge from generation to generation. The Romans feared the Druids, and tried to obliterate them and any control they may have had over the people. Facing annihilation the persecuted Druids let their sacred secrets slip out amongst men, and with the alphabet the face to face oral traditions gave way to the written word.

ETYMOLOGY OF YEW

In the oral traditions which were passed down intact through centuries from generation to generation by bards, minstrels and gleemen, the yew acquired a certain stature, a body of belief based on its physical as well as associated spiritual qualities, that survive for us today. Eventually, once the taboos against writing or pronouncing the sacred syllables were lifted, men began to scratch their stories on hides, parchment, tablets of wood and paper. The written history of the victorious began. Those first intrepid authors must have felt some moments of terror severing the sense from the sound; leaving behind the practiced inflections, intonations and individual modulations of the voice. The progression from oral sound through the labyrinth of the mind into alphabetic symbols and the written word must have run up against many walls and into myriad pitfalls. The etymology of the word 'yew' alone demonstrates the difficult task of those first wordsmiths.

The Greeks named the yew *toxus*, after two important aspects of the yew: *toxon* which meant bow, and *toxikon* which meant poison. The Latin name, which is derived from the Greek, is also associated with poison, as Pliny pointed out:

> ...for he asserts that arrows were dipped in the juice to render them deadly, and that poisons were named *toxica*, formerly *taxica*, from the name of the tree *taxus*.[45]

There are varying etymologies for the word 'yew'. According to Dr. Johnson, 'yew is derived from the original Anglo-Saxon Ip, or Welsh yw.' And Dr. Price says it is derived from the Latin, Iva. J. G. Cumming says the word:

> ...is ancient British and signifies existent and enduring, having the same root as Jehovah, and yew in Welsh means it is, being one of the forms of the third person present indicative of the auxiliary verb *bod*, to be.[46]

The first writers of any language must have struggled mightily to capture with alphabets the sounds of spoken words which constantly changed. In the case of English, they borrowed from Latin, Gallic, Teutonic and other Celtic languages and correspondingly wrote the word 'yew' in a Babel of ways: Eugh, Ew, Ewe, Ewgh, Ibe, Iuu, Ive, Ivel, Iw, U, Ugh, Vew, Vewe, Viewe, Yeo, Yeugh, Yewgh, Yewe, You, Yowe, Yugh, and Yw.

As oral myth and legend gave way to the written word, early writing turned to history for its inspiration. The yew tree's mythic image also changed, became more prominent with the advent of the yew wood longbow in military affairs. Kingdoms full of oral tales, which the Druids had kept alive, began to be written down, but not everyone could do it. Those who could came quickly under the aegis of the prince.

CHAPTER THREE

HISTORICAL IMPACT

ISTORY, commissioned by victorious monarchs, became in large part the study of their battles. Just as Greeks and Romans did, ancient Britons knew the value of yew wood pikes, spears, staves and bows to fight those battles. In earlier British history, according to John Lowe, the bow was not thought a formidable weapon for war.

> Bows have from the earliest times, been made of various kinds of hard and elastic wood, and we have the testimony of Homer and Virgil that the yew was one of the principal of these. There is little doubt that it was used by the Saxons for this purpose, though Meyrick says they only used it for killing birds, and in all probability the ancient Britons made their bows of it. Certainly they used it for making spears, for I have in my possession a spear of this wood, dug up from beneath the peat in the fens of Cambridgeshire.[1]

TIP OF MIDDLE-PALEOLITHIC YEW WOOD SPEAR

The early bows were about four feet long, with an effective range of about 50 yards. Although the Saxon words 'boga' and 'arewe' have changed very little in the past 1,500 years, the bow went through considerable transformation. In 1855 a prehistoric yew wood bow was also found in a peat bog near Cambridge. Just shy of five feet long and perfectly formed, it suggests a gradual evolution from the primitive hunting bow to the much more powerful six-foot longbow. Although Meyrick may have thought the Saxons to use the bow to hunt birds only, they were also known to mark the advent of war by sending out heralds with strung bows, and the return of peace by heralds with their bows unstrung.[2]

WILLIAM THE CONQUEROR

William the Conqueror invaded England in 1066, and at the Battle of Hastings on August 16, the Saxon King Harold was struck by an arrow from a Norman four-foot yew wood bow. Shot through the eye, Harold died on the field and the demoralized Saxon troops were easily vanquished.

PANEL FROM THE BAYEUX TAPESTRY OF THE NORMAN CONQUEST

It is said that King Harold owned a manor house in Sussex, where today a venerable female yew tree stands nearly 40 feet tall in the churchyard of St. George in Crowhurst. It has a girth of 28 feet. According to J.H. Wilks, it stands:

> ...between the manor and the church, and the general opinion is that the tree is older than manor or church, both of which began

their recorded history about 1250. King Harold owned the Manor of Crowhurst at the time of the Conqueror's landing, and a legend records that the Reeve was hanged on the yew tree for failing to disclose the king's hidden treasure when requested.[3]

THE CROWHURST YEW, SUSSEX

William was crowned King of England on Christmas day 1066 and during his reign, which lasted until 1087, he replaced the Saxon nobility with his own Norman peers, creating problems for his less capable son, William II. William Rufus, as he was called in honor of his red beard, reigned for thirteen years, but was neither as strong nor as politic as his father and could neither dominate his subjects nor command anything but their hatred. He was killed in the New Forest, which had been planted by decree of William, twenty years earlier. He too was shot by an arrow from a yew wood bow. His brother, Henry, succeeded him and shortly thereafter enacted a law forgiving the accidental killing of another while engaged in the pursuit of archery. This point has not gone unnoticed by those who suggest William may have been victim to something other than accident.

Sometime between the Norman invasion and the end of the 12th century, the short Norman bows gave way to the six-foot longbow which could send, in the hands of a skilled archer, a 'cloth-yard' arrow to its mark 250 yards away. Although the Norman bows and the longbows were both made of yew wood, the full value of the yew was realized in the latter, for which it was far superior to any other wood. Historians claim a preeminent place for the yew wood longbow in the context of English history, particularly from the 11th through the 16th centuries, when archers were a most effective component of battle. For this reason as historian W. J. Bean pointed out in 1970, 'No tree has become more woven into the history and folklore of Great Britain than the yew.'[4]

Henry died in 1135 and for a short while there was no king; fierce competition for the throne arose between Henry's daughter Mathilda and his nephew Stephen. Stephen pronounced himself king and embroiled England in civil war for 15 years. The war ended in a compromise when it was agreed that Mathilda's son Henry would become king on the event of Stephen's death, and that Henry's heirs would be first in succession to the throne.

HENRY II

Henry II (1154 –1189) had to contend with the Scots and the Irish, but eventually subdued them. In so doing he discovered much about the tactical value of archers armed with yew wood longbows. Giraldus Cambrensis, writing in the late 12th century, said that yews were planted by holy men and that Henry quite shocked the Irish when he 'sacrilegiously laid hands on a group of yews in a most irreverent and atrocious manner.'[5] Presumably Henry laid hands on these yews to get wood for bow staves, for during his reign archery became a regal priority and the skill of the armed English citizenry became legendary; exemplified by the tales of Robin Hood, who is referred to variously as a 'yeman', 'yoeman', 'yew-man' and 'yoman', all of which are of course antecedent spellings of the modern word yeoman, which has come to mean a stout-hearted citizen.

Saint Thomas à Becket, Archbishop of Canterbury, who was assassinated on Henry's order, is reported to have preached to a group of parishioners beneath the branches of a yew tree which just barely survives today in the Capel Churchyard at Tudeley in Kent. The trunk is hollowed out and some of it is missing. P.E. Norton measured the circumference at two feet from the ground to be 24 feet.[6] The tree would have certainly been alive (possibly 700 years old) in Becket's time. There are several yews on the grounds at Canterbury, although none of this venerable age.

THE CAPEL YEW

Richard Lion Heart was more interested in the crusades than in England and spent much of his time marching off to war under the Christian banner. Gibbon alluded to the efficacy of the English archer when he said of their King, 'Richard, with seventeen knights and three hundred archers, sustained the charge of the whole Turkish and Saracen army.'[7] As the story goes, he made Robin Hood 'Chief Yemen' of all his forests. Richard was killed on a raid in Normandy; shot by a Norman with a yew wood crossbow.[8]

King John (1199–1216) began the 13th century by signing the Magna Carta at the armed insistence of English noblemen. On a nearby hillside near present day Staines, Middlesex, overlooking the field at Runneymede where the document was signed, stood a magnificent yew tree. This renowned and oft-recorded tree measured over 30 feet in circumference.[9] In 1920 Wilson reported it to be 30 feet 9 inches in girth.[10] An anonymous poem about the Ankerwyke Yew:

> What scenes have pass'd since first this ancient Yew
> In all the strength of youthful beauty grew!
> Here patriot Britons might have musing stood,
> And plann'd the Charta for their Country's good;
> And here, perhaps from Runnymede retired,
> The haughty John with secret vengeance fired,
> Might curse the day which saw his weakness yield
> Extorted rights in yonder tented field.[11]

In the 13th century the role of the archer in war became pre-eminent. Statutes were enacted to ensure widespread, intimate experience with the art of archery. King John began the practice of calling a standing militia of English yeomen.

EDWARD I

Led by Edward I (1274–1307), the English archers fought the Scots in the Battle of Falkirk. The longbows accounted for 12,000 Scottish dead compared to 100 English. The Scots had bows but the bows were weak; Dallimore reported that they were no match for the English in the art of archery:

> The Scots had a proverb to the effect that 'every English bowman carried 24 Scotts under his girdle' – meaning that every English arrow would account for a Scot.[12]

Dallimore paraphrased a 16th century description of Scots archers, by Roger Ascham the King's Chronicler:

> ...[Scots] are surely good men of war in their own way; but as for shooting they can neither use it with any use or profit. He goes on to say that James the First of Scotland, at the Parliament held at St. John's town, or Perth, commanded under pain of a great forfeit that every Scot should learn to shoot; yet neither the love of their country, the fear of their enemies, punishment, or the receiving of any profit that might come of it, could make them to be good archers, which they may be unapt and unfit for by

God's providence and good nature.[13]

Edward turned John's policy of arming the common man into law, and eventually the English military could draw on all men between the ages of seven and 70, unless they were priests or judges. In the 13th century, according to Lowe:

> ...every person not having a greater revenue than one hundred pence was obligated to have in his possession a bow and arrows, with other arms offensive and defensive; and all such as had no possessions, but could afford to purchase arms, were commanded to have a bow with sharp arrows, if they dwelt without the royal forests, and a bow with round-headed arrows, if they dwelt within the forests...It was also ordained by the forementioned Statute that proper officers should be appointed to see that these weapons were kept in good order, and ready for immediate service.[14]

THE HUNDRED YEARS WAR

Edward II (1307–1327) did not succeed in subduing the Scots, as had his father, and was eventually deposed by their efforts and subsequently murdered. Edward III (1327–1377), more aggressive than his indolent father, not only subdued the Scots but began the Hundred Years War with France with a naval battle at Sluys in 1340. This enabled the English to occupy the French port of Calais and gave them control of the Dover Straits and the Channel. In 1341, preparatory to further aggression, Edward ordered the sheriffs of most counties to provide 500 bows and 500 bundles of arrows for the intended war against France.[15]

Six years later, on August 24, 1346, at the Battle of Crécy, the power of English archery struck with the force of a technological revolution. Outnumbered ten to one, 7,000 English archers, armed with their best yew wood longbows, darkened the sky with 100,000 arrows per minute. An eyewitness chronicler wrote:

> ...our archery was such that the arrows, flying in the air as thick as snow, with a terrible noise, much like a tempestuous wind preceeding a tempest, they did leave no disarmed place of horse or man unstricken.[16]

Roger Ascham, from the English point of view in 1545:

> Kynge Edward the Third at the battle of Cressie ageinst Philip ye
> Frenche Kynge, as Gaguinus the French Historiographer plainlye
> doeth tell, slewe that daye all the nobilite of Fraunce onlye wyth
> hys archers.[17]

According to one account, the French nobility held the common
archer in contempt and had hired Genoese archers.

> In the early part of the battle a shower of rain came on which
> thoroughly wet the [Genoese] archers' bowstrings; on being
> ordered to discharge their arrows they were unable to do so on
> account of wet strings. This so enraged Philip VI that he ordered
> his mounted troops to ride them down. The English archers,
> meanwhile, had kept their bows in cases during the shower, and
> so kept them dry, and as they had been long accustomed to shoot
> strongly at a mark, they made short work of the French horse-
> men.[18]

The war was to be taken up again. According to Dallimore, Edward
III wrote to the sheriffs of London on June 12, 1349, issuing an edict
that:

> ...sets forth how 'the people or our realm, as well of good quality
> as mean, have commonly in their sports before these times
> exercised their skill of shooting arrows; whence it is well known
> that honour and profit have accrued to our whole realm, and to
> us, by the help of God, no small assistance in our warlike acts.'
>   Now however, 'the said skill being laid aside, as it were
> wholly,' the King proceeds to command the sheriffs to make
> public proclamation that 'every one of the said city, strong in
> body, at leisure times on holidays, use in their recreations bows
> and arrows or piles, and bolts, and learn and exercise the art of
> shooting, forbidding all and singular, on our behalf, that they do
> not after any manner apply themselves to the throwing of stones,
> wood, or iron, hand-ball, foot-ball, bandy-ball, cambuck, or
> cock-fighting, nor such-like vain plays, which have no profit in
> them.'[19]

Ten years later, represented by his son the Black Prince, Edward
marched again on France and after skirmishes here and there over
certain parts of the Norman countryside, fought the decisive battle at

Poitiers. Froissart describes it thus:

> Then the battle began on all parts, and the [battalions] of the
> marshals of France approached, and they set forth that they were
> appointed to break the array of the archers. They entered a-
> horseback into the way where the great hedges were on both
> sides set full of archers. As soon as the men of arms entered, the
> archers began to shoot on both sides and did slay and hurt horses
> and knights, so that the horses, when they felt the sharp arrows,
> they would in no wise go forward, but drew aback and flung, and
> took on so fiercely that many of them fell on their masters, so that
> for press they could not rise again, in so much that the marshals'
> battle could never come at the prince...True to say, the archers
> did their company that day great advantage, for they shot so thick
> that the Frenchmen list not on what side to take heed.[20]

Roger Ascham wrote of the casualties:

> Such lyke battle also fought ye noble Black Prince Edwarde
> beside Poitiers, where John ye French Kynge with his sonne and
> in a manner all ye peers of Fraunce were taken beside XXX
> thousand which that daye were slayne, and verie few Englyshe by
> reason of theyr bowes.[21]

Edward III reigned for fifty years, but the Black Prince died and
Edward became quite incapacitated in the waning years of that reign.
His third son, who came to be known as John of Gaunt, was essentially
the ruler, attending to pressing needs until young Richard, the Black
Prince's first son, became king in 1377. Richard II upheld his
grandfather's edict that men should practice archery on Sundays and
holidays rather than play frivolous games. The act further required that
all servants be compelled to shoot. Richard also, apparently under some
duress from factions (minions of John) who would challenge his reign,
was required to hold parliament under special circumstances. According to Pennant in 1397, 'Richard II, holding a parliament in a
temporary building, on account of the wretched state of Westminster
Hall, surrounded it with 4,000 Cheshire archers, armed with tough
yew bows, to ensure freedom of debate.'[22]

In 1399 Richard sailed to Ireland to deal militarily with some minor
uprising. During his absence, his banished cousin Henry, son of John

of Gaunt, returned and convinced England to accept him as Henry IV.
When Richard returned from Ireland, his throne and the hearts of the
people had been captured by Henry. Richard died soon after, in some
northerly castle, of unknown causes. Henry did not lack for decisive
methods. Because the supply of bow wood was running out, in an effort
to augment the national armory he ordered Nicholas Frost, his royal
bowyer, 'to enter upon the lands of private individuals and cut down
yew or any other wood for the public service.'[23]

Nicely provided by his father with authority to get yew wood from
anywhere in England, Henry V, who succeeded to the throne in 1413,
set about immediately to prepare for another assault on France. Two
years later came the battle of Agincourt. The final expedition of what
was to become known as the Hundred Years War left few aspects of the
English domestic economy unaffected. Twenty-five thousand horses
were readied. Six feathers were taken from every goose in England to
fletch the hundreds of thousands of arrows. Nearly all of England's
peerage made the trip across the channel, some lured by pride, many
by the promise of riches. There was a contingent of the standing militia
numbering 7,000 yeomen, which also made the crossing.

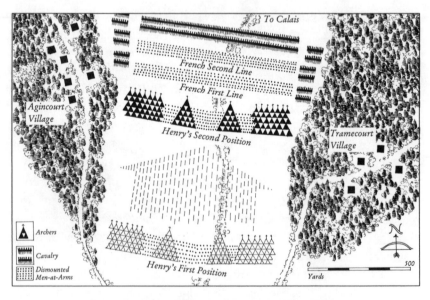

THE BATTLE ALIGNMENT AT AGINCOURT (AFTER KEEGAN)

Even so, when the battle was joined, the English were outnumbered ten to one. The French, preparing to crush the English invaders once and for all, had gathered a force of 60,000. For the French nobility, who had apparently not learned the lessons of the past hundred years, this was to be their last hurrah. Drinking, eating and quarrelling among themselves, they watched the smaller English force set up positions. As in previous battles, the French came mounted and over-dressed in heavy armor.

Henry spoke to his archers, telling them that his spies had learned that each archer captured by the French would have three fingers removed from his right hand, and would be sold in lots as a slave. Accordingly Shakespeare imagines it thus in *Henry V:*

> And you good yeomen,
> Whose limbs were made in England, Show us here
> The mettle of your pasture; let us swear
> That you are worth your breeding; which I doubt not;
> For there is none of you so mean and base
> That hath not noble lustre in your eyes.[24]

Henry also told them that he would rather die in battle than be taken prisoner and cost England a king's ransom. He was roundly cheered by his men, and then just before the battle he offered a prayer, 'Remember us Lord.'

English archers advanced to within 500 yards of the French positions. Each planted a long, stout, sharpened stake pointed at a thirty degree angle in the enemy's direction. The French knights began slowly at first to advance across the open field, many with their visors still raised. As they began to trot into range, all English eyes were on the raised baton of Sir Thomas Erpingham, the King's Archery Master. He threw it in the air and a hiss of English arrows blackened the sky. The few French knights who reached the inclined sharpened stakes fared poorly. Their horses were impaled through the breast; they, unseated and clumsy in armor, were quickly dispatched by archers with short swords. When the battle had ended, according to Roger Ascham, the French dead numbered 40,000. The English lost twenty six.[25]

At one time, probably under King Phillip, the French too had tried to establish a citizen archer army, but it is said that the nobility, noting the power which such a group of common men had in war, quickly thwarted all efforts to do so, presumably in the vain hope of maintaining their own traditional preeminence as the warrior class. As a consequence the French knights, thinking themselves invincible against common English yeoman, had no substantial archer force and thereby committed a fatal mistake. In the aftermath Henry ordered many of the prisoners and wounded put to death. This harsh excess eventually came due in the reign of Henry VI (1422–1461) and gave Joan of Arc enough emotional ammunition to drive the English from most of France in 1453. It is conceivable that had the English lost any of their major battles of the Hundred Years War, this book might have been written in French.

THE WAR OF THE ROSES

The War of the Roses, between the Houses of York and Lancaster, lasted the entire reign of Edward IV (1461–1483), and it seems the archers were equally balanced in military effectiveness. Roger Ascham rued, '...shafts flew from both sides, to the destruction of many a yeoman whom foreign battle could never have subdued.'[26] John Lowe recounts a regal imperative enacted by statute during the reign of Edward IV:

> '...every Irishman dwelling with Englishmen, should have a bow of his own height, made either of yew, wych-hazel, ash, or anolune laburnum.' The Act directs that butts should be erected in every township, which the inhabitants were to shoot at up and down, upon all feast days, under the penalty of one halfpenny for every time they omitted to perform this exercise.[27]

Edward petitioned the House of Commons so that, 'no bowyer might sell a bow to any of the King's subjects for more than three shillings four pence.' He petitioned also for a tax to be paid in yew:

> ...such bowstaffes as be brought within this realm, be sett now to outrageous prices,' and prays that for every tun-tight of merchandise as shall be conveyed in every 'Carik, Calee, or shipp, four bowestaffes be brought, upon pain of forfeiture to your Highness.'[28]

ARCHERY PRACTICE AT THE BUTTS

The War of the Roses was fought primarily by noblemen aligned with either the House of York or the House of Lancaster and their retainers. For the most part it passed over the heads of the average Englishmen's lives. When Edward died in 1483, his young son was to become Edward V, but due to the machinations of his uncle Richard, the hunchback Duke of Gloucester, the young king and his even younger brother didn't live long, and the Duke was crowned Richard III.

Richard III reigned for less than two years in those tumultuous times at the end of the War of the Roses. He decreed at the start of his reign that there be a 'general plantation of yew trees for the use of archers.' He was rightly nervous, for he was soon killed at the Battle of Bosworth by Henry Tudor, the last champion of the House of Lancaster. The victorious earl was crowned Henry VII in 1485 and reigned until his death in 1509. During his reign, England began to emerge from the dark ages.

HENRY VIII

Henry VIII (1509–1547) inherited a united kingdom at peace with the world. It is said that the Ankerwyke Yew, previously mentioned witness to the signing of the Magna Carta, also provided a proper environment for one of Henry's ill-starred romances.

> Here too the tyrant Henry felt love's flame
> And sighing, breathed his Anna Boleyn's name.
> The royal lover woo'd the ill-starred maid,
> And yet that neck round which he fondly hung,
> To hear the thrilling accents of her tongue;
> That lovely breast, on which his head reclined,
> Forms to have humanized his savage mind;
> Were doomed to bleed beneath the tyrant's heel
> Whose selfish heart could dote but could not feel.[29]

Henry himself was an expert with the longbow, but because there had been a long period of peace and Europe was running out of yew wood bow staves, archery began to fall into general disuse. In order to bolster the indolent populace to increase their proficiency with the national weapon of offence, he decreed that:

> ...every man, being the King's subject, not lame, decrepit or maimed, do use and exercise shooting with longbows, and also do have a bow and arrows ready continually in his home to use himself in shooting...[30]

Henry further decreed that every male child over the age of seven was to have a bow; that the price of a child's yew bow should not be more than 12 pence; that the price of bow and arrows for servants could be deducted from their pay and that the fine for any and every infraction of these enactments was to be six shillings and eight pence.[30] Roger Ascham, Henry's Chronicler, wrote *Toxophile* in 1545 just before Henry embarked upon his war with France. He explains his purpose in the introduction, 'To all Gentle men and Yoeman of Englande':

> By this matter I meane the shotying in the long bowe, for English men; which thyng with all my hert I do wyth, and I were of authorite, I wolde compel all the gentle men and yoemen of Englande, not to chaunge it with any other thyng to be; but that

styll, accordyng to the oulde wont of Englande youth shoulde vse it for the moost honest pastyme in peace, that men myght handle it as a moost sure weapon in warre.[32]

About selecting the proper longbow he wrote:

If you come into a shoppe and fynde a bowe that is small, long, heavie and stronge, lying streighte, not wyndynge nor marred with knottes, gaule, wyndeshake, wen, freat or pynch, bye that bowe on my warrant...As for brasell, elme, wyche, and ashe, experience doth prove them to be mean for bowes; and so to conclude, ewe of all other things is that whereof perfite shootinge would have a bowe made.[33]

THE MARY ROSE

In the same year, Henry finished refitting a 35 year old ship, Mary Rose, with 91 pieces of heavy artillery and furnished it with a crew of 415 men. A much larger French fleet was attacking in the Solent near Portsmouth, and Henry had deployed his ships in a narrow passageway to block their entry. On that fateful July 19, there were an additional 285 heavily armed soldiers aboard, 'many of them longbowmen whose job was to blanket the French ships under a steady hail of arrows.'[34]

The weight of the guns, the extra weight of the soldiers and the archers positioning high in the masts, combined to topple the Mary Rose to one side as she wheeled to face the French. Water rushed in through the gunports and within a minute she sank to the bottom. Only 30 survived of a crew of 700. Henry, less than a mile away, heard one long collective cry as she foundered. Over four centuries later what was left preserved in the mud of the Solent was brought to the surface a piece at a time, yielding valuable artifacts and information about archers of the Tudor period. A recent article on the discovery relates:

Deadly accurate within 300 yards, longbowmen on the ship's upper deck and fighting tops could clear an enemy deck with a shower of arrows. Using leather spacers as 'ammunition clips' for two dozen steel-tipped, armor-piercing arrows, an archer could shoot about 12 rounds a minute. His six-foot-long yew bow was probably fitted with horn tips on its ends, though none survived attack by marine organisms over the years. An embossed leather or horn bracer protected his wrist from abrasion by the bow-string.

The 2,500 arrows and 139 longbows recovered from Mary Rose were found in remarkable condition. Many of the bows examined by the author were so well preserved that they could be restrung and used today.[35]

Salvaging the Mary Rose provided valuable information about the men who shot the longbow all their lives by yielding two sets of archers' bones. The older man's bones:

> ...confirmed that he was a professional archer. Two of his middle vertebrae had been pulled forward and twisted to the left, suggesting chronic pressure on his spine from that side. Also his lower left arm bone was noticeably enlarged and flattened, the result of prolonged strain. Obviously he had been right-handed and had spent long hours at the butts, as archery ranges are called.

Before the salvage of the Mary Rose it was thought that archers were only deployed on land, but as related in the article:

> ...the archer on the gun deck had obviously been prepared for action at the moment Mary Rose went down. Elsewhere in the hull we found longbows and arrows at what clearly were battle stations...

We also learned that fire was used:

> ...with the discovery of two leather mittens packed in a wooden box among the longbows and arrows. The mittens were used by archers to protect their hands while shooting fire arrows. Only the hand holding the bow needed protection, as shown by the fact that both mittens were left-handed.[36]

The loss of the Mary Rose was not a factor in the battle; the English repulsed the French and relationships between the two countries improved. Henry still had to keep England prepared and to that end he arranged for huge quantities of yew bowstaves to be imported to England from Germany, Austria and Poland. Henry also imported the landscaping phenomenon of topiary and formal gardening from France, notions he had acquired while on a royal tour. The yew, heaven-sent for these purposes, was soon trimmed and tamed into fantastic shapes in manor house gardens throughout England and Scotland. This craze has endured for centuries and there are today many fine examples of these pursuits, which we will examine in an ensuing chapter.

Upon Henry's death his sickly son Edward V took the throne, but he never actually ruled. A statute was decreed in his name however, to the effect that every Englishman living in Ireland was to have a longbow of his own height made of yew, hazel or ash. The minister Latimer summed up his own enthusiasm for archery in a sermon given before young Edward:

> In my tyme, my poore father was diligent to teach me to shoote as to learne any other thynge and so I thynke other menne dyd their children. He taught me how to drawe, how to laye my bodye in my bowe, and not to drawe with strength of armes, as other nacions do, but with strength of bodye. I had my bowes bought me according to my age and strength; as I increased in them, so my bowes were made bigger; for menne shall never shute well excepte they be brought up in it. It is a goodly arte, a holesome kind of exercise, and much commended in phisike.[37]

QUEEN ELIZABETH I

Edward died in 1553 at age 16 and was succeeded by his sister Mary who enacted a statute setting the price of bows. Mary was beheaded in 1558 after five short years as queen and was succeeded by her sister Elizabeth whose reign lasted 45 years. Though the longbow was giving way to firearms, its production and use was still enforced by statute under Elizabeth. It is apparent that by this time the efforts of earlier monarchs to acquire yew wood for bows had been so successful that there was very little servicable yew wood remaining in England. The best bow-wood was imported from the continent. According to Williamson:

> In Elizabeth's reign the yew bow was no longer such a common item, the stocks of wood, both at home and abroad, obviously having been depleted. Her Act of Bowyers ordained that every bowyer should have fifty bows made of elm, wych-hazel or ash...[it directed] that yew wood staves be imported from the Hanse towns and other places. Again, the price of bows was fixed:

'Bows meet for men's shooting being outlandish, Yew of the best sort, not over the price of 6 shillings and 8 pence; bows meet for men's shooting of the second sort 3 shillings and 4; bows for men, of a coarser sort called livery bows 2 shillings and 2 pence, bows being English Yew 2 shillings.' By then the tree had become so scarce that yew wood had to be shared around.[38]

Lowe adds, concerning Queen Elizabeth's statute:

Yew at length became so scarce, that to prevent a too great consumption of it, bowyers were directed to have four bows of witch-hazel or elm to one of yew. And no person under seventeen, unless possessed of moveables worth forty marks, or the son of parents having an estate of ten pounds per annum, might shoot 'in a yew bow.'[39]

And about archery in the time of Elizabeth:

In 1570 the art of bow-making had so much declined that the bowyers and fletchers petitioned Queen Elizabeth to enforce the Statue of Henry VIII. Grounds were marked out, and batteries erected, and the people enjoined to practise at Newington Butts...

One of the rules laid down by the founder of Harrow School in 1592 ordained that the implements of archery should be supplied by the parents of every boy entering the school. 'You shall allow your child,' it said, 'at all times, bow-shafts, bow-strings, and a bracer.'[40]

Lowe also recounts that Elizabeth:

...enjoined that they [yew] should be planted in churchyards and cemeteries, partly to ensure their cultivation and protection, and partly to secure their leaves from doing injury to cattle.[41]

During the years between 1530 and 1560, through orders of the various monarchs, England imported over half-a-million yew bowstaves from the province of Nuremburg in what is now Germany. At this time Austria and Poland were protesting the amount of yew exports and in the last half of the 16th century yew exports from these countries ceased because they ran out of yew wood.[42] Regardless of statutes and royal policy, the scarcity of yew wood brought about the demise of archery as an instrument of war. Stow lamented in 1598:

In the east end of Fore Street is More Lane; then next is Grub Street, of late years inhabited, for the most part, by bowyers, fletchers, bowstring makers, and such-like occupations, now little occupied; archery giving place to a number of bowling-alleys and dining-houses, which in all places are increased and too much frequented.

What should I speak of the ancient daily exercises in the long-bow by citizens of this City, now almost clean left off and forsaken? I overpass it; for by the means of closing in the common grounds, our archers, for want of room to shoot abroad, creep into bowling-alleys and ordinary dining-houses, near home, where they have room enough to hazard their money at unlawful games.[43]

THE ENGLISH CIVIL WAR

Charles I (1625–1649) suffered much rebellion during his reign, by the Scots and Irish outside his own borders, as well as by his fellow countrymen from within them. It was during the English Civil War at the siege of Devizes under Cromwell, that the yew wood longbow was last used as a viable instrument of war. Charles was defeated by the Roundheads and captured at Little Giddings. He was beheaded in 1649 and thus the first English experiment in government without a king in over a millenium began. A yew tree stands today in the churchyard of Holy Cross Church in Durley, Hampshire, that is claimed to be 1,500 years old, 1,200 years old at the time of Cromwell. It is said:

> ...that Oliver Cromwell tethered his horse to the yew tree. He visited Durley because he had a sister, Bridget, who married the celebrated General Ireton, and they supposedly resided in Durley for some time. True or not, the yew has stood many centuries marking the comings and goings of countless Durley folk bringing their children to Baptism, coming to weddings, and finally coming to burial in the churchyard.[44]

The longbow reigned as the major factor in English warfare for nearly 500 years. Ironically, even when the longbow began to fade from the scene, it was not because the rifles and muskets of the time were more proficient in killing the enemy. Indeed, to every ball fired by a musketeer, the archer could discharge six arrows with better accuracy and over a further distance. Archery was no longer viable because fifteen centuries of war had all but eradiacated the natural stands of European yew. No real efforts were made to cultivate the slow-growing tree, although it was planted in churchyards, archers supposedly grew it near their dwellings and manors had their yew wood groves. Despite these efforts, the demand far outstripped the capability of the slow-growing yew to provide. But still it remains an integral part of the daily lives of Englishmen through its mythic and poetic image, to which we will return in Chapter 13.

PART II

BOTANY AND GEOGRAPHY

*I had measured the trunks of other trees, but the girth
of this could not be taken unless a man went down on
his belly and drew himself snakewise through the
protecting natural hedge. May no sacrilegious hand
with hatchet or billhook ever cut a way through it.*

– William Henry Hudson

CHAPTER FOUR

THE GENUS *TAXUS* WORLDWIDE

E have seen the impact common yew *(Taxus baccata)* has had on western civilization. It is only one of several species distributed throughout the northern hemisphere and we can surmise from the available information that the others played similar roles in the cultures where they grew.

ANCIENT TAXUS

The Yew is an evergreen Gymnosperm of the order, *Taxales*; family, *Taxacae* and genus, *Taxus*. Botanists disagree on the exact taxonomy and divide the genus into from six to ten species distributed through-out the northern temperate zones of Asia, Asia Minor, India, Europe, North Africa and North America. There is little over-lap of species from one region to the next. All species survive and most thrive when moved from one temperate region to another and the differences between them are eclipsed by their similarities. Regardless of the number of species, all are thought to descend from *Paleotaxus rediviva*, which was widely distributed across the land mass before it separated into the continents of today. The form of *Paleotaxus rediviva* was imprinted on a Triassic Age fossil laid down 200,000,000 years ago.[1]

Two more recent fossils of yew have been found. *Taxus jurassica*, which dates from the middle of the Jurassic Age (140,000,000 years ago), contained the various characteristics of the modern species *Taxus*, specifically *T. baccata* (European yew), *T. cuspidata* (Japanese Yew) and *T. brevifolia* (Pacific yew). *Taxus grandis* from the Quarternary period (less than a million years ago) is very near to the European yew.[2] Judging by pollen counts taken from peat bogs in Europe, yew trees grew there in much greater abundance during the sub-boreal and sub-atlantic eras than they do now. Since the last Ice Age the yew has been in decline.[3]

PALEOTAXUS REDIVIVA

Peat bog excavations in the southern half of the Fenland basin have exposed remnants of ancient English forests. As Oliver Rackham reports, in *Ancient Woodland,* 1980:

> The trees were rooted in clayey or sandy mineral soil under the peat and were the last generation of trees that grew before the peat formed. They were killed by a sudden rise in the water-table; they rotted and were felled by storms; and their stumps and trunks were entombed by the growth of peat. Most of the trees on the clay were oaks and had grown up closely-spaced to a height now seldom seen in Europe; lengths of 90 ft. to the first branch have been reported. In the eastern Fens, where the soil was more sandy, pines of similar size and yews of great age predominate. Trees later grew on the peat itself but never reached these sizes.[4]

In interglacial forests elsewhere in Europe, *T. baccata* composed up to 80 percent of the primeval plant population. In Poland botanists have traced the yew back to the Holocene, nearly 10,000 years ago, when it grew all over Europe. The occurrence of yew in Europe has declined dramatically because of its continuous harvest by man.[5]

SEVEN SPECIES

Yew's natural habitat ranges from as far north as the 61st parallel in Sweden and the Amur River basin of Russia to as far south as Sumatra and El Salvador. Taxonomists have not always agreed on the number of species and their differentiation. Pilger in 1916 classified seven subspecies under *Taxus baccata: eubaccata* (Europe, Western Asia, North Africa), *wallichiana* (Himalayas), *cuspidata* (Japan), *brevifolia* (western North America), *canadensis* (eastern North America), *floridana* (Florida) and *globosa* (Mexico).[6]

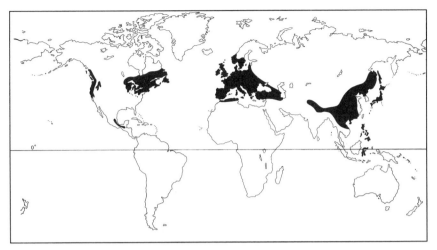

WORLD DISTRIBUTION OF THE GENUS *TAXUS*

Contemporary taxonomy divides the genus into seven species, although, as U.S. Forest Service botanist Charles Bolsinger points out:

> Where different species grow near each other, interspecific hybrids frequently occur, lending support to the view that there is but one species. Further evidence of the close similarity of the species of *Taxus* is provided by bark analyses which show that most species contain taxol [an anti-cancer agent], and by an analysis of heartwood constitutents of *T. baccata, T. brevifolia, T. cuspidata,* and *T. floridana*: the four species were found to be 'chemically almost indistinguishable.'[7]

The genus *Taxus* includes eight species: *T. baccata, T. sumatrana, T. floridana, T. brevifolia, T. canadensis, T. wallichiana, T. cuspidata* and *T. globosa.* The above *taxi* are so closely related that according to some investigators they constitute geographic variations of the same species and they are considered intraspecific variants of the basic species *T. baccata* native to Europe and the Mediterranean countries.[8]

Like the European yew, species on other continents exist today in substantially smaller populations than they once did. They are widely distributed but in scattered sparse stands. The largest natural population of yew left is in the Pacific Northwest of the United States and Canada, where Pacific yew *(T. brevifolia)* survives in what remains of its natural habitat – the old growth rain forest.

Range, distribution and characteristics of the European and Pacific yews will be presented in Chapters 5 and 9. Briefer descriptions of the other species are given here.

NORTH AMERICAN YEW

Besides *T. brevifolia*, there are three other species of yew found in North America. *T. canadensis*, found in the U.S. and Canada, is called both American and Canadian yew or sometimes ground hemlock. It grows into a hardy, dense shrub, usually not exceeding six feet in height. However, some specimens exist in the wild that are up to twelve feet tall and appear more like trees than shrubs. Humphrey Marshall named the plant in 1785; prior to that it was thought to be a variety of *T. baccata*. In its natural state, the Canadian yew is found from Newfoundland to Manitoba and southward into New England, and as far south as western Virginia. It is also found in the states of Indiana, Illinois, Iowa and North Dakota.

Because of its predominately shrub-like nature, I found nothing regarding the use of this species for making tools or weapons. It is, however, known to be poisonous. Friedberger and Frohner give the symptoms:

> Death may be sudden, resembling apoplexy; it may be preceded by staggering and convulsions; cases of long standing show gastro-enteritis. Give purgatives as remedies.[9]

Many poisonous substances have medicinal value precisely because of their toxicity and the Canadian yew was used for a variety of medicinal purposes among Native North Americans, as Duke, who called it 'American yew', attests:

> Abenaki infused the leaves for rheumatism. Algonquin boiled the needles with wild cherry for rheumatism, taking the tea after childbirth. Chippewa employed the twig decoction, externally or internally, for rheumatism. Malecite employed the plant to bring out clots and alleviate pain following childbirth. Canada's Maritime employed yew for afterbirth, clots, fever, pain, and scurvy. Menominee steamed the plant in herbal sweat baths for numbness, paralysis, and rheumatism. Micmac used it for bowel

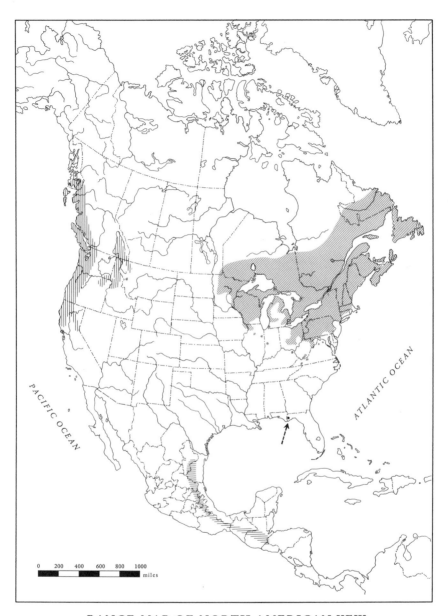

RANGE MAP OF NORTH AMERICAN YEW

Pacific Yew   Canadian Yew

Florida Yew   Mexican Yew

ailments, fever, and scurvy. Montagnai use it with Lycopodium for debility and fever. Ojibwa used leaf decoction for arthritis. Penobscot steeped the leaves for colds. Potawatomi used the leaf decoction as a diuretic, for gonorrhea. Tete-de-Boule infused the twigs with ash for dysmenorrhea and stomachache.[10]

The Florida yew *(T. floridana)* was named by Chapman in 1860. Not as hardy as its brothers and sisters, its habitat is limited to the valleys and dells east of the Apiachicola River in northwestern Florida. It attains a height of 15 feet and its curved, slender, dark-green leaves are nearly an inch long. The few Florida yew left are protected. According to Godfrey the largest is found in Torreya State Park. In 1971 it had a circumference of 1 foot 3 inches; a height of 18 feet and a spread of 28 feet.[11]

The fourth North American yew, *T. globosa* or Mexican yew, ranges from the state of Nuevo Leon in northeastern Mexico, to as far south as Guatemala and El Salvador. It too has been considered by some botanists to be a variety of *T. baccata*. Named by Schlectendal, it was first discovered in 1837. It is smaller than other species of yew, except *T. canadensis*, rarely exceeding 15 feet in height. The light-green leaves are larger and sharper than those of *T. baccata* and the mature red female aril is larger than that of other species.[12]

JAPANESE YEW

Several species of yew are found in Asia. In common with other yews, the resilient and durable qualities of the wood and the toxicity of leaves and bark have led to similar uses. It appears that, just as in Europe, the Asian species have been decimated for their utility.

T. cuspidata, or Japanese yew, was named by von Siebold and Zuccarini in 1846. It was introduced into England in 1855, and into the United States in 1862. Japanese yew attains a height of 50 feet and is said to be hardier than European yew.[13] Its common shape is upright and pyramidal, with an abundance of reddish-brown mature branchlets ascending through spreading branches. The young leaves are a lighter green than the European yew. Their undersides are tinged with yellow. Like the European yew, it also is easily shaped into hedge and topiary forms and when pruned properly, produces a velvet-like, dense foliage.

It is the fastest growing species of *Taxus* and the easiest to cultivate.[14] Japanese yew is native to the islands of Hokkaido, Honshu, Shikoku and Kyusu. It is also found in Manchuria and in eastern Russia from the Amur river basin to the forests of central Korea.[15]

Ernest Henry Wilson's book on Japanese trees, published in 1916, gives an account of Japanese yew:

> As a wild tree *T. cuspidata* cannot be said to be common any-where in Japan that I visited except, perhaps, in Kitami province, Hokkaido. On the lower slopes of Fuji-san in Suruga province, Hondo, and more especially round the villages of Gotemba and Yamanaka, there are many fine trees of this Yew, but it is impossible to decide whether they are wild or planted.
> The largest trees I saw were from 15 to 16 meters tall and about 2 meters in girth of trunk. The branches are usually very numerous...The bark is red-brown, sometimes grayish brown, and shallowly fissured. When this Yew fruits it appears to bear very large crops and many trees which I saw presented a wonderful sight with their wealth of scarlet fruits. The wood is red or reddish brown, very hard, tough and durable. It is very lasting in wet soil and on this account is valued for piles in the foundations of houses and buildings generally. It is also highly esteemed for cabinet-work, for carving and and for indoor-decorations of better-class houses. Formerly the Japanese used it for making bows, as do the Ainu people to the present day. In Hondo the common name for this tree is Ichii and in Hokkaido it is Onko.[16]

The Japanese also used yew wood for water tanks, pails, bath tubs, trays, chopsticks, and clogs.[17] Wilson saw the finest Japanese yews in Korea:

> In the Diamond Mountains in central Korea, grow more trees and finer specimens than I have seen elsewhere. Scattered through woods of spruce, fir, oak, birch and other broadleaf trees are hundreds of specimen yews – from 40 to 60 feet tall, 6-10 feet in girth, with large spreading branches forming handsome crowns. And on the Korean island of Quelpaert, in pure woods of hornbeam, I found the Japanese yew in bush form to be a common undergrowth.[18]

Duke tells us that the leaves were used for an abortifacient and antidiabetic. More recently it has shown promise as the producer of an anti-cancer agent.[19] Most of the remaining stands of *T. cuspidata* are found in Eastern Russia. When first brought to America in 1833, the Japanese yew was known as 'Fir of the Goddess of Mercy'. It has since, according to many, become 'the most valuable evergreen Japan has given America,' and as an ornamental shrub or small tree it does well in sun or shade.[20]

CHINESE YEWS

Taxus mairei grows in China and Taiwan, and was named by the botanists Lemee and Leveille. It is called za shen, which means 'purple fir'. It may or may not be a distinct species. Various experts disagree; some think it is *T. celebica* (Warburg); others call it *T. speciosa* (Florin) or *T. sumatrana* (De Laubenfels). It grows into a large tree, up to 50 feet in height and 9 feet in circumference. Like other species of Taxus it has reddish bark, but the two-tone leaves are dark green on top and pale green underneath with two yellow bands on the underside.[21]

Silba states that the following species named by De Laubenfels, *T. chinensis, T. celebica, T. mairei* and *T. speciosa*, are all actually *T. sumatrana* (Asian yew) also named by De Laubenfels, which according to Silba is found in India, Burma, China, Vietnam, Indonesia, Sumatra, Celebes, Philippines and Taiwan at altitudes of 1,300 to 7,000 feet. He describes Asian yew thus:

> A large broad shrub or a small tree 15–30 meters tall, to 1 meter in girth, with short, fine branches. Bark reddish-purple, smooth, thin, fissured...Leaves [are] dark shiny green above, bright green below with 2 large gray bands of stomata.[22]

HIMALAYAN YEW

Taxus wallichiana, or Himalayan yew, named by Zuccarini, is found in Afghanistan, Burma, Bhutan, China, India, Nepal, Philippines and Tibet at altitudes of 5,000 to 10,000 feet. The tree is similar in appearance to the European yew and grows into a large shrub or tree as high as 60 feet. The leaves are longer and narrower than the European yew with a glossy deep-green color on top and paler underneath.[23]

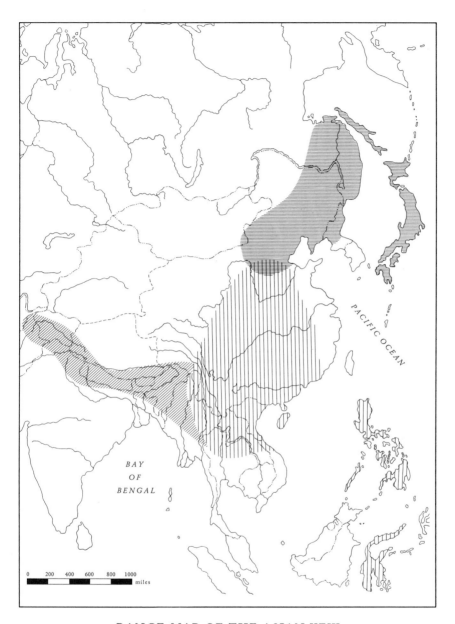

RANGE MAP OF THE ASIAN YEW

Himalayan Yew   Chinese Yew   Japanese Yew

In the Punjab Himalayas the yew is called *rakhal*[24], elsewhere in India it is called *tingschi*. According to Lowe, it is used for:

> ...native bedsteads...jampan poles, upholstery, and clogs. Whip-handles are also made of the branches, and from time immemorial it has been the principal wood used for bows.The bark (*sang, sangha*) is exported to Ladak from Kunawar, to be mixed with tea and to be used as a red dye.[25]

Brandis says, in his *Forest Flora of India:*

> The tree is held in great veneration in some parts of the northwest Himalayas; it is called Deodar (God's tree); the wood is burnt for incense, branches are carried in religious processions in Mamaon and in Nepal the houses are decorated with the green twigs at religious festivals.[26]

Brahmins in some parts of India mark the little red dots on their foreheads with a paste made from powdered yew bark and oil, and according to H.A. Rose: 'The god of the dwelling in Kula in the Punjab Himalayas is called *bastar*, and a sprig of yew is offered to him.'[27]

Although there is much confusion about the number, names and differentiation of species, it is clear that all are very similar. It is also clear that civilization has been the major predator of the yew. Imagine fitting out the armies of Alexander, the legions of Rome, the crusaders and the medieval armies of Europe. Still it survives in small, revered and studied pockets throughout most of the northern hemisphere.

YEW CULTIVARS

It survives in another way as well. Since the 17th century many varieties of yew have been planted in private and public gardens, parks and arboretums. Today it is one of the most popular genera of plants for landscaping. From the seven or so original species, hundreds of cultivars have been developed with a multitude of differing characteristics. They vary in height from 18 inches to 90 feet, in girth from one inch to 30 feet; in color from black through blue and green to red and gold; in needle length, from one-half inch to an inch and a half; in shape, from low-lying shrub to tall, cone-shaped columns; from the unruly specimen in the wild to the sculptured topiary in the garden.

The reason for this wide variety is the high morphological variability of the yew. According to one European botanist, Wladyslaw Bugala:

> Yew is one of the oldest conifers, a relict genus, which is becoming extinct, just as tree ferns or Ginkgo trees, yet it is distinguished by a large scale of variability and has a great ability to produce new varieties...Its innate ability to produce various habitat and color forms has been increased by crossing species from distant geographical regions.[28]

And Adam Czartoryski, another botanist:

> The old spatial specific isolation of yew gave rise to its possessing a group of genetic characters, uniform and close-knit, unmarred since the Tertiary (1,000,000 years ago) by a crossing of species or geographical races. The yew has thus many characters of 'old', 'relict' species. It is hardy; variable, yet resistant; rare and inexpansive, but lasting; it grows slowly, but for a long time.[29]

Another reason yew survives today is that toxic urban environments apparently do not bother it; it has in fact an 'astounding resistance' to combustion engine fumes.[30] It adapts to many different habitats and can resist serious setbacks such as heavy browsing by animals or unfavorable climatic conditions for years, resuming healthy growth when favorable conditions return.[31]

One article published in 1923 recounts the many virtues of yew:

> But for the purpose of making a decorative garden, no other material is so well adapted. When thickly planted; the yews produce wind-breaks, and in the outskirts and suburbs of the city, where no other evergreen will thrive because of the soot, smoke, dust and gases, the yew will still grow luxuriantly. It also withstands the pruning knife like no other plant. The twigs may be cut or mutilated, always new shoots are made, and the needlelike leaves become thicker and denser.[32]

Yews, for the most part, are easily cultivated, transplant well and survive throughout the northern temperate zone. They withstand repeated pruning, eventually forming dense, velvet-like foliage. They are easily contained in formal shapes and serve the modern gardener well as hedges, screens, topiary and as natural specimens like those found in many English churchyards. Low-growing varieties, like the

Canadian yew make good ground cover beneath woodlands and serve well as a deterrent to erosion.

Yews are not particular about the soil they grow in, though they prefer moist, fertile, sandy loam. They will not grow well in water-logged ground or sticky, wet clay soils. They are propagated through cuttings, seed, grafting or layering. Cuttings taken from lateral branches generally produce shrub-like plants, while those from erect, topward branches are more likely to produce a tree. Yew has been found to be beneficial in propagating other species; cuttings soaked in an infusion of crushed yew and water produce quicker and healthier root growth.

In addition to the seven or eight natural species of yew, two hybrids have been created. *T. media* was bred for the hardiness of Japanese yew and the ornamental nature of European yew. Large specimens reach a height of 40 feet, are densely branched and can grow into either broad or conical shaped trees. The older branchlets of *T. media* range in color from olive-green to red. *T. hunnewilliana*, a second hybrid, is less common. Its parent species are Japanese yew and Canadian yew. Its light-green leaves take on a reddish tint in winter.

An article written by E.H. Wilson in 1920 describes the most popular varieties of *T. baccata*:

> The principal varieties of the English Yew are about a dozen in number and of these the Irish or Florence Court Yew (*fastigiata*) is perhaps the most strikingly distinct and best known...The Dovaston Yew (*dovastonii*) is another well-known form...This is a tree or wide-spreading shrub with branches arising in whorls and becoming quite pendulous at their extremities. The original tree was planted as a seedling about the year 1777, at Westfelton, near Shrewsbury, England, and is a female tree. There is a form of this Yew (*aureo-variegata*) in which the leaves are variegated with yellow. There is another Weeping Yew (*pendula*) which is a low dense shrub with no definite leader.
>
> There are several forms of Golden Yew and one is known to have been growing in Staffordshire in 1686. The best known (*aurea*) is male and is a dense shrub or low tree with narrow sickle-shaped leaves which are variegated with yellow. Another good sort is *Washingtonii*, a low, dense shrub in which the leaves on the young shoots are golden yellow. Of low-growing forms there are several including *horizontalis*, *recurvata*, and

procumbens, sufficiently distinguished by their names. But another dwarf form which is grown in the Arnold Arboretum under the name of *Taxus baccata repandens* is worthy of fuller mention. Its origin is unknown and it is remarkable as being the only form of the English Yew which is properly hardy...It has widespreading semi-prostrate branches and broad, black-green leaves.

Wilson goes on to say that another fifty or more varieties of European Yew have received names and 'they exhibit the widest possible range of variation in form and general appearance.' Of the Japanese Yew he says:

> In Japanese gardens it is a favorite as a low, clipped bush and it is also used as a hedge plant, but not extensively. It was one of these garden forms (*nana*) that was first introduced to this country, and this has been propagated largely by cuttings. It is a low, wide-spreading shrub with short leaves. There is another form (*densa*) which is also a low, compact shrub – but when seedlings from these dwarf forms are raised they revert to the tree type.
>
> The first tree forms of this Yew raised in this country were from seeds collected in Japan in 1892, by Professor Sargent and the tallest of these in the Arnold Arboretum is now 8 feet. Quite recently an erect form (*Hicksii*) has appeared in the Hicks Nurseries on Long Island. As time goes on and the Japanese Yew is freely raised from seeds, other forms will arise; and there is little doubt that it will ultimately produce as great a variety as the English Yew has done. This is a matter that our nurserymen should pay attention to.[33]

In 1926 he added to his praise of Japanese Yew:

> For any and every purpose in which evergreens are required the Japanese Yew can be recommended. For placing beneath windows, for flanking doorways, as specimens on the lawn or in the formal garden and as a hedge-plant there is nothing better. Perfectly hardy, immune from disease or pest, accommodating to an extra-ordinary degree, withstanding shade or full sunshine, black green at all seasons of the year, small wonder that the plant has been acclaimed Japan's greatest gift to the gardens of the colder parts of North America.[34]

Besides the natural and hybrid species, there are hundreds of varieties of garden yew, or cultivars. The most famous yew cultivar is

T. baccata fatigeata, or Irish yew. It is sometimes referred to as *T. baccata stricta*. Not purposely bred, this female yew was found by a farmer named Willis in the mountains of Fermangh in Ireland in 1780. He found two trees; one of which he planted in the home of his landlord at Florence Court; the other, in his own yard. The one at Florence Court survives and every existing Irish yew was obtained from a cutting or graft from this yew. Its foliage is black-green and the berries are bright red. It is more erect than the European yew and grows naturally in a tall columnar shape. In 1927, the existence of male Irish yews was discovered when shoots bearing male characteristics were sent to Kew Gardens from Sussex.

IRISH YEW AT WARWICK CASTLE

From my experience looking for yew trees in the United States and England, I would venture to say that there are probably more yew trees alive in urban parks and the front yards of suburbia then there are in the wild. It is ironic that this indomitable species has crept back into our midst in this fashion despite our efforts to obliterate it in its natural habitat.

CHAPTER FIVE

EUROPEAN YEW
(TAXUS BACCATA)

DISTRIBUTION

HE most well-known species of yew is *Taxus baccata*, named by Linnaeus in the 15th century. It is also called European, English or common yew. It grows to an average height of 30 feet, but in some instances as high as 90 feet and attains a girth in excess of 20 feet under optimum conditions. Ancient remains of yew trees preserved in peat bogs indicate that they grew at one time to tremendous size and age. For most of the past 10,000 years yew has been at least a co-dominant species in the European and English forests. *T. baccata* is now sparsely distributed throughout:

> ...the British Isles, southern Norway and southern Sweden. In the Scandinavian countries it reaches up to 61 degrees northern latitude. It grows in the Baltic countries. In the Alps it reaches the altitude of 1,100–1,400 metres above sea level, in the Carpathians 1,660 metres, in the Caucasus 1,500 metres, and Asia Minor 2,300 metres. It also grows in the Mediterranean countries and North Africa.
>
> The eastern limit of the range of yew in Europe runs from the Gulf of Riga, through Bialowieza to the Carpathians (along 23 meridian), and from the East Carpathians southeast. Yew avoids areas with the continental climate, hence this limitation of its occurrence in Eastern Europe.[1]

The fate of the yew tree in Europe is well documented in a work published in 1975, *Cis Pospolity*, which is a collection of articles by

ANCIENT SPECIMEN OF THE EUROPEAN YEW
THE WARBLINGTON YEW, ENGLAND; 1600 YEARS OLD, 25 FEET IN GIRTH.

Polish scientists. One point made by several contributors is that despite intense study, all efforts to save yew trees in their natural habitat seem to be failing. According to Stanislaw Krol, this does not mean that the yew or its natural forest communities have undergone any essential changes in their requirements for normal development, but as Krol points out:

> The fact is unquestionable that the yew is a perishing species – that is, a species with a shrinking natural range not only in Poland and Central Europe but also in the peripheries of its area.[2]

There are yew reservations throughout Europe and individual trees are noted. There are yew trees in some public parks and churchyards in France and Italy. In Germany the yew is completely protected. Single trees are found in the mountains, but it is very rarely found in the north German flatlands and has disappeared over wide areas. As of 1932 there were still quite a few yew trees in Austria and the Tyrol. The largest remaining stands of yew in Germany are found in the Verreland.[3] There is a venerable yew tree near Balderschwang which is the center of controversy. Like the Fortingall yew in Scotland, the Balderschwang

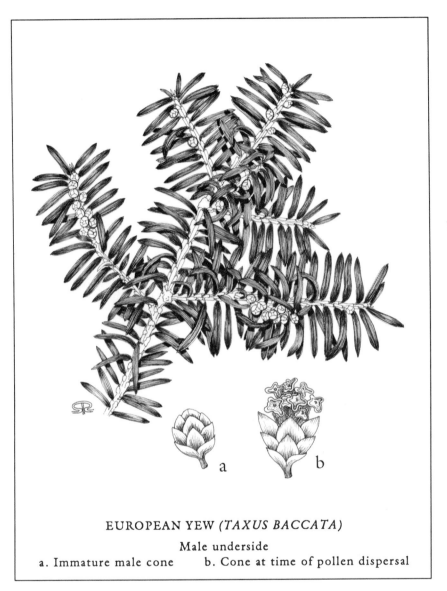

EUROPEAN YEW *(TAXUS BACCATA)*
Male underside
a. Immature male cone   b. Cone at time of pollen dispersal

Eibe has two gnarled trunks opposing one another with a meter of space between them. Some German dendrologists think it is one tree with the middle rotted out, others that it is actually two trees. If it is one tree, then its circumference would be about 24 feet and its age between 1,500 and 2,000 years old. Another yew called the Hintersteiner Eibe, near Bargundele, is nearly 10 feet in circumference and is said to be 2,000 years old.[4]

In Poland yew trees and groves have been studied for many years. The first law regarding its protection was enacted by decree of King Wladyslaw Jagiello early in the 15th century.

> Anyone who, entering a forest, would fell trees of a high value, such as the yew or its like, can be detained by the landlord or the squire...[5]

Apparently this was to keep valuable yew wood out of the hands of the Teutonic Knights and allied merchant guilds who were exporting large numbers of logs to England.

In Poland in 1975, the largest stand of yews was in the reservation in Wierzchlas Forest on Mukrz Lake. In 1892, Conventz counted 5,533 yews; the tallest was nearly 40 feet and the largest girth was about 4 feet 6 inches. The largest yew tree in Poland, in Henrykow, measures over 15 feet in circumference, another in Bystrzyca is 11 feet 6 inches, one in Mogilno is 10 feet and the Raciborski Yew in Harbutowice is 8 feet 6 inches in circumference.[6]

There are concentrations of yew in Hungary; 100,000 yews near Great Fatra in 1975 and about 45,000 mature yews in the Bakony Forest. There are also yew reservations in Czechoslovakia, in the Ukraine (about 35,000 trees near Kolomya), Rumania, and the Caucasus.[7] In Greece, where once it provided the armies of Alexander with stout weapons, the yew is found sparsely in remote places; usually on limestone, in wild deciduous forests at elevations 800 to 2,200 meters. It rarely regenerates on its own.[8]

There is a handful of notable old yew trees in Greece including one on the Sithonia with a girth of 15 feet, several in Arcoudolaccas ravine near Mt. Cholomon, and near the ruined Aghios Dionysios monastery are trees nearly 10 inches in girth.[9]

PLACE NAMES

European yew is found today in over 30 countries and its various common names relate back to Latin (*taxus*), Gaelic (*an-t-iuchar*) or Celtic (*yewar*).[10] According to W.J. Bean, many place names were

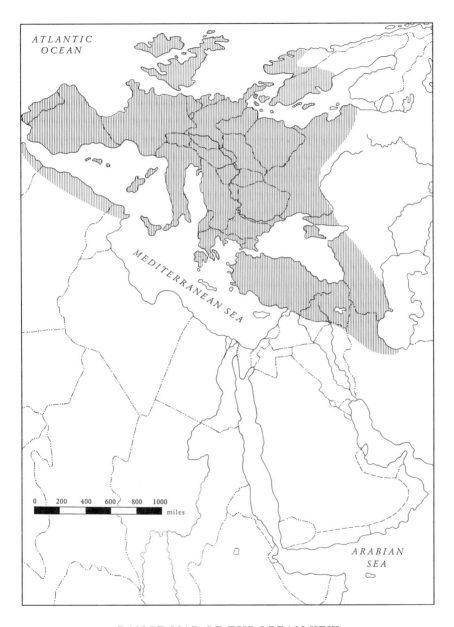

RANGE MAP OF EUROPEAN YEW

▥ *Taxus Baccata*

derived from the yew:

> In Europe the yew has been on the retreat ever since man
> acquired the ability to fell it. Many ancient stands on the
> continent have been reduced to stunted remnants or extermi-
> nated; place names often indicate its earlier presence in areas from
> which it has long since disappeared.[11]

The yew grows throughout Great Britain and Ireland, although the
natural distribution patterns have been rearranged by man; it once
grew in denser stands, but was less widely distributed. Some place
names derived from yew in England, are:

Ebernoe	spur of land by a yew
Eudon	yew hill
Eridge	yew ridge
Ewhurst	yew wood
Ewshott	yew grove
Ibrook	yew brook
Iburn	yew stream
Ifield	yew field
Ifold	yew vale
Iford	yew ford
Iridge	yew ridge
Ive	from *iwa*: yew
Ivegill	valley of the yew
Iwade	yew ford
Iwerne	a river named yew
Iwode	yew wood
Iwood	yew wood
Yeo	river on whose banks yew grows
Yeoford	ford in the Yeo river
Yeovil	town on the river Yeo
Yewdale	yew valley[12]

Various public houses in England have taken their name from the
yew. There is a Yew Tree Inn in Derby, near Matlock. In Barrowdale,
Cumbria, where the Four Brethren immortalized by Wordsworth once
lived, is the Yew Tree Pub. A nearby stretch of steep chalk hillside called
The Yew Tree Crags is sprung throughout with gnarled, wind-sculpted
yew trees.

The name York is also derived from yew.[13] Before the Romans arrived there were vast forests of yew in York. A principal Roman outpost, Eburacum (which means essentially yewtown), was situated just north of the river Humber. Today there are few yews left in York, not even in the churchyards, because the Romans logged the trees for chariot axles, and spears, lances and bows to arm their legions. The Saxons and Danes no doubt took care of whatever the Romans left behind, for they too hunted and made war with yew wood weapons.

In Ireland, Dr. Conventz found 'more than a hundred place names compounded with yew.' He also found yew fossils in many places where there were no yew trees living.[14] Adrian Room cites Irish place names associated with yew:

Aghadoe	field of the two yews
Ahoghill	ford of yew trees
Killenure	secluded spot of yew
Killure	church of the yew
Loughanure	lake of the yew
Mayobridge	bridge of the plain of the yew trees
Moynoe	plain of the yews
Newrath	yew land
Newry	the yew tree
Terenure	land of the yew tree
Ture	the yew tree
Uregare	short yew tree
Virginia	field of the yew tree
Wood of O	yew tree wood
Youghal	yew wood[15]

Names derived from yew are found throughout Europe, even in places where there haven't been yew trees for centuries. For instance, one form of Spanish for yew is *Ibe* and early records show that yew trees grew in great profusion on the Iberian Peninsula, where today there are few. Speculation as to the true etymology of the name 'Europe' itself is tempting. There was Eburobriga in the heart of Europe; there was also 'an Eburomagus in Aude (Bram), an Eburodunum in Switzerland (Yverdon) and an Embrum in the High Alps.'[16]

"THE WOOD IS TIGHT-GRAINED, HARD AND RESILIENT."

USES AS WOOD

The yew has been employed by man since he first stood under a tree for shelter, or used sticks for firewood and clubs, bark for pigment or leaves for poison and medicine. Yew trees are slow growing; the wood is tight-grained, hard and resilient; well-suited to the woodworker's art. It resists rot and endures; ancient yew wood implements can be found in museums throughout Europe.

The oldest known wooden implement is a spear made of yew in Clacton-on-Sea, Essex. It is said to be about 50,000 years old.[17] Another spear was found in Lower Saxony between the ribs of a straight-tusked elephant.[18] The oldest known yew wood art objects are two sculptures of the Egyptian Queen Teje, wife of Pharaoh Anemenhet III, from 1400 B.C.[19], one of her face and one full-bodied statuette.

The lake dwellers in Switzerland used yew wood tools over 10,000 years ago:

QUEEN TEJE

In the lake or pile dwellings of the Swiss, bows and knives were

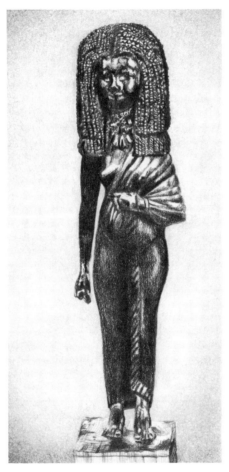

EGYPTIAN STATUETTE OF QUEEN TEJE

found made of this wood and in spite of the thousands of years of dampness, they are in perfect condition.[20]

Many afficionados of wood have praised yew over the years, lauding its many uses, as did Selby in 1842:

The wood of the Yew possesses qualities of first-rate excellence, being not only hard, compact, of a fine and close grain, and elastic, but susceptible of a very high polish and almost incorruptible. The colour of the matured wood is peculiarly rich, varying from shades of the finest orange red to the deepest brown, and near to the root and at the ramification of the branches it is marbled and veined in a way surpassed by few of the finest foreign cabinet woods; the sap wood, also, which is white and of a firm and hard texture, may be worked up with the other kind, and thus add to the numerous shades of colour it exhibits. From the qualities above enumerated, the Yew may safely be pronounced, not only one of the most valuable among European trees for cabinet purposes, but scarcely, if at all, inferior to the most costly exotic woods that have been introduced; unfortunately, from the neglect of not having been treated as a timber tree, or planted extensively with a view to profit, it is not, at present, to be procured in quantity sufficient to make it generally available for the larger articles of furniture, and its application is, therefore, restricted to the making of small tables, work-boxes...veneers... inlaid work and the smaller wares of the turner.[21]

Dr. Conventz wrote of a somewhat bizarre use put to yew wood, in Germany, where it is made into:

...A die with signs and letters cut in it, with which cakes are marked, which are then given to mad dogs in order to cure them. In Sweden patterns for printing wall-papers were formerly made of yew; in several countries shuttles...on the Aland Island the may-poles are decorated with yew twigs.[22]

John Lowe in *The Yew Trees of Great Britain and Ireland*, published in 1897, says:

It was formerly much used in the manufacture of Tunbridge ware. It is converted into 'cogs for mills, posts to be set in the ground, and everlasting axle-trees.' Bows also are made from it, and spoons, cups, and 'flood-gates for fish-ponds, which hardly ever decay.' ...the wooden part of a bed made of yew 'will most certainly not be approached by bugs.' 'Cabinet-makers and inlayers most gladly employ it...there is none to be compared with it...likewise for bodies of lutes, theorboes, bowls, wheels, and pins for pulleys; yea, and for tankards to drink out of.'[23]

Other European sources add that yew wood was also used for: '...household ware, combs, tool handles, pegs, veneers, turner's products, wood-carving, and sculptures.'[24] It should be noted that 'even the powder produced in processing yew wood is harmful to craftsmen.'[25]

POISON AND MEDICINE

The yew is poisonous and was used for fish and animal poisons as well as arrow poison by primitive and early historical cultures. It was also used for murder and suicide. It is known to be harmful to most animals, particularly cows and horses, as is shown in this toxicity chart presented by Lowe:

For each kilogramme of weight of the live animal,

Horse	2 grammes
Ass or Mule	1 gr. 60
Sheep	10 gr.
Goat	12 gr.
Cow	10 gr.
Pig	3 gr.
Dog	8 gr.
Rabbit	20 gr.[26]

If a man were like an ass or mule, then at 150 pounds 4 ounces of wet yew leaves would be fatal. There are many instances of deadly mishap and misfortune with yew berries. Lowe recounts:

Taylor records two cases of poisoning thus caused, one of which died comatose four hours after the berries had been eaten, and the other nineteen days afterwards, evidently from severe inflammation of the bowels. Another case is reported by Mr. Newth in which death resulted from eating the berries, and two are given in the Gardener's Chronicle for 1881. A lunatic in the Sussex County Asylum had eaten large quantities of them and was found dead. At the post-mortem examination evident signs of irritation of the stomach and intestines were discovered.[27]

The foliage is also poisonous as Dr. Percival of Manchester, wrote in 1774:

...three children of a labouring man, near Manchester, were killed by taking a small quantity of the fresh leaves on the recommendation of an ignorant person, for the cure of worms. A spoonful of dried leaves was first given, followed by a drink of sour buttermilk. This produced no ill effect, and two days afterwards the same dose of fresh leaves was administered, causing the death of all three children. Two hours after the leaves were given they began to be uneasy; were chilly and listless; yawned much, and frequently stretched out their limbs. The eldest vomited a little, and complained of abdominal pains. The others expressed no signs of pains. No agonies accompanied their dissolution; no swelling of the abdomen ensued; and after death they had the appearance of being in a placid sleep.[28]

Mark Silber recounts a tale from *The Gardener's Dictionary* in 1807:

A clergyman, who was a curate in Sussex, informed me that a young lady and her servant, his parishioners, being seized with an ague, were advised to take a decoction of Rue, which they unhappily mistaking for Yew, sent to the church-yard, where a large old tree grew, and gathered a quantity of the leaves, of which they made a decoction and drank it upon going to bed. The next morning they were both found dead. This was Sunday: on the Thursday following, the clergyman was called upon to bury them: he performed the office on the servant, but the young lady had so fine a bloom on her countenance, that they entertained hopes of her being in a state of suspended animation, and even then the corpse remained totally unchanged. What made it more remarkable was, that the accident happened in November, and the weather was of that damp murky kind in which the flesh keeps the worst.[29]

Many cultures used yew for medicine; teas were made of leaves and bark, powders from the bark; even the wood itself was thought to have healing properties. Europeans used the yew as an abortifacient and as a cure for hydrophobia and heart ailments. Claudius suggested in the 1st. century A.D. that the juice of yew served as an antidote to the bite of the viper. Du Monceau and Lowe noted its use as a heart tonic and one Anglo-Saxon remedy, translated by Cockayne from a 10th century leech-book, said:

If a man is in the water elf disease, then are the nails of his hands livid, and the eyes tearful, and he will look downwards. Give him this for a leechdom. Everthroat, Cassuck, the netherward part of Fane, a Yew berry, Lupin, Helenium, a head of Marsh Mallow, Fen, Mint, Dill, Lily, Attorlothe, Pulegim, Marrubium, Dock, Elder, Felterrae, Wormwood, Strawberry leaves, Consolida; pour them over with ale, add holy water, and sing this charm over them thrice.[30]

Folklore has provided many leads for modern scientists who screen plants for possible medicinal use. Plants that are known to be toxic to humans, or those used for fish and animal poisons, seem to show the most promise.[31] This is certainly the case for yew, as will be fully discussed in Chapter 11.

YEW FORESTS

There are native stands of yew trees in England, particularly in the south, where remnants of the old forests remain, which have been studied, measured and described for centuries. John Evelyn wrote in *Sylva: Discourse On Trees* in 1664:

> He that in winter should behold some of our highest Hills in Surrey, clad with whole Woods of these two last sort of Trees [yew and box]...might without the least violence to his Imagination, easily phansie himself transported into some new, or enchanted Country...[32]

John Selby in 1842:

> The Yew is indigenous to Britain, growing naturally in various parts of England and Scotland, and particularly affecting rocky and mountainous wooded districts. It is also found in similar situations in Ireland, advancing to as high a range as 1,200 feet. It seems to prefer a northerly or cool aspect, and grows freely under the shade of many deciduous trees... It is not, however, a tree of much power of occupancy, being seldom found growing in large masses together, but usually solitary or intermingled with other trees.[33]

W.D. Dallimore in 1908:

> It is a common tree in the British Isles, and is fairly evenly distributed, plants which must have originated as wild examples being met with in many different places, whilst ample evidence is at hand to prove that it formed at least a portion of the woods and forests of pre-historic times.[34]

The most complete surviving stand is in Kingley Vale on the South Downs near Chichester. William Henry Hudson (1841–1922) described it:

The grove is an isolated wood, or rather forest, composed almost wholly of yew trees, growing in a broad combe [hollow] in the side of a down; and above about the dark green of the yews the round light-green summit is seen like a head crowned with a row of immense barrows. In one part of the wood, on the right hand as you go up from the vale, there is no undergrowth, and in this part you may walk freely among the dark religious trees with trunks like huge rudely-fashioned pillars of red and purple ironstone. One has here the sensation of being in a vast cathedral; not like that of Chichester, but older and infinitely vaster, fuller of light and gloom and mystery, and more wonderful in its associations. Coming from this sacred dim interior, I have found on its threshold a tree the like of which is hardly to be seen in England. This is a large and very perfect yew with horizontal branches of great length, the lowest of which come down to the ground on all sides, and are interwoven with and form part of an immense and most beautiful tangle of juniper, thorn, bramble and briar, grown through and overgrown and bound together with honeysuckle and deep green ivy and light green traveller's joy, the last hoary-silver with its profusion of downy dry seed-feathers. I had measured the trunks of other trees, but the girth of this could not be taken unless a man went down on his belly and drew himself snakewise through the protecting natural hedge. May no sacrilegious hand with hatchet or billhook ever cut a way through it.[35]

Wilks ventures a reason how Kingley Vale came to be:

Tradition notes that yews were planted here about the beginning of the 9th century, to commemorate a defeat of the Vikings by men of Chichester. The grotesque and somber antique trees permit nothing to grow beneath their dim canopy. Rain rarely reaches the earth through the ever-green crowns, and the sunlight seldom penetrates to the soft, composted floor. The coomb covers more than 200 acres, and the oldest trees grow at the bottom of the valley. At one time the belief that the grove had been an ancient pagan preaching site was so strong that few would venture near their eerie cloisters after daylight hours. The coomb slopes over 600 ft. upwards to a plateau, the top of Bow Hill.[36]

There are small stands of yew in forests near Mickelsham, Surrey. Norbury Park consists of a group of ancient yews called the Druid's

Grove; two trees there are over 20 feet in circumference.[37] New Forest, planted at the decree of William the Conqueror beginning in 1085, is still in good health today. One New Forest yew tree in the churchyard of St. Peter's in Brockenhurst, Hampshire had, according to Lowe, a girth of 18 feet and a height of 45 feet in 1897.[38]

The yew grows on a wide variety of soils and according to Williamson:

> The distribution of yew has probably been seriously affected by the influence of man, since many early religious beliefs and pagan cultures centered around the tree... It was also used as a boundary marker and as a tombstone in unconsecrated ground.[39]

Wilks suggests that many small groves in the south of England may have been planted by archers:

> Although the best yew bows came from the Continent in medieval and Tudor times, the supply was inadequate to equip the whole force of the standing army and the militia, so large numbers of yews were planted in the homeland. Even so the species must have become seriously depleted by Plantagenet times. The natural indigenous groves of these slow-growing conifers had therefore to be felled very circumspectly. The demand resulted in primitive forms of woodland mangagement – at least in differentiating between the sexes of the trees, and in learning the correct felling procedures to ensure natural regeneration...
>
> All over the British Isles today we can find strange glades of yews of varying ages, legacies from our warlike economy. These were often venerated for superstitious reasons that have baffled later inquiry. The most interesting groves are still evident in the South of England. At Hod Hill, near Shroton, Dorset, areas of the yews still grow where their prototypes were planted after the Battle of Agincourt to ensure vital supplies of bows.[40]

Sloden Enclosure in the New Forest is occupied by clumps of yews said to be descended from trees planted by yeoman for the purpose of making longbows.[41] Remnants of a famous grove called the 'Black Grove' still stand in Sherwood Forest where Robin Hood was wont to select a good yew bow stave. Hambledon Hill in Dorset:

> ...has a dense yew forest that has produced a number of traditions explaining its origin. Generally held to be an unlucky place, some

say that it was planted by the Druids as a grove in which to worship, others that it was planted by archers in later years to provide a ready supply of wood for their bows.[42]

There are hundreds of ancient yew trees growing in England. While the most venerable specimens are found in churchyards, there are some fine yew trees found along the Pilgrim's Way, a thoroughfare that stretches from Stonehenge to Canterbury, in use since the Neolithic Age. According to Walter Johnson (1908):

> ...One can understand how valuable as guides these trees would be at dusk and dawn, and during foggy weather. The white chalk itself, where worn a little, would help travellers to keep the track... The yews, almost black, would accentuate this distinction. Dark on white, or dark on the grey-green turf either trail would be easily picked out.
>
> We turn to the facts which, being verifiable today, cannot possibly be in dispute. In Surrey, the yews occur at intervals from St. Martha's Hill to the back of Albury Park. At Newlands Corner they are found but a few steps from the path. Then they occur intermittently from Wooton Church, by way of Ranmore Common, to Dorking. Just under Box Hill, four ancient yews stand in a field by themselves. The ridge East of Reigate is marked by another line, and numerous fine specimens are met with from Merstham to White Hill.[43]

The Pilgrim's Way winds through the counties of Kent, Surrey, Hampshire and Wiltshire. Yews were so common in these districts that they are still called 'Hampshire weeds'.

HEDGES AND TOPIARY

In the early 16th century Henry VIII visited the fabulous gardens at Blois and Gaillon in France, where he saw shrubs and trees cultivated in straight lines, trimmed to geometric shapes and woven into knots and mazes. Henry, not to be bested by the French, brought the impetus to England for stylized hedges, topiary and formal gardens. By the end of Queen Elizabeth's reign in 1603, formal gardening had reached a peak of popularity which it retained for another century.

The yew was a preferred species for hedges and topiary as John Evelyn wrote in 1664:

This English yew tree is easily produced of the seeds, washed and cleansed from their mucilage, then buried and dried in their sand a little moist, any time in December, and so kept in some vessel in the house all winter, and in some cool shady place abroad all the summer, sow them the spring after. Some bury them in the ground like haws. It will commonly be the second winter e'er they peep, and then they rise with their caps on their heads. Being three years old, you may transplant them and form them into standards, knobs, walks, hedges, etc. in all which works they succeed marvellous well, and are worth our patience for their perennial verdure and durableness. I do again name them for hedges, preferably for beauty, and a stiff defence to any plant I have ever seen, and may upon that account (without vanity) be said to be the first which brought it into fashion, as well for defence, as a succedaneum [replacement] for cypress, whether in hedges, or pyramids, conic-spires, bowls, or what other shapes, adorning the parks or other avenues with their lofty tops thirty foot high, and braving all the efforts of the most rigid winter, which cypress cannot weather. I have said how long-lasting they are, easily to be shaped and clipped; nay, cut down and revive: but those which are much superannuated, and perhaps of many hundred years standing, perish if so used.[44]

There are scores of formidable yew hedges in England. Montacute House in Somerset, dating from the end of the 16th century, is built on an ancient site, 'Mons Acutus', which had been a fortified position during the Norman conquest of 1066. On the grounds, hundreds of yards of thick yew hedges have grown so tightly together that they no longer require pruning. They seem to be made of a gray-green, crushed velvet, with undulating dimples and ridges. At Montacute House there are also 15 pairs of manicured Irish yews on the west drive, 44 more in the sunken courtyard, and 22 on the cedar lawn.

A hedge at Blickling Hall in Aylsham, Norfolk is over 300 years old. Today it is 310 feet long, 17 feet high and 14 feet wide. Few in England can match this one for sheer mass. An impressive collection of conifer trees at Bodnaut Garden, Gwynedd, Wales, features a canal; one end is bordered by a striking yew hedge. The gardens at Castle Drogo in Devonshire sport dramatic hedges and screens of yew including a large circular lawn completely encircled by a tall, dense yew hedge. Formal gardens are marshalled by yew and holly hedges at Courts Hold in

THE YEW LINED WALKWAY AT MONTECUTE

Wiltshire. At Wightwick Manor, in West Midlands, a magnificent walkway is bordered by rows of alternating Irish yew and holly. Also to be found there are large, drum-shaped yew trees, one of which is golden in color.

Other ancient hedges of particular renown can be found at Hampton Court Palace in London where there is also an exquisite maze that was layed out in 1700. Hever Castle in Kent has a maze and hundreds of yards of hedges, Melbourne in Derby has a yew tunnel planted in 1704 that extends 120 yards, as well as some fine old hedges. Rockingham Castle in Northampton has a 'Mount' on the grounds with a few yew trees growing on it and a very dense undulating hedge bordering an 'old yew walk.' These are a few of the more notable hedges in England; there are scores of others.[45]

A more specialized form of plant sculpture is topiary, which has been well established in England since the 17th century; according to Evelyn Cecil:

> The idea that cut trees were generally yews is very prevalent, and the remains of topiary work in old gardens still in existence confirm this impression. All the cut trees in the garden at

Heslington, near York, are yews. This garden was laid out soon after the house was built, about 1560. The quaintly-rounded hedge at Rockingham, and the hedges and trees at Erbistock, are two examples of the cut yews of this date. But in the books of the period other shrubs are spoken of more favourably than yews. It seems, therefore, that it is only because the yew is a slow grower, a sturdy tree, and an evergreen that more yews than other shrubs have survived.[46]

E. H. Wilson gives a thumbnail sketch of the rise and fall of the topiary phenomenon in an article published in 1920:

In ornamental gardening the English Yew was employed as early as the Tudor times to form hedges, and was pleached and clipped into the forms of grotesque beasts, birds, cones, pyramids and other fantastic shapes. During the 17th century the taste for this kind of art increased and in the time of William and Mary reached its highest point. Even today in Europe there are many old places famous for this topiary art – and in this country at least one, the Hunnewell Garden, Wellesley, Massachusetts – but in general it has fallen into disrepute. Pope helped it to this end by his comment: 'An iminent town gardener has arrived at such perfection that he cuts family pieces of men, women, or children in trees. Adam and Eve in Yew, Adam a little shattered by the fall of the Tree of Knowldege in the great story; Eve and the serpent flourishing. St. George in box, his arm scarce long enough but will be in a condition to stick the dragon by next April; a green dragon of the same with a tail of ground-ivy for the present...Divers eminent modern poets in bays somewhat blighted to be disposed of a penny-worth. A quickset hog, shot up into a porcupine by its being forgot a week in rainy weather.' Very many fine Yew hedges and sculptured trees were swept away in England in the middle of the 18th century by the celebrated landscape gardener 'Capability' Brown, who dealt ruthlessly with all clipped material and topiary work.[47]

A very popular and surviving subject for yew topiary works was the *Sermon on the Mount,* or some variation of Christ and the twelve apostles. The legendary Packwood House collection in Hereford is described by Blomfield in 1892:

At the entrance to the mount at the end of the garden, stand four tall yews 20 feet high for the four evangelists and six more on either side for the twelve apostles. At the top of the mount is an arbor formed in a great yew tree called the 'Pinnacle of the Temple', which was also supposed to represent Christ on the mount overlooking the evangelists, apostles and the multitude below.[48]

Blomfield learned from the gardener that the 'Apostles and the Mount' had been there since at least 1756. Packwood House was one of the first estates in England where formal gardens were created. The 'Apostle' theme is found at Dartington Hall in Devon, which was founded in the 14th century on the site of an old 'tilt yard', where jousting tournaments were held and chivalry abounded. Another 'Twelve Apostles' can be seen at Manor Cleeve, Worcester.[49]

Along with Christian themes, topiary developed into more fantastic forms. At Hidcote on the edge of the Cotswolds is a well-kept collection dominated by huge yew columns. New Place was built by Shakespeare in Stratford-on-Avon when he retired from the theater. The house has vanished but a formal garden surrounded by yew hedges and sculptured squirrels remains. A peacock aviary styled of yew can be seen at Great Dixter, Sussex. Galloping figures and a serene Irish harp are hewn in yew at Mount Stewart. Earls' Hall, Fife, Scotland boasts another impressive collection of strange shapes fashioned of yew. It was built in the middle of the 17th century and its perimeter is guarded by dense yew hedges. At Knights Hayes Court, immense old hedges are accentuated by classic yew topiary work, about which William Lawson remarked in the 18th century, 'Your Gardener can frame your lessor wood sculpture to the shape of...swift running hounds to chase the deer.'[50]

A garden featuring extraordinary topiary shapes was layed out by Monsieur Beaumont before 1687 at Heslington House near York. Another amazing collection of topiary forms by Beaumont is at Levens Hall, Cumbria. Levens Hall was begun in the 13th century and had its last major overhaul in 1580; little has changed since. Mrs. Jane Curry provides current information:

The gardens of Levens Hall were laid out circa 1690–1720. The topiary was planted then, and has been clipped yearly since. It

TOPIARY GARDEN AT LEVENS HALL

takes three gardeners three months to clip. The highest are over 8 metres and are clipped from scaffolding using electric shears. The golden yew topiary is 170 years old.

Monsieur Beaumont designed the gardens here and else-where, but only Levens survives – other formal gardens and the yew topiary they contained were removed as garden fashions changed to the 'Capability Brown Landscapes' of the 1750's. All the yew topiary pieces are different – some have been given names, e.g. Judges Wig, Dutch Oven, Crowned Arch, Pyramid, Top Hat, Coach and Horses, Castle Wall, Great Umbrellas and Victorian Cake Stands.[51]

After over a century of formal gardens and clipped yew trees, according to Julia Berrall:

England was due for a change in garden styles, for she had been gardening in prescribed patterns for more than five hundred years. In criticizing topiary work as 'vegetable sculpture', essay-ists provoked a reaction. In 'The Spectator' of June 25, 1712, Joseph Addison wrote, 'Our British gardeners, instead of humouring Nature, love to deviate from it as much as possible. Our trees rise in Cones, Globes and Pyramids. We see the marks of the scissors upon every Plant and Bush. I do not know whether

TOPIARY AT KNIGHT'S HAYES COURT

I am singular in my opinion, but, for my own part, I would rather look upon a tree in all its Luxurancy and Diffusion of Boughs and Branches, than when it is thus cut and trimmed into a Mathematical Figure; and cannot but fancy that an Orchard in Flower looks infinitely more delightful than all the little Labyrinths of the most finished Parterre.'[52]

In 1791, near the end of the topiary craze, William Gilpin spoke out in defense of the yew in its natural form:

I profess myself a great admirer of its form and foliage. The Yew is, of all other trees, the most tonsile. Hence all the indignities it suffers. We everywhere see it cut and metamorphosed into such a variety of deformities, that we are hardly brought to conceive it has a natural shape, or the power which other trees have of hanging carelessly and negligently.

Yet it has this power in a very eminent degree; and in a state of nature, except in exposed situations, is perhaps one of the most beautiful evergreens we have. Indeed I know not whether, all things considered, it is not superior to the cedar of Lebanon itself.[53]

There are scores of fine collections of topiary of various ages throughout England; mainly on manor house grounds.[54] However, let us turn again now to the unkempt tree form of the yew. Although there is little natural yew left in England, several hundred very old trees survive in churchyards, some of which sprouted in the days of myth and legend.

"OUR TREES RISE IN CONES, GLOBES AND PYRAMIDS."

PART III

LIVING WITNESS TO HUMAN HISTORY

*The Druids, as recorded by Caesar, preached a
doctrine of the immortality of the soul, the yew being
their* cultus arborum. *Since the yew is a commoner
kind of tree than, say, the oak in the Iberian Peninsula, whence the pre-Celtic peoples came, it is prob-
able that they brought the cult of the yew – or at least
the custom of using yew groves for their religious rites
– to these Isles.*
                                              – John Wilks

CHAPTER SIX

ANCIENT LIVING YEWS

ANY taxophiles (yew lovers) over the years have written wonderful things about yew trees, noting a certain sanctity emanating from old yews. Robert Graves said that yews were greatly venerated, considered to be of 'most ancient fame' and 'the oldest of woods.'[1] This may mean that yew trees were the first trees to be revered because they were the most useful and certainly the most long-lived. There are few stands of yew left in Britain, but there are some very large, old yew trees, a few in Ireland and Scotland, but nearly all in English and Welsh churchyards. There has been much speculation as to how they got there. John Selby wrote in 1842:

> For there is little or no doubt but that Yew trees existed in places of Druidical worship previous to the erection of Christian churches upon the same sites.[2]

The Reverend W.T. Bree, quoted in 1842:

> ...suggests the probability that churches were more frequently built in Yew groves or near old Yew trees, than that Yew trees were planted in the churchyards after the churches were built.[3]

Mr. Charles Coote, quoted in 1897, says:

> But of these old-world superstitions, that connected with the yew tree is the most interesting. For as of old it was connected with the passage of the soul to its new abode, so ever since the introduction of Christianity into this country it has continued to adorn the last resting-place of the body, which the soul has left.[4]

W.D. Dallimore wrote in 1908:

> Previous to the Christian era historians tell us that the Yew was looked on as a sacred tree, and that the vicinity of a Yew, or a group of Yews, was often a place of heathen worship. The majority of the oldest Yews in Britain are to be found in churchyards, and the generally accepted opinion prevails that these Yews were not planted as adjuncts to the churchyard, but that the churches were built near the Yews, which were already of mature years. The probability is that these old Yews were looked on as sacred trees in druidical times, and missionaries would so far respect the feelings of their converts as to erect their religious houses on, or as near as possible to, sites that had long been held sacred.[5]

Hudson wrote in the 1920's:

> The stones we set up as memorials grow worn and seamed and hoary with age, even like men, and crumble to dust at last; in time new stones are put in their place, and these, too, grow old and perish, and are succeeded by others; and through all changes, through ages, the tree lives on unchanged. With its huge, tough, red trunk; its vast, knotted arms outstretched; its rich, dark mantle of undying foliage, it stands like a protecting god on the earth, patriarch and monarch of woods; and indeed it seems but right and natural that not to oak nor holly, nor any other reverenced tree, but to the yew it was given to keep guard over the bodies and souls of those who have been laid in the earth.[6]

Vaughn Cornish wrote in 1946:

> In pre-Christian times the symbolism of Nature had great religious influence in Britain. One of the ancient beliefs of pagan Britain which has not only survived, but become incorporated with Christian observance, is reverence for the churchyard Yew as an emblem of immortality.[7]

John Wilks wrote in 1972:

> ...the Druids, as recorded by Caesar, preached a doctrine of the immortality of the soul, the yew being their cultus arborum. Since the yew is a commoner kind of tree than, say, the oak in the Iberian Peninsula, whence the pre-Celtic peoples came, it is probable that they brought the cult of the yew – or at least the

"CHRIST IS MY DRUID"

custom of using yew groves for their religious rites – to these Isles...there is a higher proportion of yews in Welsh churchyards than in England generally.[8]

Cornish confirmed that five yew trees over 30 feet in circumference were alive in Wales in 1946.[9] In the churchyard of Llantheyw Bach, Monmouth there is a hollow stunted tree with a girth of 32 feet that in 1897 could hold six people inside.[10]

Three dozen yew trees in England and Wales are 30 feet in circumference or larger.[11] The Fortingall Yew in Scotland is the largest with a girth of 56 feet 6 inches. No trees of these dimensions are found in Ireland. Rarely since the advent of man were yew trees able to attain in the wilds of Europe the great age and size of those found in consecrated ground today. The fact that these trees were sacred put them beyond the clutches of man, allowing them to run their full course.

THE FORTINGALL YEW

It is difficult if not impossible to judge the age of yew trees by any method other than cutting them down. Many have tried and there is no real consensus to be found, but for the sake of discussion a reasonably accurate average of growth per year needs to be established. There is information upon which to base an estimation.

THE DARLEY DALE YEW

The annual growth rings of the Darley Dale Yew, a female tree in the churchyard of St. Helen's in Derby, were measured in 1888 by Mr. Paget Bowman who cut nine cylinders (core samples) from it with a trephine. All samples were taken on the same plane. He found from 33 to 66 years to the inch of radius growth, and an average of 46 years per inch.[12] In 1867 the tree's girth was measured by C.S. Greaves at 31 feet, four feet from the ground. In 1879 the parish clerk measured it to be 31 feet 8 inches. In 1926 Mr. F. Williamson measured it to be 32 feet 3 inches and again in 1938 he measured it to be 32 feet.[13] In 1972, according to Wilks it was measured to be 32 feet 10 inches.[14] Between 1867 and 1972 the tree grew in circumference by 22 inches, or an increase of 3.5 inches of radius over a 105 year period, or a growth of 30 annual rings to the inch. At this rate of growth the tree in 1972 would have been 20 years shy of 2,000 years old. Using Bowmans estimate of 46 years to the inch of radius growth, the tree would have been just over 3,000 years old. Others have agreed, as expressed in this news clipping from the *News* of July 8, 1892:

> In the churchyard at Darley Dale is the most venerable yew tree in the world. Many authorities claim for it a fabulous age, making it as much as three thousand years old. It is thirty-three feet in girth, but its trunk has suffered not a little from the modern goths and vandals who have carved their name in the bark, and employed other methods of mutilation.

The tree is now fenced round to save it from further insult; and, 'whatever may be its precise age,' says the Rev. Dr. John Charles Cox,

> ...there can be little doubt that this grand old tree has given shelter to the early Britons when planning the construction of the dwellings that they erected not many yards to the west of its trunk; to the Romans who built up the funeral pyre for their slain comrades just clear of its branches; to the Saxons, converted, perchance, to the true faith by the preaching of Bishop Diuma beneath its pleasant shade; to the Norman masons chiselling their quaint sculptures to form the first stone house of prayer erected in this vicinity; and to the host of Christian worshippers who, from that day to this, have been borne under its hoary limbs in

women's arms to the baptismal font, and then on men's shoulders to their last sleeping place in the soil that gave it birth.[15]

In 1979 according to an article in the local news of October 18, the Darley Dale Yew was:

...savaged by the cruel winter which broke its limbs under the weight of frozen snow. But the tree, which has a girth of 34 feet, is so strong it would probably need an Ice Age to kill it. Yesterday it looked full of life, leaves, berries and colour, not a day over 1,000 years![16]

And in another article of April 5, 1980:

When...William Wildgoose, a Kniveton farmer and parish councillor, heard of the wood he decided it should be saved. He took it to Mr. Simon Manby's studio and told him to carve exactly what he wanted – a responsibility which both thrilled and terrified the sculptor. But it so happened that Simon had been waiting 20 years for just such a piece of wood to carve a crucified figure of Christ. After months of labour, he has just finished the work. It now hangs in pride of place.[17]

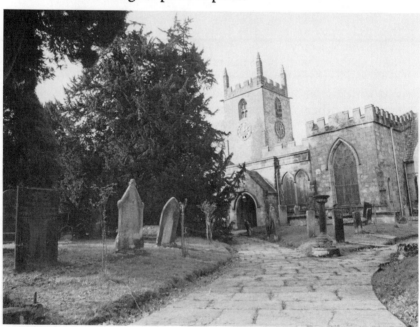

DARLEY DALE CHURCHYARD

DETERMINING THE AGE OF YEW TREES

Getting back to determining the ages of yew trees, Williamson reported instances of much slower and faster growth:

> ...a yew dug up in an Irish bog, which during the last 300 years of its life had put on 100 rings to the inch. I have found one which had 80 rings to the inch. This was a tree of exactly 2 inches diameter which had been stunted beneath its brothers and sisters. They had achieved varying success in life too, although all were exactly 80 years of age. They all grew in a rough circle, like a family seated around a 5-foot-wide circular table, except for the 'runt' who was underneath the table. Their diameters in inches were as follows: 2, 5.5, 7.75, 11.25, and 15.5. The latter had all the sun and possibly the benefit of the downhill drainage too.[18]

The average of these samples measured by Williamson is 30 years to the inch. Other estimates, ranging from 10 years to the inch to 100 years, have been made of the age of other trees. There are many factors that account for the difference in various estimates. Not all trees grow at the same rate; it depends on the site and weather. Because of the gnarled irregular trunk growth in most old yew trees the girth-size will vary greatly depending on the level at which the measurement was taken. Some measurements were taken at ground level, others at one foot, two feet and higher. Some people took measurements at the widest possible spot; others at the slimmest. Today it is common to measure the circumference at breast height (4 feet). In the case (which often occurs) of an earlier recorded measurement being larger than a more recent one it is probably because the earlier measurement was taken at the widest point rather than at a standard height, or that the more recent measurement was taken at a slimmer point instead of a standard height. In some cases where more than one tree grew in a churchyard, the one remaining might have been mistaken for an older, larger one measured at some earlier age for a posterity that has come. In other cases it might have been combinations of wishful thinking and rubber tape measures. Still another factor that may skew estimates of longevity is that some trees of large girth may actually be two or more trees grown together.

My best estimate, derived from historical measurements of various individual trees and from actual ring counts taken, is 35 years to the inch of radius growth. In my experience with the Pacific yew, 40 annual rings to the inch is normal. The 'Yew Tree Campaign' people in England today are estimating the ages of some trees at 45 years to the inch.[19] Taking 35 annual rings to the inch of radius growth to be a reasonable average, a tree more than 30 feet in girth would be more than 2,000 years old, which implies that some yew trees in English churchyards predate the church by centuries. The oldest may predate Christianity by millennia and might easily have been associated with the rites of pagan Romans, Druids and pre-Celtic immigrants from the Iberian Peninsula, who quite probably brought the worship of the yew tree with them.[20]

The Fortingall Yew, using 35 years to the inch, would be almost 4,000 years old today. The Braeburn Yew which is long gone was reported by Evelyn in the 17th century to be 58 feet, 6 inches in girth.[21] It would have been over 4,000 years old then. The Hampstead Marshall Yew that used to grow in Berkshire, reported in 1836 by Loudon to be 37 feet in circumference, would have been 2,500 years old then. The yew tree in the churchyard of St. Mary in South Hayling, Hampshire, at 33 feet 6 inches in 1961,[22] was 2,300 years old then. Mr. F.G.S. Thomas wrote:

> In 1225 a middle-aged tree dominated the landscape, and a chancel was built where meetings of every sacred-secular kind had been held, perhaps since the time of Augustine, Birinius or Wilfred.

And according to Vicar George Royle:

> Colonel Sandeman, a parishioner, now buried near to the Yew, at his own expense had the Yew attended to by experts from Kew Gardens and had it railed for protection.[23]

THE TISBURY YEW

Another venerable yew tree survives in the churchyard of St. John the Baptist in Tisbury, Wiltshire, where there were at one time two yews in excess of 30 feet. Now there is only one.[24] The survivor was measured to be 32 feet in girth in 1959[25] and may well be over 2,000 years old. In regard to the larger yew that died, Sir Lauder was quoted in 1897:

> ...there is now standing, and in fine foliage, although the trunk is quite hollow, an immense yew tree, which measures 37 feet in circumference and the limbs are proportionately large. The tree is entered by means of a rustic gate; and seventeen persons lately breakfasted in its interior. It is said to have been planted many generations ago by the Arundel family.[26]

Jill and Peter Drury tell us that the estimate of the surviving yew's great age has been revised upward:

> Estimated previously at just over 1,000 years old, it has been scientifically tested recently and is now reckoned to be 4,000 years old. Trunk is 31 feet in circumference, and height is adjudged to be between 40 and 50 feet.[27]

If this estimate of age is correct, the Tisbury Yew would have grown at a rate of one radius inch every 60 years. The Drurys also inform us that the tree, though the trunk is bound together by concrete, 'still grows vigorously,' and an offspring is growing in the 'Haven's Grace churchyard in West Tisbury, on Martha's Vineyard, off the coast of Massachusetts.'[28]

All of the above mentioned trees were of considerable age during the Roman occupation and must have given pause for consideration, for as Mr. Bowman, quoted in 1842, said:

> It seems most natural and simple to believe that, being indisputably indigenous, and being, from its perennial verdure, its longevity, and the durability of its wood, at once an emblem and a specimen of immortality, its branches would be employed by our pagan ancestors, on their first arrival here, as the best substitute for the cypress, to deck the graves of the dead and for other sacred purposes.[29]

As we have seen in an earlier chapter, Romans worshipped the yew and it may be that they added more layers of associations to the yew tree's symbolic mystique during their 400 years in England. Indeed, some of these trees may have been sacred to a number of pagan cultures, Iberian immigrants, Druids, Romans, Danes and early Saxons.

DRUID SITES

There are a number of churches built on what were obvious earlier sites of worship or at least unusual human activity. Guy Underwood wrote in 1969:

> At Knowlton in Dorset a ruined church stands within a circular prehistoric bank almost covered by yews. The church of Norton Malreward near Bristol has a barrow with a yew growing in its centre, opposite the west entrance; and two yews in the church-yard at Mells, in Somerset, are also on mounds which have the appearance of barrows. There are many similar examples else-where.[30]

Wilks mentions that the yew tree in the churchyard in Preen, Shropshire was associated with an ancient Druid site.[31] In 1971 Francis A. Knight wrote:

> One of the finest yews in these islands is at Church Preen, in Shropshire. It measures forty feet and five inches in girth at its base, and twenty-one feet and nine inches at a height of four feet from the ground... The top of the tree was long ago broken off. Young shoots then sprang up round its stem forming at length a solid ring round the original trunk. The original trunk then died, leaving a cavernous hollow in which twenty-one men can stand upright.[32]

According to Wilks, in Penpont, Brecon, Wales, there is a:

> ...circle of yews on the site of another circle of yews (now gone). Many churches in England and Wales have similar circular designs so the the 'devil cannot enter at any corner.'[33]

Underwood pointed out a very practical reason why yew trees might have been associated with ancient sacred places:

> It seems likely that, since it grows its best on a blind spring, the yew was planted in churchyards with the intention of marking and protecting such spots.
> I have examined many old yew trees in churchyards with reference to geodetic phenomena, and all were located on blind springs or nodes. At Amesbury in Wiltshire there are fourteen yews in the churchyard, and eighteen at Bradford-on-Avon, and

SACRED WELL YEW TREE

all are on blind springs. The 'ninety-nine' yews in the churchyard at Painswick, near Gloucester, are famous. It is said that all attempts to plant another has failed, and will always fail, but in fact there are a hundred trees, and some occasionally die, while attempts to replace them are not always successful. The main paths to the church are aligned on avenues of aquastats which make many nodes on each side of the paths, and it is on these nodes that the yews grow. Of sixty trees tested, all were on nodes or blind springs.[34]

One such tree survives today in the churchyard of St. John the Baptist in Hope Bagot, Shropshire. The Hope Bagot Yew is 24 feet in circumference and was recently certified:

> Measurements of the tree were sent away, and in return the parish has been sent a certificate from the 'Country Living' yew tree campaign signed by among others, David Bellamy, the Archbishop of Canterbury, and the actor Robert Hardy.
>
> This states: 'Using all the data we have to hand, the age of the yew tree at St. John the Baptist Church, Hope Bagot, is at least 1,600 years. Please do all you can to prolong the life of this venerable member of your local community.'

According to Commander John Elgar:

> A remarkable tree is the yew at Hope Bagot Church, St. John
> Baptist. This has an ancient well beneath its branches, which is
> said to be beneficial to eye problems.[35]

EARLY CHRISTIANITY

The Hope Bagot Yew sprouted near the end of the Roman era, in
the beginning of the 5th century, when native Britons were primarily
pagan but Christianity had begun to take root. In 397 A.D., St. Nenian
travelled from Wales to Scotland to found churches; at each one he
planted a yew tree. Many of the 50 churches he founded have yew trees
of such an age growing in them today.[36] Most yew trees in Irish and
Scottish churchyards were probably planted at the founding of the
church. This became the case in England and Wales, but as we have
seen, the oldest trees predate Christianity.

The Romans left Britain by 425 A.D., leaving small congregations
of Christian Britons behind to face the invading pagan Saxons and
develop as they could. The Druid tradition had already faded into the
Roman pagan pantheon which was in turn beginning to fade into
Christianity. When St. Augustine came from Rome in 597 A.D. to
preach the gospel, he found enthusiastic Britons waiting for him, for
the Queen was already Christian. Ethelbert, the king, allowed Augustine to establish his mission in Canterbury. Thus began the long
struggle between the established Church of Rome and the British
version of Christianity, which had evolved on its own for centuries.

In the churchyard of Stanford Bishop in Herefordshire stands a yew
tree with a circumference of 26 feet and a fine umbrage that covers a
circular area of 400 square feet. This tree is supposed to have shaded
one of Augustine's early efforts at conversion and by my count must
have then had a girth of 5 feet and been about 350 years old. It is said
that St. Augustine sat under the tree with Welsh Bishops in 606 A.D.
to discuss church matters. At that meeting Augustine displayed a
'dictatorial manner' and an 'overpowering personality.' The Bishops
did not know what to make of Augustine and according to Nellie
Duncan, they consulted an anchorite who suggested:

'Take the Bishop's chair out of the church. Place it near the yew tree and ask Augustine to sit there with his followers. When he is seated, approach him. If he rises to greet you, adhere to his request, as this will prove him to be a humble man and a true follower of Christ. However, if Augustine does not rise, have nothing to do with what he asks, as this will show him to be a proud and unfeeling man.'

The Welsh bishops did as instructed. Augustine remained seated and the Welsh churches continued to celebrate Easter in the Asian Way. It was not until 200 years later in 768 A.D., that all Churches in Britain agreed to celebrate Easter on the first Sunday after the first full moon after the vernal equinox.[37] [The Bishop's Chair still graces the church.]

Early missionaries found an interesting mix of religious notions among their prospective converts. One theme common to all was an identification with the Virgin Mary because feminine deities and lesser goddesses were revered among the pagans. For example, Sulis of Bath served as an intercessor for people in their business with other deities. Missionaries took every opportunity to identify with the prospective local flock by referring to beliefs or concepts that they already understood. St. Columba in the 7th century, said to his quarry, 'Christ is my Druid.'[38]

As a matter of policy missionaries would often co-opt the ancient holy groves for their church sites. Augustine was enjoined by Pope Gregory to convert the heathen temples into churches by removing the old objects and replacing them with new ones.[39] On one hand it was the best way to get potential converts to attend services, and on the other it served well to disrupt whatever pagan uses the people had for the holy site. Within 100 years of Augustine's arrival the British were almost entirely Christian, but of two sorts: those converted by missionaries from Rome and those who preserved a Celtic version, formed apart, descended from the earlier contact with Rome 600 years before.

Whether the first churches were built near yew trees because the early Christians recognized them as holy from their experience on the continent, or whether the trees were actual places of pagan worship, the churchyard, 'God's Acre', was built arround them and they became participants in the lives and deaths of generation after generation of parishioners.

NORMAN CHURCHES

During the first 150 years after the Battle of Hastings in 1066, the Normans built hundreds of churches; in each churchyard they planted two yew trees situated in accordance with established custom. According to Cornish:

> The established positions of Yew trees in relation to the church doorways indicates frequent planting of these trees during the period of the Norman dynasty, for their situations are identical in England and Normandy, as is shown by the record that of nineteen in Normandy, thirteen are on the south side of the church, five west, one north, and none east; a proportion similar to that in English churchyards. It seems evident that the practice of planting churchyard Yews was general among the clergy in England after the conquest by the Normans. Archbishops Lanfranc and Anselm both came from Northern Italy, where the cypress had been planted in graveyards since Roman times. This may have influenced them to adopt the churchyard Yew of Britain as its equivalent.[40]

Yew trees are still found in churchyards in Italy, and that may have had some influence on Norman practices, as J.G. Strutt pointed out in 1822:

> It was formerly not less common in the churchyards of Italy; and in the original charter for building the church at Perone, in Picardy, dated in the year 684, a remarkable clause is inserted containing directions for the proper preservation of a particular yew tree. This individual yew tree was in existence in the year 1799, nearly 1,100 years after this notice in the charter.[41]

In some cases in England, the Normans built churches in or near ancient groves. It is recorded that monks lived in the adjacent yew grove while they built the Fountains Abbey in Yorkshire, which was completed in 1132. Today, hundreds of yew trees, remnants of the original grove, still grow around the ruins. Although Lowe and others refer to an enormous tree, nearly 30 feet in girth that grew here at one time,[42] I could not find it on a hike through the grounds and none of the later taxophiles mention it. It is probably gone.

CAD GODDEAU

Whatever the reasons for the association between yew trees and churches, some of the trees have been in existence since before oral tradition gave over to the written word. Written down for the first time in the 13th century, a Welsh minstrel poem, the *Cad Goddeu*, or *Battle of the Trees*, recounts a battle waged in the 4th century B.C. which according to Robert Graves, can:

> ...be explained as the expulsion of a long-established Bronze Age (Fourth Century B.C.) priesthood from the national necropolis by an alliance of agricultural tribesmen, long settled in Britain and worshippers of the Nanaan god Bel, Beli, Belus or Belinus, with an invading Brythonic tribe...[43]

The *Cad Goddeau*, in a version that has come down to us today, is a series of riddles in which trees represent major characters in this ancient human event. Belus, one of the first male deities to wrest power from the Great Goddess, was leading his people against her people. In the *Cad Goddeau*, the poet Gwion says of the yew, 'The dower-scattering yew/Stood glum at the fight's fringe.'[44] The yew tree, symbolizing the Druid and the Great Goddess, is placed to witness the battle where the gender change was made. A Druid would not actually engage in battle, but watched the proceedings from a hill top with a Druid from the opposing side. Then together they would render a decision as to which side actually won. Regarding the symbolism of 'dower', in the 13th century the yew was found at the doorway of most churchyards and it could be that its scarlet berries were considered a dowry, a blessing, or 'dower' could mean a gift of nature and refer to the many uses of the yew. In the 4th century B.C., it certainly was not found in churchyards, but near sites of pagan significance, such as the 'national necropolis.'

In this ancient poem is a glimpse of the yew tree in transition. By the 13th century it was in decline and from prominent neolithic forest tree, through centuries of exploitation, it has become today a denizen of the churchyard.

ONE OF THE HANCHURCH YEWS

CHAPTER SEVEN

THE CHURCHYARD YEW

RELIGIOUS FUNCTIONS

THE puzzle as to why yew trees were kept in or planted in churchyards has been answered by taxophiles in many different ways. William Caxton (1422–1491) explained:

> Wherefore Holy Chirche this day makyth solemn processyon, in memory of the processyon that Cryst made this day. But for the eucheson that we have none Olyve that beareth grene leef, algate therefore we take Ewe instead of palm and olyve, and beren about in processyon, and so is thys day called Palm Sonday.[1]

John Evelyn in 1664 said that the purpose of planting yews in churchyards had been to supply sprigs and boughs to the church services and that it was emblematic of 'a refreshing state to come.'[2] Brady mentioned in *Clavis Calendaria*:

> Among our superstitious forefathers the palm-tree or its substitutes, box or yew, were solemnly blessed, and some of their branches burnt to ashes and used by the priests on the Ash Wednesday of the following year, while other boughs were gathered and distributed among the pious, who bore them about in their numerous processions...a practice which was continued in this country until the second year of Edward VI, when it was abolished as superstitious.[3]

John Selby (1842) reasoned that yew was planted in churchyards to protect it from cattle and the cattle from it's poisonous effects; that yew was there to supply wood needed for long bows and sprigs and boughs needed for funeral rites and Palm Sunday services, and finally that it was there as an emblem of silence and death.[4]

In 1948, Reverend C.A. Johns wrote:

> ...there is far greater probability that at the period when crosses were erected in those sacred spots as emblems of the victory over death achieved by the Author of our faith, the yew tree was stationed not far off, to symbolize, by its durability and slowly altering features, the patient waiting for the resurrection, by those who committed the bodies of their friends to the ground in hope....The yew, then, we may safely conclude, is not an unmeaning decoration of our churchyards, much less a heathenish symbol, or, as some will have it, a tree planted with superstitious feelings, but an appropriate religious emblem.[5]

Cornish recounted a sermon by John Mason Neale (1818–1866) whose biblical text was, 'O all ye green things upon the earth, bless ye the Lord: praise him and magnify him for ever':

> The Yew...may be accounted a fit emblem of a Christian. You see it hath little outside bark, only a small rind; to teach us not to make a great outside show of religion. Then it is a very lasting timber, much harder than oak, to show the soundness and sincerity of a Christian. It hath many branches, large and fair, to remind us to be plentiful in good works. It is always green and prospering, to declare unto us that a Christian should always grow and thrive in grace. Yea, green in winter and the hardest weather, to show that a Christian is best in affliction; yea, then it hath berries on it, to teach us, as then we are the best Christians, so then to bring forth most fruits of righteousness. It is a long-lived and lasting tree, to be unto us a type of immortality and lasting life...All this we confess when we set up the Yew.[6]

Other, more peculiar reasons abound. For example, Mr. R. Turner, quoted in 1908:

> If the Yew be set in a place subject to poysonous vapours, the very branches will draw and imbibe them, hence it is conceived that the judicious in former times planted it in churchyards on the west side, because those places, being fuller of putrefaction and

gross oleaginous vapours exhaled out of the graves by the setting sun, and sometimes drawn by those meteors called ignes fatui, [luminous clouds associated with marsh gas] divers have been frightened, supposing some dead bodies to walk.[7]

Dallimore pointed out that yew trees liked to be in the graveyard:

...the questionable honour of being the most ill-omened tree in Britain must be ascribed to the Yew, if we are to judge by the old superstitions, which credit it with liking better to lead a solitary life amidst the dead and sending down its roots to prey on and invigorate itself on dead bodies, rather than be sociable with its neighbors and obtain its nutriment in the manner befitting well principled trees.[8]

PRACTICAL PURPOSES

Less sacred associations were made with the churchyard yew by common people throughout Europe, especially in Britain and Ireland. One use was suggested by an old church sexton in 1928 when asked why yew trees were found in churchyards.

IRISH YEW AT LORTON VALE

'Well, you see, young lady, it's this way,' he began. 'There's very elastic wood in the yew tree, and they do say in the old days it were used for making bows. Sometimes they'd call a bow a yew, for the wood it were made of. But the trees all belonged to the gentry, the earls, and the lords of the manor, and the like. The only land the poor folk owned was the bit of ground they was to be buried in. And, however doughty they was, they dast not strip the trees of their betters for wood for their bows. So they set to and planted their own yew trees in the churchyards, which was common property, and many a stout weapon the peaceful graves gave up, I warrant you.'[9]

Some vernacular versions for the purpose of yew trees in churchyards demonstrate the degree to which the yew tree influenced imagination. It is interesting that the value of churchyard yew in the middle ages was tenfold that of common yew. According to Lowe:

In Wales, great value used to be set upon the yew tree; as is proved by the ancient Welsh laws, the consecrated yew of the priests having got to supplant in value the sacred mistletoe of the Druids. The following extract of the ancient Welsh laws fixes the value of the different trees. It must be borne in mind that at the age to which it refers, fruit-trees, such as apple-trees, were comparatively scarce.

> A consecrated yew, its value is a pound.
> A mistletoe branch, three score pence.
> An oak, six score pence.
> Principal branch of an oak, thirty pence.
> A yew tree (not consecrated), fifteen pence.
> A sweet apple, three score pence.
> A sour apple, thirty pence.
> A thorn-tree, seven pence half-penny.
> Every tree after that, four pence.[10]

The difference in value between consecrated and common yew may have been because the churchyard yew was older and better for wood than the ravaged English forest trees. Or it may have been that people thought there to be more magic in the consecrated boughs and sprigs. In any case there are many tales involving churchyard yews rather than the profane variety.

SUPERNATURAL POWERS

There are other reasons, not religious or practical, why yew trees are found amongst the graves. Mercatante wrote that according to European folklore, yew:

> ...is planted in graveyards to prevent witches from destroying church buildings or overturning gravestones, thereby upsetting the dead, who in turn would then disturb the living. In fact, sometimes yew was buried with the dead to ward off the possibility of such trouble from witches or demons.[11]

Or in Cambridgeshire, for protection:

> It was most unlucky to cut down or damage a growing yew tree; this is not surprising for the yew was among the most potent of trees for protection against evil, and was therefore often planted alongside a house, or where it might form a windbreak against the invisible wind as well as against unknown powers of evil.[12]

But also in Cambridgeshire, the reverse is mentioned:

> The yew trees so often seen growing in old churchyards were feared in many parts of Cambridgeshire because, in addition to their gloomy, somewhat frightening appearance, especially at night, the trees were thought to afford shelter to witches.[13]

In the Lake District, in 1886, according to Rev. H.J. Bulkley, yew branches could be a magical periscope:

> ...it was believed possible, but risky, to see the spirit form of the recently buried by watching in the churchyard at night. For this, a long branch of yew had to be cut with a wide, V-shaped notch at the end. The branch had to be held in the left hand, together with the knife. The end of the branch rested on the ground, while the watcher, kneeling on his left knee, supported his right elbow on his right knee and with his right hand firmly closed his right eye, then by peering beyond the notch and open knife it was said that he would see the spirit of the dead light. One bold youth fulfilled all the conditions and reported that he actually saw a dead light approaching in the dark, but jumped up in 'a fright' to flee from the apparition so that he injured his left eye.[14]

In Herefordshire, the churchyard yew was a bringer of dreams:

...that if a girl placed a sprig of yew under her pillow which she had picked in a churchyard she had not previously visited, she would dream of her future husband.[15]

In Somerset:

Branches were placed under the deceased, and, being evergreen, were, 'beautifully emblematical of the resurrection of the body.' this was most probably a Christianization of a pagan belief. Yew is popularly associated with the Druids, though, being poisonous, it has been said they were planted in the churchyard to prevent farmers from allowing their cattle to stray over the then unfenced cemetery.[16]

Once again we must recall the vigorous legends throughout Britain and parts of Europe of the roots of yew growing into the throats of corpses buried in churchyard graves:

Even now in Celtic districts extreme veneration exists for trees growing in cemeteries or other places. It is dangerous to cut them down or to pluck a leaf or branch from them, while in Breton churchyards the yew is thought to spread a root to the mouth of each corpse...these embody the belief that the spirit of the dead is in the tree.[17]

On the continent there are said to be sacred groves near Marseilles, and from Brittany come accounts both sacred and secular:

In the cloister of Breton, in Brittainy, there grew a Yew tree which was said to have sprung from the staff of Saint Martin. Beneath it the Breton princes were accustomed to offer up a prayer before entering the church. This tree was regarded with the highest reverence; no one ever plucked a leaf from its sombre boughs, and even the birds refrained from pecking the scarlet berries. A band of pirates, however, happening to visit the locality, two of them spied the tree, and forthwith climbed into its venerable branches and proceeded to cut bow-staves for themselves; their audacity speedily brought its own punishment, for they both fell and were killed on the spot.[18]

Or a more practical French 'wives tale':

The 'bonnes femmes' of Bress gather cross-shaped yew branches from the churchyard at Saint-Denis to put in their chickens' nests to help them lay more eggs and prosper. The crosses also protect the chickens from insects and vermin.[19]

In Scotland where, as we have seen in earlier chapters, there are many beliefs concerning the yew, one is very specific about the power of churchyard yew:

A chieftain could by holding a piece of churchyard yew in his left hand, threaten or denounce his enemy without the latter hearing. Others present did hear, however, so that it could not be said that he attacked his enemy without warning.[20]

And from a modern *Encyclopedia of Magical Herbs,* we learn that the yew's gender is feminine, its planet is Saturn, its element water and:

This poisonous plant is sometimes used in spells to raise the spirits of the dead. Though it has a long mythic history it is little used in magic due to its high toxicity.[21]

Whether yew trees are in churchyards to mark ancient springs or sacred spots, or to either shelter witches or drive them off; whether they are there to suck in 'oleaginous vapors' or exude them, or whether they are places where ghosts congregate, or are actually instruments through which any of the above transformations occur, all are facets of the mythic, paradoxical image of the yew. To complement these images there are today in England and Wales over 250 yew trees that are as old or older than the churchyards they live in; each has accumulated generations of individual associations within its respective community. In my visits to England and through correspondence with parish vicars, I have found that there is still a latent reverence for yew trees among people there. Most of those I talked with knew that yew trees belong in churchyards but few knew why they were there and some thought it peculiar that anyone should want to know.

FAMOUS PREACHERS

Famous preachers took advantage of the churchyard yew tree's shade. One such tree, immortalized in verse by Wordsworth, is found in the churchyard of St. Cuthbert, in Lorton Vale, Cumbria. Cornish recounts:

George Fox (1624–1691), founder of the Society of Friends (the Quakers), preached his doctrine...in the churchyard of Lorton, Cumberland, where people climbed up the ancient Yew in order to obtain advantages for listening.[22]

Wilks says the Lorton Yew is called Wesley's Yew because John Wesley preached under it on May 28th, 1725. Some time in the latter half of the 19th century the top of the yew was either blasted by lightning or broken off by the wind. According to R. C. George, a chair carved for William Wordsworth from the fallen top of the Lorton Vale Yew is now being used as the seat of the Chairman of the Cockermouth Council. And about the Lorton Vale tree he adds:

> Wordsworth's Lorton Yew was obviously very old when he wrote, but possibly not quite as old as his poem suggests. As I have said above, it still stands, though looking somewhat the worse for the passage of the years. Local lads are supposed to have climbed into it to listen to John Wesley preaching in 1725, but there is no firm evidence that he did preach under the tree. Since then it has lost a number of limbs to the weather and, for safety reasons, the axe-man.[23]

Thomas à Becket is said to have preached in the early part of the 12th century to a group of parishioners in the Capel Churchyard at Tudeley in Kent under a yew tree that was over 500 years old then. According to Wilks:

> The tree still survives close to St. Thomas à Becket church. The girth suggests that the existence of the yew in the martyr's day cannot be discounted, and for this reason preservation and treatment to the tree has been arranged.[24]

The tree survives just barely today, according to P.E. Norton:

> Yes it's still here at Capel and it's alive even though the main trunk is completely hollowed out and quite a lot of the sides are missing. I have measured the circumference and the measurement is just on 24 feet at a height of about 2 feet from the ground.[25]

Some of the ancient yews were mentioned in the *Domesday Book*, which was a sort of inventory of Britain begun in 1066 by William the Conqueror. One tree recorded in the *Domesday Book* is the great yew at St. Mary's in Breamore, Hampshire. Lowe reported it to be 30 feet in girth in 1897 as did Cornish in 1956. Today Canon Blake writes:

> The middle is hollow (seven can walk around inside) with a 20 foot circumference inside measurement; in the middle of our churchyard, which is surrounded by other large yew trees, which are also of considerable age. The yew trees that date from Saxon times (as ours does) may well have had pagan uses originally.[26]

Another tree of similar girth at St. Mary's in Cusop, Hereford, is according to Mr. Ridger:

> ...believed to be over 1,000 years of age as it is mentioned in the *Domesday Book*. It is one of four yews, one at each corner of the church. Yews were religious trees, symbols of fertility and immortality. This raises the query as to the probability of the church being in a former pagan site. The girth of our yew is now approximately 31 feet.[27]

THE CUSOP YEW

THE SELBORNE YEW

As I write these words, the life of another ancient, the Selborne Yew, is hanging in the balance. Gilbert White was a taxophile, a naturalist and also curator of St. Mary Church in Selborne, Hampshire. He mentioned the Selborne Yew in his *Journals 1768-1793*, pointing out that it was a solid male tree with a girth of 23 feet supporting a large head.[28]

THE SELBORNE YEW
"A PAINSTAKING OPERATION BY ARBORCULTURALISTS MAY HAVE RESTORED IT TO LIFE"

A recent news report speaks of crisis:

The yew, in the Hampshire village of Selborne, which overtopped the 45 foot tower of the Norman church of St. Mary, was 26 feet in girth and said to be 1,400 years old. It was felled during the great gale of January (1990) and given up for dead. The congregation said prayers over it a few days later. But a painstaking operation by arborculturalists may have restored it to life.

...partial confirmation of the tree's antiquity came with excavations beneath its roots. Seven complete burials were found with the oldest dating from the late 12th century.[29]

James Anderson, Vicar of Selborne, says the best estimate of the yew's age takes it back to the evangelization of Wessex by St. Birinus in the 7th century, when it may have been planted to commemorate the founding of a church. He added: 'It's a shadow of its former self today but yews have tremendous powers of regeneration. The yew has always been a symbol of immortal life. They are almost immortal.'[30]

The above measurements indicate that in the last 210 years of its life the Selborne yew has grown 3 feet in girth at a rate of 35 years to the radius inch.

THE CROWHURST YEW

A yew tree mentioned by John Selby in 1842, survives to this day in Crowhurst, Surrey in the churchyard of St. George. In 1959, Alan Mitchell measured the tree to be 30 feet 3 inches in girth.[31] Mrs. Pamela Cook reports from Crowhurst in 1990 that the yew tree has been recently certified to be 4,000 years old by the Country Living Yew Tree Campaign Committee. She adds:

The tree is about two yards from the northeast corner of the Church (which is 800 years old). The tree was hollowed out in the 1820's when a door was put into the side of the trunk. A wooden bench seat was put inside the tree (believed to seat 12 persons), also a small wooden table. It is understood that this was done to provide shelter for those attending the annual Palm Sunday Fayre in the Churchyard. When the tree was hollowed out, a cannon ball was found embedded in the side of it, which was assumed to date from the time of the Civil War (about 1652). Mansion House, opposite the road from the Church, is believed to have been a Royalist stronghold.[32]

THE CROWHURST YEW, SURREY

MORE OLD YEW TREES

Perhaps John Lowe's favorite tree, though only 24 feet in girth, was the Harlington Yew in the parish churchyard near Hounslow, Middlesex:

> The old yew tree at Harlington, Middlesex, was clipped in 1729 into a series of circles, and must have been about 50 feet high. In 1780 or 1790 it ceased to be clipped, and was allowed to assume its natural form. It is now one of the finest trees in existence.[33]

An article published in 1975, tells that the Harlington Yew has suffered in recent years:

> The magnificent yew in Harlington churchyard, Middlesex, was for centuries one of the mighty trees of England. This tree, too, is at least ten centuries old. At five feet from the ground the trunk was between 24 and 25 feet in circumference. After some tempestuous weather in 1959 the main trunk collapsed, and it took the men of the church council nine months to saw it up. Fortunately for the continuity of history a substantial stump survived, about 20 feet high. This has taken on a new lease of life and is growing vigorously.[34]

THE HARLINGTON YEW IN 1729

One yew tree in the churchyard of St. Peter in Hambledon, Surrey was measured by Alan Mitchell in 1959 to be 31 feet in girth.[35] Apparently it is the survivor of a pair of trees. The other, larger of the two, recorded by Lowe to be 39 feet at three feet from the ground in 1897, must have met its demise, because by 1941 there was only one massive tree, according to Eric Parker:

> In Hambledon Churchyard stands as fine a yew as any in the south of England. It is vigorous, green, whole; no branches are broken, none need chain nor prop; there is no sign of decay without or within. For size, it measures as nearly as possible 30 feet in circumference; it is hollow, with an inside diameter of 6 feet, and its cavity is clean, housing only a watercan for flowers, But that is not all. It has a neighbour. Indeed, I am not sure that having such a neighbour is not its chief distinction, for many churchyards possess a great yew, but I do not know of another that besides a thirty foot giant owns a perfect specimen of the columnar yew.[36]

E.R. Yarham gives an interesting account of the momentous trek of the Buckland Yew across the churchyard of St. Andrew in Buckland-in-Dover, Kent. The tree was dug up and moved by Mr. William Barron and co-workers in 1880:

> The tree originally stood 62 feet to the east of where it stands today, and the purpose of moving it was to extend the nave of the church and so increase the seating capacity. No doubt the sceptics...were convinced that such an extensive operation would bring about the tree's decease, although nowadays such trasplantations are commonplace. This yew is still in a flourishing condition and shows vigorous signs of new life each spring.[37]

It seems that some of these trees have lived forever, or that they will live forever, but the recent fate of several of them suggests that these relics of bygone ages are in fact mortal. One, at St. Cross Church in Bognor Regis, Sussex, according to Rev. Hugh Pruen:

> ...stood in our churchyard until October 1987. Then in the great gale of that month, the most severe in England for almost three centuries, it was blown down. Part has been used in the church for the display of flowers.[38]

Another was the great yew in the Kingston St. Mary vicarage in Broomfield, Somerset, reported by Lowe to be 24 feet at ground in 1897, but a recent update from Rev. G.C.H. Watson spells disaster:

The Broomfield Yew Tree won a prize in a recent competition for the oldest churchyard yew tree in Somerset. It is certainly older than the 13th century church. Unfortunately the severe storm of the 25 January 1990 badly damaged the tree, bringing down a large portion of the tree onto the church porch. We are advised that the remainder of the tree was in a dangerous condition and is therefore being severely lopped back in the hope that it will regenerate and a new crown form but inevitably the tree will never again be what it was. The timber salvaged from the yew is to be seasoned and it is hoped to make some into furniture for the church, for example a new lectern and priest's desk.[39]

There are some European yew trees in America although according to Edward Roark they do not fare so well:

In early America, George Washington tried growing English Yew at Mount Vernon, but was 'not pleased with the hardiness thereof.' Elizabeth Haddon, the Quakeress, heroine of Longfellow's poem *Elizabeth*, planted two English Yew trees at Haddonfield, New Jersey, early in the Eighteenth Century. They're alive today, but they brown badly in winter, as do specimens on Long Island and at the Arnold Arboretum, near Boston.[40]

Several hundred yew trees greater than 10 feet in circumference can be found in churchyards throughout England, Ireland, Wales, Scotland and Normandy. In 1983 I went to England and Scotland to see and touch some of these old trees. In 1990 I wrote to the vicars of churches where yew trees were supposed to be according to Lowe and Cornish. I received scores of replies with updates on the conditions of some of the largest trees.[41] Many of these remarkable old trees bear their mythic and historical significance, their stories, legends and poetic inspiration well, surviving a past so long that the entire duration of humankind on earth is only a minute in the day to the span of the yew, whose own ancestors stretch back 200 million years in time.

PART IV

CULTURE AND GEOGRAPHY
OF PACIFIC YEW

*We know the sap which courses through the trees
as we know the blood that courses through our veins.*
— Chief Seattle

CHAPTER EIGHT

NATIVE AMERICANS AND PACIFIC YEW

SACRED FORESTS

THE abundant rainfall of the Pacific Northwest at one time sustained a dense forest through which many rivers ran down to the sea, filling twice each year with salmon. The forest was full of birds and animals, the lowland river valleys abundant with camas. Salmon, camas and game sustained life for Northwest natives and the forest provided shelter, clothing and implements for their survival. Through folk memories we can surmise that trees and forests had spiritual significance, as exemplified by these words attributed to Chief Seattle of the Suquamish and Allied Tribes who inhabited the central Washington coast:

> Every part of this earth is sacred to my people. Every shining pine needle, every sandy shore, every mist in the dark woods, every meadow, every humming insect. All are holy in the memory and experience of my people.
>   We know the sap which courses through the trees as we know the blood that courses through our veins. We are part of the earth and it is part of us.[1]

A northwestern Washington myth, *The Beginning Of The Skagit World*, speaks of the forest:

> The creator gave four names for the earth. He said that only a few people should know the names; those few should have special preparation for that knowledge, to receive that special spirit

power. If many people should know the names, the world would change too soon and too suddenly. One of the names is for the sun, which rises in the east and brings warmth and light. Another is for the rivers, streams and salt water. The third is for the soil; our bodies go back to it. The fourth is for the forest; the forest is older than human beings, and is for everyone on the earth.

After the world had been created for a while, everyone learned the four names for the earth. Everyone and everything spoke the Skagit language. When the people began to talk to the trees, then the change came. The change was a flood.

The legend goes on to tell of survivors who spoke of a change yet to come, prophesying:

> ...that a new language would be introduced into our country. It will be the only language spoken, when the next change comes. When we can understand animals, we will know that the change is halfway. When we can talk to the forest, we will know that the change has come.[2]

CHIEF OF THE FOREST

This tale brings to mind Celtic Druids who also would not allow the names of their deities to be spoken, perhaps for the same reason: to prevent the world from changing 'too soon and too suddenly.' The sacred relationship between man and forest which is inferred here has been forgotten, but when it was acknowledged, the yew tree, most long-lived of trees, was woven into the beginings of North American myth just as in the myth of other cultures (Greeks, Romans, Celts and early Christians), whose 'cultus arborum' was the yew. Another story from the Northwest coast suggests it:

> O friend Ya yag Exts!a, I came sent by our friends to let you know the end of their speeches last evening when chief Yew tree called in those who have him for their chief, all the trees and all the bushes. And this was the speech of Yew tree, 'You have done well to have called for mercy all the trees and all the bushes and also done well that you have purified yourself twice and rubbed your body with hemlock branches in the pond.'[3]

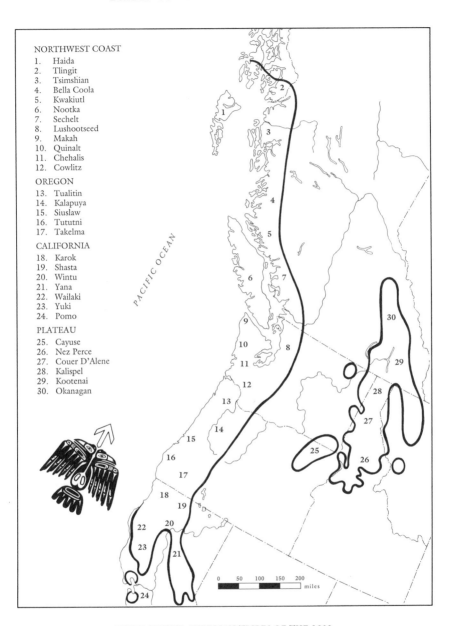

NORTHWEST COAST

1. Haida
2. Tlingit
3. Tsimshian
4. Bella Coola
5. Kwakiutl
6. Nootka
7. Sechelt
8. Lushootseed
9. Makah
10. Quinalt
11. Chehalis
12. Cowlitz

OREGON

13. Tualitin
14. Kalapuya
15. Siuslaw
16. Tututni
17. Takelma

CALIFORNIA

18. Karok
19. Shasta
20. Wintu
21. Yana
22. Wailaki
23. Yuki
24. Pomo

PLATEAU

25. Cayuse
26. Nez Perce
27. Couer D'Alene
28. Kalispel
29. Kootenai
30. Okanagan

PACIFIC OCEAN

0   50   100   150   200
miles

MAJOR NATIVE AMERICAN TRIBES OF THE 1800s
WITHIN THE RANGE OF PACIFIC YEW

NORTH COAST TOOLS

From southeast Alaska, the northern tip of Pacific yew's range, south to the Olympic Peninsula, the coastal seafaring tribes favored the pliable, tough heartwood of the yew for their most vital implements. It could be worked to a smooth finish; it bent without breaking and could be molded into shape. People fished for salmon with yew wood spears and nets on yew wood frames. They pursued seals, sea lions and whales, propelling their sixty-man cedar canoes quickly across the sea with yew wood oars. On shore at low tide women and children pried chitons and mussels off the exposed rocks with fire-hardened yew wood sticks. Men and boys hunted deer, elk and bear with yew wood bows four fingers wide. The northerly Tlingit and Haida made war clubs and fish clubs of yew on which they carved intricate anthropomorphic and animistic designs. The Haida name for yew means 'bow' or 'bow plant.'[4]

HALIBUT HOOK

HALIBUT HOOK

The Kwaikutl, Nootka and Makah of Puget Sound favored yew for canoe paddles: one oval-shaped for peace-time and another for war, tapered to a sharp point and honed to a razor edge, thus also serving as a formidable weapon. Bill Holm of the Burke Museum in Seattle says that the yew occurs in Native American mythology because of 'its toughness and springiness, rather than any special spiritual qualities.' He cites a Kwaikutl tale about two canoes of mythical heroes passing one another, one with yellow cedar paddles and the other with yew paddles. The yellow cedar paddles all broke.[5]

CANOE UNDERWAY WITH YEW WOOD BATTLE PADDLES

Ethnologist Nancy Turner, mentions specific uses of yew:

> The Kwaikutl bound a bundle of yew branches to a hemlock pole to make a tool for gathering sea urchins; the spines of these animals became entangled in the branches. Young Kwaikutl men tested their strength by trying to twist a yew tree from crown to butt.[6]

Forest tribes made strong durable wedges of yew for splitting
and shaping cedar into planks for
houses, quarter-rounds for spirit
poles and half-rounds for canoes.
They had no way to fall huge cedar
trees but they did know how to use
them once they had blown down.
They also knew how to take single

HALIBUT HOOK

planks from living trees by driving wedges into them along two parallel
and perpendicular lines: when the massive trees swayed back and forth
in high winds a plank would pop out from between the wedges. The
Hesquiat tribe of Vancouver Island had two names for the yew: *wita-*

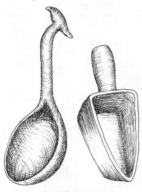

pt meaning, 'plant used for warring', and
xatmapt or *xanat* meaning, 'wedge'. Turner
says that it means 'wedge plant' in Saechelt,
Suquamish, and Nootka as well.[7]

Makah of the southern Puget Sound
region hunted whale with yew wood harpoons and made durable frames for their dip
nets as well as canoe-bailers and a variety of
fish spears. They made halibut hooks from
slim yew twigs which they cut to length and

CANOE BAILERS   smoothed. They cut the bulb end of a kelp

whip to the same length and put the yew twig inside, filled it with water
and stuffed both ends with moss and laid it in warm coals overnight,
until the steamed yew could be bent. Then they put it into a wooden
mold and left it to assume its final shape. They rubbed dry deer tallow
into the hook to make it water-resistant, then lashed a bone barb to it.[8]

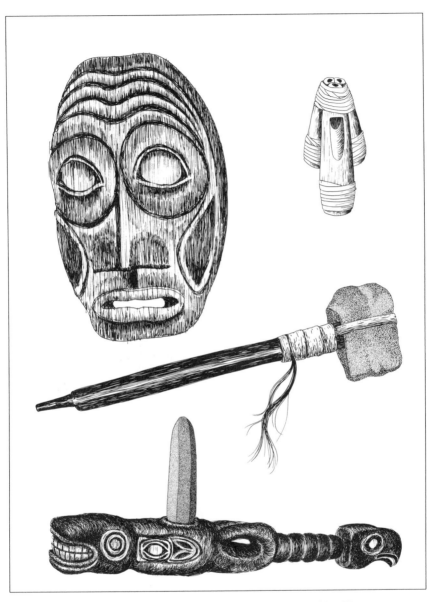

YEW WOOD ARTIFACTS OF THE NORTHWEST COAST TRIBES
(NOT TO SCALE)

Death Mask   Spirit Whistle
Pipe
Slave Killing Club

Saanich of Vancouver Island employed similar steaming techniques to shape the ends of their yew wood bows. They used trunks of living yew trees as catapults for throwing spears. Women used yew twigs to remove underarm hair. Quinault who lived on the Olympic Peninsula, made bows, clubs, combs, digging sticks, spear and harpoon shafts, needles for sewing cattails, mauls, chisel shafts, traps and spring poles for deer traps. Utensils and tools were carved from yew: awls, spoons, dishes, bowls, hammers, handles for knives, adzes and scrapers; dowels and pegs, drum

GAMBLING STICKS

frames and boxes. Several tribes, among them Quinault, Slahelem and Tillamook made small polished sticks or button-like discs out of yew with which they gambled, sometimes for very high stakes.[9]

There are numerous yew wood objects of the Northwest coast Indians at the Burke Museum in Seattle. From the Haida is a totemic

stick, associated with the 'one-legged fisherman', the figure of a shaman and a collection of gambling sticks. From the Tlingit is a cermonial staff with a raven and human head and a shaman's box made of a single piece of yew representing a human face. One Tlingit mask carved from yew represents the face of a corpse with dried, wrinkled skin and catches the 'spirit of a dead man'. There is also a fine collection of Tlingit fishing gear, featuring intricately carved halibut hooks.

TLINGIT MASK

MEDICINAL USES

Northeastern Native Americans used Canadian yew for many ailments: rheumatism, clots, fever, pain, scurvy, numbness, paralysis, bowel ailments, colds, gonorrhea, dysmenorrhea and stomachache.[10] Northwestern Native Americans made similar use of Pacific yew. Haida believed that women who ate yew berries would not conceive.[11] Makah and Nootka crushed yew needles in hot water to brew an astringent bath for the elderly and children; branches were used for scrubbing. Quinault pulverized the needles into a paste to put on wounds, as did the Cowlitz. Yew bark boiled in water made a tea for lung ailments. Swinhomish youths rubbed smooth sticks of yew on their developing bodies to gain its strength.[12] Needles were ground and smoked, sometimes in a mixture with kinnikinik, which was said to make a person quite dizzy.[13] Erna Gunther wrote in the 1930's that, 'features of the old culture, like medicinal usages, cling with amazing tenacity.'[14]

INTERIOR VALLEY TRIBES

In the interior valleys west of the Cascades from British Columbia to the western slopes of the Sierra Nevadas gathering and hunting were more important elements in survival than fishing, so the implements used to get food were different. As in other cultures, yew wood was especially prized for making bows. The bow is featured in northwest creation myths, usually associated with some mythical hero who brought the knowledge of survival to humans. Tribal names for yew allude to its use as bow-wood; Hesquiats called it 'plant for warring'. Haida called it the 'bow plant'. The Lillooet tribe who lived in the interior west of the Monashee Mountains and east of the Coast Range in British Columbia called it *texw-ats-az*, or 'bow-tree'. They also called it *tiemk-az*, or 'female tree with berries'.[15]

Yew wood was prized by people living outside the range of the tree and was often traded:

> ...the Shuswap in the Interior made bows from it, although yew is fairly scarce in their territory. They and the Upper Thompson often obtained the wood from the Lillooet and Lower Thompson. The Flathead Salish of Montana also made yew bows, seasoning the wood well and varnishing the finished product with boiled sinew to waterproof it and prevent it from warping.

The eastern limit of Pacific yew's range is the western slopes and foothills of the Montana Rockies. It is a dominant species over a considerable portion of the forest in Idaho, in the south fork of the

Clearwater basin east of the Bitteroots and west of the Snake River. The Nez Perce from that region were quite dependent on their yew wood hunting bows.[17]

Chinook, who lived along the Columbia River in eastern Oregon made bowls, boxes, spoons, ladles and bows out of yew wood.[18] Their access to yew trees was limited but they lived between yew producing regions and had frequent opportunity to trade for the yew they needed.

OREGON COAST TRIBES

On the north Oregon coast, Nehalem Tillamook made bows and other items of yew wood, and from a folktale we learn that they thought highly of it. Two young women painted tattoos on their faces and went among the trees to ask, 'How do I look? Do I look nice?' According to each tree's answer, desireable or undesirable properties were bestowed upon them by the women. Younger Wild Woman asked Yew, who said, 'You are quite nice looking, that tattoo looks well on you.' She said to Yew:

> They will go a long distance to obtain you. They will carve needles from your wood, and even spirit-power poles and fish clubs will be made from you. People with power will scrape your hard surface and make little flat discs for gambling games. Large wagers will be made over you, even slaves will be wagered.[19]

KALAPUYA

Further inland and south in the Willamette Valley, Kalapuya hunted game with bow and arrow. It was also their chosen weapon of war and while oak or ash would suffice, yew was thought to be the very best wood available. Native Americans were in the southern Willamette Valley very early, as attested to by a 'clovis' projectile point found in the surface gravel of the Mohawk River, left there 10,000 years ago. According to Kalapuya expert Bill Burwell:

TLINGIT STAFF

In precontact time they figured that the Kalapuya numbered between 100 and 200 thousand and they held all of the territory up the Willamette Valley from the Tualitin River drainage on the north all the way to the Umpqua rivers; the Yoncalla were the southernmost tribe of Kalapuya and there were about 16 different major bands and about 12 different, completely separate dialects. Linguists think that it took probably about 4,000 years for the break down into all of these different dialects from a common linguistic stock. The Kalapuya were probably indigenous here in the southern part of the valley for at least three and probably four thousand years.[20]

FISH CLUBS

Kalapuyas had a diversified food base, not dependent on fishing like so many Northwest tribes. The Willamette Falls was a physical barrier to the salmon, so very different cultures developed in the northern and southern ends of the Willamette Valley. In the north the way of life resembled the seafarers and fishers of the north coast. In the south, the camas, a starchy bulb, was the staple food. Kalapuya women dug this abundant food with a sharp, stout stick, topped with an elk antler handle. Straight yew saplings that grew to a point made the ideal digging sticks. The tough, resilient wood was fire-hardened into an indestructible tool. When a woman died her digging stick was stuck in the ground to mark her final resting place.[21] Kalapuya men were often buried with their yew wood bows.

Like other Native American cultures the Kalapuya used the yew medicinally. According to Bill Burwell:

They used yew wood in a skin salve in which the needles and the bark were soaked in water and then prepared with grease into a concoction that was used on the skin as a protection against sunburn. The Yoncallas used it as a tonic for old people who would ingest a tea made out of yew needles.

Burwell tells several Kalapuya stories about yew wood and its various uses. In one tale about Coyote and the Frog Women, Coyote employs several guises involving yew wood implements: a shinny stick, a camas root digging stick and a salmon spear:

> Shinny is a game much like lacrosse or field hockey. There were two goals set up and entire families and bands would play against each other. They used yew wood sticks that were cut almost like field hockey sticks and they used a hard ball made out of yew wood. They would hit the ball back and forth around the field trying to get it through the goal. It was almost identical to a game that is played in Ireland called hurling; exact same format and everything, the rules were that there were no rules.

Another Kalapuya tale is about Coyote who runs into a one-legged man who is fishing beside a river:

> The man was fishing with a yew wood spear, made by hardening a yew wood limb in the fire and then abrading it with a rough stone down to a sharp point. Coyote goes through a period where he comes down every day and goes fishing with the man, basically sitting on the bank. When the man speared a fish and brought it in by himself then Coyote would jump down and club it with the man's yew wood fish club.
> The first day that Coyote was there the man speared two salmon and gave Coyote one and took one home. The second day the man speared three salmon and gave Coyote one and took two home and the next day he speared four, gave Coyote two and took two and the next day he speared five and took three and gave Coyote two. Coyote went home very upset because the man was not even giving him half the fish that he was spearing and Coyote was helping him out so much by sitting up on the bank and hollering when he sees a fish and jumping down and clubbing it after the man does all the work himself.
> So Coyote decides that he's getting short changed by the man and turns himself into a giant chinook. The next day the man is back at the falls

HARPOONS

fishing, waiting for a fish to come by and no fish come except for this giant chinook. The man was suspicious of it, but finally because the chinook is scaring away all the rest of the other salmon around he finally spears the giant chinook that is really Coyote in disguise. Coyote's plan is to grab the man's yew wood spear and drag him into the water and drown him. The one-legged man sits down behind a rock and braces himself so Coyote can't pull him into the water. Coyote breaks off the point of the yew wood spear that is piercing him and heads down river, turns back into Coyote and goes home and complains to his wife that his side is hurting and she finds the broken off yew wood spear point in his side, pulls it out and throws it out the door.

The one-legged man in the meantime hadn't been able to get any fish and he figured that that giant chinook was Coyote, so he goes home and gets some fish that he had dried from the day before and takes it over to Coyote to see how he was doing. Coyote thanks him for the fish and the man sees his broken spear outside and says, 'Aha! I knew that was Coyote all along.'

Burwell indicates that yew was the wood of choice for critical implements.

Yew wood was the most important wood to the Kalapuyas as far as their ceremonial tools and also their tools that needed great strength and durability. It was much harder to work than cedar, ash, filbert or some of the other woods. At the start of every  gathering season, they would have a first gathering or first fruit ceremony. In the case of the camas bulb the shaman would go out and dig the first camas bulbs to be used that year with a particular digging stick to be used only for the first camas bulb ceremony. He would dig enough bulbs for the entire group to partake in – just one small bite – and with this ceremony they gave reverence to the spirit that provided for the camas to come back every year. The shaman would put away the yew wood digging stick until the next year. All the tools that they used in the first gathering ceremonies were almost always made of yew wood, passed on through successive generations from shaman to shaman.

KNIFE HANDLE

Kalapuya bows were almost always made of yew wood. They would take a piece of clear trunk stock, free of knots. They would shave out a blank in which just a thin line of the sapwood was left on the outside or the flex side of the bow. They grooved this out and then glued deer back-sinew into the grooves to give it even more strength. The very best bow strings around here were made out of the single filament fibers of the wild blue flag, the blue irises.

They also made drinking vessels, serving bowls and platters of yew wood. Sometimes red cedar was used, but ceremonial objects were made of yew wood because it was so lasting. They would rough out a piece of wood into the approximate shape that they wanted and during the winter time when they were largely confined to their dwellings because of bad weather they would use the burn and abrasion method to make their cups, platters and bowls. They would take a hot coal out of the fire and set it on the piece of wood and blow on it until the coal glowed and charred out the area around it. Then they would take an abrasive stone and rub out the charred area; then start all over again with the coal. This was a time consuming process but they ended up with wonderfully polished, hand-burnished utensils.

With the Kalapuya, everything that had form in the physical world was really a manifestation of its spiritual aspects. The yew wood was a manifestation of endurance and strength and an intractable nature.

It was common for a person making a new salmon spear from a long straight yew limb to perform a gathering ceremony before he would even begin to cut off a limb to use. This offering to the spirit was sometimes a song that was made up which would become an integral part of the spear. The person, sitting on a rock waiting for a fish to come by, would sing the song to call in the yew spirit to help him attract salmon. 'Wouldn't you love to be killed by this beautiful yew wood spear that I have made instead of getting caught by some bear upstream.'[22]

UMPQUA

Further south, below the Umpqua River, the Cow Creek band of Umpquas trapped deer in rope snares and hunted them with bows and arrows as well. George Riddle, who grew up with Cow Creek boys, described the technique:

INDIAN BURIAL PLACE, OREGON 1841

In order to approach the deer to make the arrows effective they dressed themselves to resemble the deer by covering themselves with a deer skin with the head and neck mounted to look natural, keeping the deer to the windward and going through the motions of a deer feeding. At fifty yards the Indian arrow was as deadly as a bullet.

On our arrival most of the Indians were armed with bows and arrows. The bows were made of yew wood, the backs covered by the sinews of the deer held by some kind of glue. The bows were about thirty inches long and very elastic. They could be bent until the ends would almost meet. The quiver holding the bow and arrows was made of the whole skin of the otter or fox and swung across the back so that the feather end of the arrow could be reached over the shoulder. They were so expert in reaching the arrows and adjusting to the bow that they could keep an arrow in the air all the time.[23]

Riddle also described the 'kamass' harvest which was done with a digging stick made of 'arrow wood'. I think this refers to straight-grained yew wood, since elsewhere the Kalapuya employed yew wood for digging sticks. It was readily available in the Umpqua River drainage and the hard yew wood was used to make arrow points [24] and the straight-grained yew was used for shafts as well.

YEW WOOD KAMASS DIGGING STICKS

The squaws were the workers. The greatest part of their winter food was the 'kamass' – a small onion shaped bulb about one inch in diameter which was plentiful in the low lands of the valley. In the early morning the squaws would be out in the kamass field provided with a basket, a cone shaped affair open at the top, swung on the back and carried with a strap across the forehead – a manner in which the Indians carried all their burdens and which left both arms free. Each squaw would be armed with a kamass stick made of Indian arrow wood fashioned to a point at one end by burning and rubbing the charred wood off leaving the point as hard as steel. At the top end was fitted a curved handle, generally a piece of deer horn. Locating the bulb by the seed top above ground they would insert the stick under the root with the weight of the body, prying up the kamass, which they would deftly throw over the shoulder into the basket. In this manner if the expert squaw worked all day she could bring home about one bushel...The kamass was cooked by excavating a pit, filling it with wood with rocks on top. After the rocks were sufficiently heated they were covered with dry grass and then a great lot of kamass, covering them up with earth for several days when they came out they would be of a reddish brown color and were sweet and really good to eat.[25]

NORTHERN CALIFORNIA TRIBES

In northern California, Yurok, Hupa, Karok, Shasta, Maidu, Wintu and Yahi made their best bows of yew. As with the northern tribes the size of the bow varied according to its intended purpose:

The bow was self [made of one piece], long, and narrow in the south, sinew-backed, somewhat shorter, thin, and broad in northern and central California. Of course light unbacked bows were used for small game and by boys everywhere. The material varied locally. In the northwest [California] the bow was of yew and shorter and flatter than anywhere else; the wood was pared down to little greater thickness than the sinew, the edge was sharp, and the grip much pinched.[26]

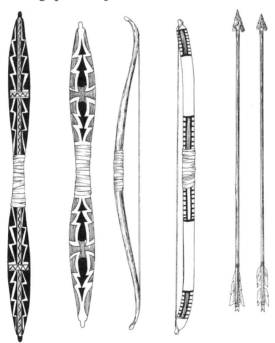

YEW WOOD BOWS AND ARROWS

ISHI

In 1911, a ragged, half-starved man staggered into a yard in a northeastern California town; barking dogs held him at bay until the sheriff came and took him away. The man was the last survivor of the Yahi tribe, which had had trouble with the white settlers when he was a boy. The small band of Yahi stayed hidden for years just beyond the reach of encroaching civilization. Bewildered and lonely, he had come to realize that the old ways were gone forever. Anthropologists from the University of California adopted him and named him Ishi, which in his language meant 'man'. He never told them his own name. One of the anthropologists knew a few words of the Yana language, a tribe to whom the Yahi were related. When he tapped his fingers on a pinewood table and uttered the yana word for pine, *siwini*, Ishi's eyes brightened and communication between his lost world and modern man began.[27]

He returned with his new acquaintances to the land of his people and taught them many primitive survival skills. He showed them how to make critical tools from yew wood; bows for hunting, spears for fishing. He was familiar with yew wood's strength and knew also that it was poisonous. He called it *hulogos'i* in his native Yahi tongue.[28]

Although Ishi was an excellent hunter, he demonstrated little proficiency in target shooting. When asked to select the best of the many bows in the museum at the University of California at Berkeley, he chose a sinew-backed Yurok yew wood bow. Saxton T. Pope, an archery afficionado, described Ishi's ability to make primitive tools as the best he had ever seen. He also said that his 'eye for form and symmetry was perfect.' About Ishi's skill as a bowman, Pope wrote in *Yahi Archery*:

> Ishi called the bow *man'i*. He made bows of many woods while under observation...eucalyptus, tanbark oak, red cedar, hickory, ash, juniper and yew...All of these were of the same general shape and size, and all were backed with sinew. Yew, of course, produced the best weapon. His standard of measurement for a good bow was to hold a stave diagonally across his chest with one end in his right hand at the hip, and the left arm extended straight out at an angle of 45 degrees from the horizontal. The distance

ISHI STRAIGHTENING AN ARROW

between these points was the proper length for a bow. This measured in his own case four feet and two inches. The width of the bow at the middle of each limb was three or four fingers, according to whether a light hunting bow or a powerful war bow was wanted. The shape of his bow was a short, flat stave, with limbs wider at their center than at the handle, sometimes recurved at their outer extremity, tapering gracefully to small short nocks at the ends.

On cold days, Ishi warmed his bow over a fire before attempting to brace it. The ideal bow, to his mind, curved in a perfect arch at all points, and at full draw represented a crescent. The center bent with the limbs and was the bow's weakest point. A forty-five inch bow he drew twenty-five inches. No yew wood could stand such an arc without backing. In fact he broke two bow-staves, testing them at my request, prior to the application of sinew.

Usually Ishi made no effort to decorate his bow, though he spoke of painting it, and led me to infer that this was done only after the implement had shown some peculiar virtue, or had figured in some deed of valor. The one bow he embellished while with us he marked with three green transverse stripes just above the handle and below the nocks, and three long snaky lines running down the back. He said that red also was an appropriate color.

A good bow was one whose string made a high musical note when tapped with an arrow or snapped with the fingers. It should sing the note 'tin, tin, tin'. This was the 'chief's bow'. One whose note was dead and unmusical, Ishi treated with contempt.[29]

It is interesting to note similar uses to which the yew was put by various cultures. Certain Asian musical intruments and quite an array of European stringed instruments including lutes, theorbores and violins were made in part or entirely of yew. Bows for playing these instruments were also made of yew. It is likely that plucked or bowed string instruments evolved from the practice of playing the strung bow with finger or arrow. Ishi made such music:

> By placing the upper end of his braced bow at the corner of his open mouth and gently tapping the string midway between the end and center he caused clear musical notes to be produced. This sounded like our jew's harp, and by altering the shape of the buccal cavity he was able to create a series of tones sufficient to form a melody relating to a story of wonderful deeds with the bow. He sang of a great archer who dipped his arrow point in the sea, then in the fire, drew a mighty bow, and shot at the sun. His arrow flew like the north wind, and entering the door of the sun, put out its light. Then all the world became dark, men shivered with cold, and from this time they grew feathers on their bodies to make them warm.[30]

In the short time that he lived in civilization Ishi became somewhat of a folk hero, a symbol of vanishing Native American cuture. When he died in 1916, his passing closed the books on a culture which had thrived for 10,000 years, and though Chief Seattle promised that the spirits of his people would dwell among the cedars, rivers and rocks of the north coast, and that the trees and all other living things would be forever relatives of his people, we are left with a profound sense of loss at the passing of these people who managed to live in harmony with the bountiful forests of the Pacific Northwest. Today even the old ways vanish into vague memories, as described by Erna Gunther in about 1915:

> I talked with old men who knew bows were made of yew wood, but had never used one seriously. A few had made them of commercial lumber, as tourist souvenirs. Many an old woman wished she could dig camas for a meal, but instead she cooks navy beans or macaroni.[31]

The lore that endures about the yew tree lingers as a connection between our culture and those that have vanished, embodied by the few surviving wooden implements, most of which were made from yew. But the most direct link are living yew trees who witnessed those bygone times. Today this connection is gravely threatened.

PACIFIC YEW

CHAPTER NINE

PACIFIC YEW
(TAXUS BREVIFOLIA)

DESCRIPTION

PACIFIC yew is similar in most respects to the European yew except that the leaves are lighter in color and shorter, which accounts for its name 'short leaf', *Taxus brevifolia.* The evergreen foliage, mottled rose to chocolate-brown bark and brown seeds are poisonous. The fleshy red aril (berry) that surrounds the seed is not poisonous and is attractive to birds and animals who play an important part in the yew's natural dissemination. In the coastal forest Pacific yew attains a height of 50 to 75 feet, but from northeast Washington through northern Idaho and Montana it grows in a shrub form similar to *T. canadensis.* Like its European cousin the Pacific yew played a significant role in the lives of people who lived near it primarily because its combination of red-brown heartwood and yellow-white sapwood is elastic and durable. Grand specimens found beneath the remaining old growth canopies of the Pacific Northwest are the oldest trees left in the forest as well as the last significant natural stand of yew on earth. They are sights to behold, as Donald Peattie points out in *A Natural History of Western Trees*, published in 1953:

> To recognize it, look for a tree with flat and prickly-tipped needles, for the Sitka Spruce is the only other species locally present which has such. But the needles of the Sitka Spruce bristle stiffly all around the twig, while the Yew's are soft and lie all in

one plane. And there are other distinguishing features, such as the beautiful, peeled-looking bark, whose papery purplish scales are always curling and sloughing away to reveal the flower-like clear rose of the inner bark. The trunk is usually fluted and twisted and often unsymmetrical; in intense forests, however, it is straight and slender though usually clothed in fine down-sweeping branches right to the ground. Sometimes it grows so densely...as to form veritable jungles. Slender whip-like twigs depend from the boughs, giving a weeping appearance, and the whole tree has a sort of wood-sprite grace, mingled with mystery in the very dark mass of foliage – quite the most somber of all the western trees, but lightened, when seen from below, by the silvery white undersides of the needles.[1]

RANGE

Taxus brevifolia was named by Thomas Nuttall in 1849 and it was introduced into England as a species apart from *T. baccata* in 1854. It has been variously called Pacific, American, Western, California and Oregon yew, and mountain mahogany. Its habitat is beneath fir, cedar and hemlock canopies in what remains of the Northwest rain forest from the Santa Cruz Mountains through the California Coast Range, Siskiyous and Trinities into the Coast Ranges of Oregon, Washington and British Columbia to the Skeena River Basin and into the tip of southeast Alaska including the islands. It is found on Prince of Wales, Queen Charlotte and Vancouver Islands as well as the Olympic Peninsula, where it thrives.

Further inland, yew grows in the pine, laurel and oak forests of the western slopes of the Sierra Nevada from as far south as Tulare County, northward into the Klamath Mountains and then in the fir and hemlock forests on the western slopes of the Cascades through Oregon and Washington and into the Selkirks of British Columbia. It is also found from the Snake River Basin on the border of Oregon and Idaho to the western slopes of the Bitterroot Range and into the Wallowa and Blue Mountains of northeastern Oregon, and in isolated pockets in northeastern Washington and northern Idaho. Its eastern boundary is the foothills and western slopes of the Rockies of Montana and British Columbia.[2]

PACIFIC YEW *(TAXUS BREVIFOLIA)*
Female
a. Ovule ready for pollination.   b. Seed with mature aril.

HABITAT

Although yew is widespread throughout the Northwest, it is not found in very large populations, surviving more in scattered pockets as an understory tree beneath old-growth canopy, or in shaded ravines, or, in drier climates, along rivers and streams. The yew, while a tenacious survivor, is susceptible to variations in microsite conditions. It can survive low temperatures to five degrees fahrenheit, and grows in places with annual precipitation of from 20 to 150 inches. Pacific yew, like other species of *Taxus*, is very tolerant of shade and is partial to those aspects which receive little direct sun. It ranges from sea level to 8,000 feet in the Sierra Nevada, in areas with growing seasons from two to ten months long. Depending on site and conditions, some yew trees grow more quickly than others, with as few as 15 annual growth rings per radius inch; others grow more slowly with as many as 50 rings to the inch.[3] Yew grow slowly compared to other trees, less than one-tenth the rate of Douglas fir. Other trees grow up through the yew's branches and it is quickly surpassed in height by fir, hemlock, cedar, pine, oak, chinquapin, laurel, ash, maple, alder and myrtle.

Dr. Charles Bolsinger, who analyzes the range and distribution of Pacific yew for the U. S. Forest Service, describes a range of habitat:

> Pacific yew grows best on deep, moist or rich, rocky or gravelly soils. In drier interior forests, the species develops best along mountain streams, and in shady canyons, ravines and coves. Within the moist maritime climate of the Pacific Northwest, it appears to grow most abundantly in drier, warmer environments.[4]

Peattie described its prime habitat in 1953:

> That great block of land that lies between Puget Sound on the east and the Pacific on the west, with the eternal snows of the Olympic range shining at the heart of it, the Western Yew reaches its best development, growing up to 75 feet in height. But big as this is for a Yew, it is fairly lost in the lowland forests of the peninsula, first because it is not a common tree even there, and further because all its coniferous neighbors are so gigantic – Douglas Firs, Grand Firs, Sitka Spruces, Western Red Cedars and mighty Hemlocks. These make the most somber, unbroken and

HABITAT OF THE PACIFIC YEW

utterly overwhelming forests on the North American continent, and in their midst the Yew must be sought out with a knowing eye.[5]

Yew trees usually grow in clusters, because damaged trees often send up new trees from the roots and in many cases what appear to be individual trees are actually offshoots of a 'mother tree' who returned to dust long ago. Only occasionally will one discover a solitary yew in the forest, even though its propagation is aided by birds which eat the red berries and pass the seed through their digestive tracts. The seed must drop onto an ideal site, of which there are apparently few, because one rarely finds yew seedlings. Peattie describes:

> Only the female trees, of course, bear the berry-like, coral-red fruit, which is really an aril, that is, a mass of fleshy pulp with an open pit in which is lodged the seed. That pulp is sweet and mucilaginous and is devoured by birds which may carry the seeds far before voiding them, their viability quite unimpaired. One would think that this would make the Yew abundantly successful, but the amount of fruiting is scarce, and seedlings are comparatively rare. More, growth in the darkness of these woods is very slow, and a trunk only 12 to 20 inches in diameter is probably 140 to 245 years old.[7]

Bolsinger reports that Pacific yew grows into a shrub in northeastern Washington, northern Idaho and Montana. As we saw earlier, on the other side of the Rockies is the Canadian yew, which closely resembles the bush-like incarnation of the Pacific yew. It too produces a fine tree in some parts of its southern range. The fact that they resemble one another in similar conditions underlines the strong similarity between the various species. Generally the Pacific yew is found in tree form as an element in the understory of old-growth forests.

LARGE PACIFIC YEWS

The largest known living Pacific yew is in Lewis County, Washington, near Mount Rainier. This record yew stands about 70 feet tall, with a girth of 14 feet 10.5 inches and is probably near 1,000 years old. Oregon's champion yew is a twisted behemoth which leans precariously over a cliff 20 feet above the Tualatin River in Washington County. It is 13 feet 4 inches in circumference[7] and is estimated to be one of the oldest trees in Oregon. The largest tree in Idaho was found by Dave Hayes east of Grangeville and west of the Bitterroot Mountains. He nominated the tree in 1987 as the largest of its species in Idaho, 10 feet 2 inches in circumference with a height of 44 feet and crown spread of 23 feet 6 inches.[8] None of these trees comes close to

THE LARGEST KNOWN PACIFIC YEW
AND FAYE O'BRIAN

one mentioned in *The Oregon Historical Journal* of 1958 as being 1,800 years old. Unfortunately it was cut down before they realized how old it was. If it had an average annual ring count of 35 years to the inch it would have been about 25 feet in circumference.[9]

IDAHO YEWS

Bolsinger indicates that dry, atypical environments for the yew are to be found in Idaho, and that in the Clearwater River (south fork) basin it is the dominant species on about 40,000 acres of federal timber land. He mentions a yew tree in Idaho growing in harsh sub-humid climatic conditions at the bottom of Hell's Canyon on the Snake River; this tree is 8 feet 9 inches in circumference and 28 feet tall.[10]

THE IDAHO CHAMPION

LARGE OREGON YEWS

I have seen fairly large yew trees throughout the Northwest, although most have been in Oregon, and just for the record I would like to mention a few of them. In Marion County are several large yew trees noted and measured by Brian O'Brian. One measures 12 feet 8 inches in circumference at breast height, another 11 feet 4 inches. On the edge of downtown Salem was the Deepwood Yew, 8 feet 10 inches diameter in its prime, which stood for centuries but recently met its demise. The Deepwood Yew was a male tree and had been a member of quite a large grove of yew trees in the past century. The area was known as Yew Park when Doctor Porter began to build his Deepwood Mansion there in 1890. Nearby, according to taxophile Brian O'Brian, there is a group of female yews surrounding an area where an old female ancestor might have grown.

Elsewhere in Marion County the Marion Yew at Parrish Gap, 12 feet 4 inches in circumference, was known to be one of the largest yew trees in the state. During the Columbus Day storm of 1962, wind gusts exceeding 100 miles-per-hour broke one of the three main trunks, causing a fatal split into the heartwood. It lingered for seven years before the last green needles disappeared. Three other mighty yews in the vicinity were uprooted by that fateful storm. Today, a handful of scrawny saplings grow nearby. There is a large yew tree in Helmick State Park in Polk County between Corvallis and Monmouth that measures 9 feet, 5 inches. In Linn County there is a single yew between Lyons and Kingston that is nearly 9 feet in girth. It is about 70 feet tall, fluted, and whorled at a jaunty angle – a beautiful specimen of a valley floor yew. There are several other smaller yews nearby.

YEW, WATER AND CAMPGROUNDS

In western Oregon pockets of yew grow in river valleys with tribal names like Umpqua, Rogue and Klamath. There is a strong correlation between water, prehistoric camps and yew trees. A few of the many archaeological sites found near water among yew trees in Oregon are: areas along the Mohawk River in Lane County, at Cascadia Cave on the Santiam River, below rock shelters on tributaries of the Willamette (Fall Creek, Gettings Creek and the Long Tom River). Yew trees are also found near waterfalls on the Siuslaw, Alsea and South Umpqua where Native Americans trapped cutthroat, steelhead and salmon. At these sites, all the necessities of life are found in one place – water, fish and game, and yew trees for making bows, spears and camas sticks (in preparation for the seasonal migration to the valley floor to dig for the roots).

OREGON CASCADES

The western foothills of the Oregon Cascades are home to some fine yew also. Southeast of Oakridge, in the Willamette watershed, Highway 58 passes through mile after mile of yew, fir, cedar and hemlock lining Salt Creek. Yews twenty feet tall and two feet around thrive here in what is left of their natural habitat. Past the Blue Pool campground, Highway 58 climbs into the Cascades and beyond the range of large yew trees. At Odell Lake, the yew grows small and brush-like, seldom more than eight feet tall. Abruptly, at East Odell Lake, the soil turns to alkaline sand; tall firs and hemlocks give way to Jack and Ponderosa pine forests, which flank the eastern slopes of the Cascades and the yew tree disappears.

THE SPIRAL YEW AT COUGAR MOUNTAIN

Bow makers believe that the southern tip of the Willamette Valley produces the clearest, straightest-grained yew available for their craft.[12] Native Americans certainly found stock for their bows here. Gettings Creek runs out of the Cascades in the foothills east of Saginaw and empties into the Coast Fork of the Willamette. Up Gettings Creek to the base of Cougar Mountain, which is connected to the backbone of the Cascades, is a scattered trail of older yew trees at elevations ranging from 1,000 to 1,600 feet. These yews grow above an underground water source that emanates from volcanic fissures in the Cascades, several found along this trail are 700 years old; two are nearly four feet in diameter and over 50 feet tall. One stag-headed yew is favored by bears and cougars where they sharpen their claws, leaving deep grooves through the bark and into the sapwood of the tree. A three-foot thick corkscrew yew looms above the deep shaded canyon of Gettings Creek; its fluted column twists in a spiral design, responding to the spinning earth and its own life force. Unfortunately this spectacular tree seems to be dying or dead.

WILLAMETTE VALLEY

Also in Lane County, on and around the Oregon Country Fair grounds, occasional clusters of three or four yews are found scattered along the Long Tom River. Some of these trees are forty feet tall and three feet wide and flare up in a network of spreading limbs. Other gnarled specimens are found nearby mixed with alder, maple, oak, ash and fir; in this area are many ancient Kalapuya encampments. These yew trees are 300 to 500 years old, having survived fire, climatic change and human exploitation. They are particularly unusual because few yew trees are left on the floor of the Willamette Valley.

YEW ON THE LONG TOM RIVER

SOUTHERN OREGON YEWS

In Douglas County on the South Umpqua River, near Tiller, where I have worked in the woods many times over the years, yew trees are so plentiful that they are considered a nuisance by loggers. In Josephine County where yew occurs frequently there is near Merlin in the Rogue River Valley a 'Ewe' Creek that is said to be a misnomer; the name should read 'Yew' Creek because of the many large yews that lined of its banks.

Further south in Jackson County, nestled into the Rogue National Forest, the yews grow profusely around the foothills of Mount McLoughlin in the vicinity of Lake of the Woods. At nearby Fish Lake is a fine collection of yew groves and thickets which are on a natural pass over the Cascades used by various tribes: Modoc, Klamath and Takelma. One can almost imagine young men walking through the pollarded trees choosing their future bow-staves, while nearby crafts-men fletched arrows to hunt geese, ducks and deer. Today beneath an aging canopy of 500 year old Sugar pine, Douglas and Grand fir, yew groves form the dominant understory species. One old yew, more than two feet thick, shares an opening in the forest with a deer-browsed yew shrub and four Druid-like stones set in velvet emerald moss.

The Fish Lake yews are draped with gray-green moss, *isothecium spiculiferum*, which highlights their somber appearance. Yews survive only on the north and west sides of Fish Lake; the south and east sides were inundated by lava over 7,000 years ago. There is one outstanding exception: on a jutting promontory of solid lava ten feet above water level, a wind swept, sun burned, rugged yew ekes out an existence with a wild gooseberry, several small conifers, some clumps of manzanita and several dwarf chinquapin. In reaction to unobstructed sunlight its needles have a reddish hue. Though it is nearly three feet thick at the base, it has attained a height of only 20 feet. This 500 year old specimen can be seen by boat on the east side of Fish Lake, about one-quarter mile from the resort.

Along the shores of nearby Howard Prairie Reservoir, a camp-ground has been named for the abundant yew and between Lake-of-the-Woods and Howard Prairie along the highway, where logging took place years ago, the effects of exposure to sun, wind and animal browsing have shaped a yew topiary garden of fantastic shapes.

EASTERN OREGON

The Pacific yew survives east of the Cascades in a few pockets, mainly in the Blue and Wallowa Mountains of northeastern Oregon. Yews here have been reduced to living fossils; some of the largest are only eight inches thick at the base. The climate is more extreme than in the rain forests west of the Cascades, but where there is water and a forest canopy, yew can be found. At the headwaters of Bear Creek and Hawkins Creek, in the old Galena mining district, yew trees cling to life around cracks in ancient basalt rim rock which guide water out of the ground. The Blue Mountains are dotted about with lush meadows surrounded by juniper and sage brush, laced with ponderosa pine, white and Douglas fir, tamarack and willow.

The most striking feature of the Eastern Oregon yew is a result of browsing by elk and deer, which has trimmed the yew into bonsai – strange, organic, close-cropped, mushroom shapes reminiscent of a Japanese garden. These wizened trees are remnants of prehistoric groves that began to recede when the climate became drier. Now, only where the water seeps from cracks in the basalt canyons do they continue to exist.

CURRENT STATUS

As we have seen, the yew shared its fate with the fir in Europe. Both were 'chieftain trees' according to ancient Brehon law, and in the Celtic Tree Alphabet yew and fir shared the same 'station of the year', the winter solstice. (The Chinese yew is called *za shen* which means 'purple fir' and one name given the Japanese yew is 'fir of the Goddess of Mercy'.[13]) The yew and fir go together in the Pacific Northwest as well, having grown side by side in the forest for millenia. Unfortunately they are just about gone together as well, with only ten percent of the 'old growth' forest left. The fate of yew in the Pacific Northwest during the last 150 years has not been so heroic as that of other species of yew in other cultures. In fact, here the yew tree has been considered to be of no value – worse than valueless; it has been in the way, a nuisance to loggers. It has been, and still is, standard procedure throughout the Northwest to knock the yew trees down before the crop tree harvest to get them out of the way of the lines. After the crop tree harvest, the downed yew trees are bulldozed into slashpiles with the rest of the debris to be burned. Often the burns are only partially successful and many of these dead yew trees escape the fire; slow to rot, they are still out there.

SPECIAL USES

Yew wood has a variety of special uses today. Woodcarvers make replicas of old native bows, canoe paddles, fish clubs and other implements. Turner says that Native American carvers:

> ...still like to use yew, but often have difficulty obtaining large enough pieces. While yew is little-used commercially, it is seldom an abundant species, and past harvesting by carvers combined with habitat destruction through logging has greatly reduced the numbers of large old yew trees in many localities.[14]

Like other species of yew, the wood is without resin; it is resilient, dense and takes a good polish. Because the supply of yew wood in Europe and the Orient dried up long ago, Pacific yew is now being used to make things that traditionally had been made from the European, Japanese and Chinese yews: furniture, religious implements, long-bows and musical instruments. None of these special uses, however, have proven to be threatening to the Pacific yew because the commercial demand for these products, though growing, is moderately small – nothing like the demand that Greece, Rome and mediaeval Europe put on the yew for armaments over the last three millenia. As we saw in an earlier chapter, yew forests that once covered large portions of Europe were literally gone by the middle of the 16th century.

Our own society has seen fit to use yew as firewood, for which it is excellent; it can be burned green and it burns slowly. Pioneers used it for building poles and fence posts, uses that every rancher knows today. Some suggest putting the yew post in upside down to increase its life two-fold. Miles of yew wood fence posts line the roads in Jackson

County along the upper Greensprings Road from Ashland, past Howard Prairie Reservoir, to Lake of the Woods. According to Chuck Edson in 1977:

> Charles Lindsay, an older member of a family which has lived on and worked a large ranch east of Ashland since the turn of the century, holds a sentimental attitude toward *Taxus*. Howard Prairie, on the Lindsay ranch, is bounded and crossed by *Taxus* fences. Mr. Lindsay remembers the tree being common over a much wider range in Southern Oregon than what remains.[15]

Yew wood posts are fine material for rustic pole buildings. Various structures in Oregon are anchored to stout yew wood posts. The Church at Triangle Lake has two large yew posts one on either side of the front entry. On Cougar Mountain, near Saginaw in Lane County, is a three story agricultural building that rests on a foundation of 24 stout yew poles. The Tillamook County Court House has yew poles integrated into its structure and the hitching post in front of the first Lane County Court House was made of yew wood.

Considered a weed for so long by so many, the Pacific yew is having something of a resurgence in popularity; other uses for it besides building poles, fence posts and firewood are being identified. Cutters are taking yew trees from government and private land and then selling

LIFE TOTEM

them to dealers, who in turn export the yew logs as ceremonial toko poles to Japan, or to Europe as seasoned wood for repair of antique furniture and musical instruments.[16]

Local carvers, sculptors and artisans know the value and beauty of yew wood. Paul Buckner sculpted *Life Totem* from a piece of yew taken off a beach on Whidby Island in the Puget Sound.

RENAISSANCE LUTES

Robert Lundberg is a musical instrument maker who resides in Oregon in order to be close to the Pacific yew which is the best possible wood for his trade. After six years of study be began making lutes in 1974. Since then he has built over 300 yew wood lutes and about 100 other instruments – classical guitars, violins, folk instruments, Appalachian dulcimers and miscellaneous others. Lundberg bases his lute design and processes on the lute during its 'yew wood phase' which began sometime in the late 15th century, when they discovered how to play the lute by hand rather than with a plectrum. In about 1530, according to Lundberg:

> Music was getting much more refined. There had been a generation and a half of people playing with the hand and they were really exploiting the instruments that they had. They needed more. They needed a better treble sound and they needed better bass. The change in the shape from a very round back to one that was more flat helped improve the treble and using yew wood ribs for the back helped give the bass an overall richer, more mellow sound. By 1540 all wooden lutes were being made of yew. There are a few that could be cypress, but the rest were all yew wood in Italy, France, Spain, southern Germany, up until I suppose they couldn't get the material any longer in around 1600. After that, fewer and fewer instruments were made out of yew, and as far as the yew wood tradition, by 1630 it was gone.
>
> My experience in reconstruction of these old lutes is that all lutes regardless of the shape and size sound much better if they are made out of yew wood. One ancient document states very explicitly that by 1600 only the married master lute makers could have enough yew for three instruments a year. That was a real limitation on the number of instruments that were built; at that point only the very special lutes were made of yew...It was so proscribed as a war material, and it was the death sentence to cut the yew tree in Germany or anywhere in the entire Holy Roman Empire. I have a workshop inventory from about 1552. They had huge quantities of materials, except for yew wood ribs; they had 1,200 sets of maple ribs, 1,200 sets of ash and only 46 sets of yew wood ribs.

According to Lundberg even here in the Pacific Northwest good quality yew wood is difficult to find:

I've had a great deal of difficulty. As a matter of fact I had almost given it up for lost after the first couple of years of searching. I was completely stymied with this. Here in the Northwest was the best yew wood grown in the world and it was almost impossible to get. When I went to a logging company that was logging in an area where yew wood was known to be, you couldn't go anywhere on their property because of insurance. They wouldn't allow me on their property. I would ask, 'What are you doing with the yew wood' and, well, the yew wood, the alder and all the branches were burned, so the site could be made completely clear.

YEW WOOD LUTE

Then I made the connection. I realized that there had been a strong industry here before the Second World War of making bows and cutting yew wood...There was one old man up in northeast Portland who had been a bow maker for years and years and told me all the stories about getting permits and going into the woods and cutting it and splitting it and carrying it back to the campsite on his back. He had done this for years; it was like a pilgrimage he would make to the woods to get his material. I bought the last yew wood that he had. No one had asked him anything about yew wood for thirty years. He couldn't remember the last time someone had asked him about yew wood.

Lundberg has gone out into the woods himself in search of good lute-making material:

It is really frustrating. It probably happened in the late 1800's or early 1900's; when the big trees were taken away the yew trees sprouted a million branches and so they are essentially no good for my use...I have to find a tree in an area that hasn't been cut, even cut 100 years ago, because the wood is no good. The wood

I cut came from the Santiam area on a Forest Service permit and it was pretty disappointing...Bowmakers have said that it was about one tree in 80 or a 100 that they looked at was suitable for a first rate bow and the wood that I have was mostly selected by bow makers in the 1920's and 1930's for their own product and out of that I end up being able to use 10 to 20 percent. For me it might be one tree in 600 or 800 that will really produce the quality of wood to make a lute.

I met Don Adams. He had good quality yew wood so I bought everything that he had. He kept some for making bows, but I bought enough to make 4,000 lutes. All of his wood was cut in the late 1930's and a lot of it is dated, and the place is marked down.[17]

YEW WOOD LONGBOWS

Don Adams, bowyer to the Royal Company of Archers and master craftsman, resides in Oregon near the greatest number of remaining natural yew trees on the planet. Speaking of his craft, he says:

> The yew wood English longbow goes back thousands of years. At the peak of its development, it was the atom bomb of its time. It won the great battles at places like Crécy and Agincourt and Poictiers...At Agincourt, 4,000 English archers with longbows kicked the crap out of 65,000 French knights. The knights were nobles and the archers were peons – diggers of ditches and scratchers of the earth. But the archers had the weapon with incredible range and the power to pierce armor.[18]

Adams makes longbows one at a time, fashioning each to take advantage of the characteristics of the wood. He was asked to examine bowstaves that were brought up with the Mary Rose. His comments, recorded in a news story:

> ...they were puzzled because there was a lot of variation in the staves. They couldn't see anything very consistent. There were differences in sizes and lengths. But once I saw them, I knew those old bow makers weren't doing anything different. It's the same now. The bow depends upon the piece of wood...the dimensions are never the same. It depends on the wood. You can't make the bow by measurement. There's a lot of artist's eye to it. It depends on the piece of wood. There are all kinds of

factors to deal with. The stresses have to be distributed perfectly or the bow will have a short life.[19]

Adams gave a brief history of his craft and some comments on past and current situations involving yew wood:

There were a lot of bowyers in the Willamette Valley area, if you look at the old magazines, which is all I have to go on. I think primarily because they were in the archery business and the yew wood was right there in the Cascades. There is even quite a bit of yew wood in the Coast Range and we're also pretty close to the Port Orford cedar which is an excellent arrow-making material. So they were kind of centrally located. If you look at the old magazine ads you see that most of the suppliers of yew wood were in Oregon.

The professional aspects of my bowmaking career began when I met a fellow in Eugene in my early teens, his name was Leonard Daley. Leonard was the flight champion [archery distance category] of the United States in 1930. I worked in his shop and that's where I learned bowmaking. He used some osage but mostly yew wood. He was a harvester of yew as well as a bowmaker and an arrow maker too.

When I harvest yew, of course the high elevation is where I look. I find where there are still some old-growth fir trees left – that's where the good yew wood will be. I look for the very straightest, clearest possible tree I can find. You can't be too choosy, because it will never look as good after you get it home as it does there in the forest. You do an awful lot of looking before you start cutting. A lot of people will bring wood in to me that they think is real good and it isn't worth packing off. I've said one out of one or two hundred, probably three or four hundred trees. You have to be that selective if you want the best wood, clear and free of pin knots, nice and straight, fine grain; all the qualities. You're talking less than half of one percent of the yew trees out there is suitable for a first-class bow.

Yew wood is the very best wood in the world for bows. That's why we use it, it's the best that I've ever found and apparently no one else has ever found anything better either. The reason it is the best is it's light weight – other woods have qualities similar to the yew, like osage, but it's so heavy. Yew wood is light and what makes it so good is the white sapwood, which forms the back of the bow – it's real stretchy. The red part, which forms the belly of the bow, gives the compression, it's got a lot of residual snap in it. So you put the two of them together and you come out with the perfect bow. It grows in the tree just like that. A lot of people think that I glue that white wood on, but that's the way it grows. It lends itself to making the perfect bow.

The first thing to do when you're making a bow of course is to decide what pound of bow you're trying to make, then you have to judge your wood and check out your staves accordingly. The lighter weight bows you would use a lighter, less dense wood; the real heavy weight bows you use a much more dense tougher wood. You don't want the more dense, tougher woods in a lighter bow, because it costs you in cast. You don't want lighter woods in heavy bows because they won't last. Choice of wood is the very first thing and that's where experience comes in. If you don't know how to do that, you will have problems and you won't ever know why.

I have never kept track of how long it takes to make a longbow. If I did I would probably raise my price to where nobody would consider buying one. It takes a long time if you consider the acts of gathering staves from the trees, cutting them up, the processing of the wood to get an actual stave ready to whittle out, from there the tillering and the shaping and the horn nocks and the finishing of it, it's a long time. You have to love it to do it, otherwise it's too much.[20]

PRICE OF YEW WOOD

The price of yew wood has been steadily increasing as more and more dealers learn of its availability for specialty products. In 1984 prices for 'number one' yew logs were reported to be $1,800 per thousand board feet, fir at that time sold for $250 per thousand.[21] More recently yew logs have been shipped to veneer factories back East in the United States as well as overseas. Later in the 1980's the price had risen to $3,600 and by 1989 some dealers were paying over $6,000 a thousand board feet.[22] For comparison, Douglas fir which has been harvested as a main crop species for years is worth a high of $500 per thousand board feet. At this comparison yew on a per board foot basis would be twelve times more valuable than Douglas fir, yet it was sold by the Forest Service in 40 log lots (less than 8 inches in diameter and less than 9 feet in length) for a $10 permit, or as single logs for $1.25

each. Ostensibly the logs were used as fence posts and firewood.

But yew wood, as valuable as it may be, is not the yew tree's main economic attraction. Ironically this tree, until recently considered to be of little or no value, now provides a potent weapon in our struggle against cancer. A compound, taxol, found in the leaves, bark, wood, roots and seeds of the genus *Taxus* is saving lives. For the moment, the only commercially viable process being used to obtain this precious substance is by extraction from Pacific yew bark. Over the course of the next five years, according to industry sources, the demand for dried yew bark may be 10 million pounds. A 250 year old tree yields about five pounds of dried bark.

PART V

A MODERN DILEMMA

The problem is that rates of extinction are escalating so quickly that if one were to find a plant that displayed interesting bioactivity, it's quite possible to go back and find its habitat destroyed. It is a race against time.

– Michael Balick, New York Botanical Garden

CHAPTER TEN

TAXOL, CANCER, YEW BARK

TAXOL

GREEKS, Romans, Druids, the indigenous people of Japan, Russia, China, Southeast Asia, North America and India have used the yew for medicinal purposes since long before history began to record such things. Emperor Claudius told the Roman senate that the juice of yew was an antidote to viper bites. He also knew that Celtic Gauls used it to poison the tips of their battle arrows as well as for ritual suicide. We have come to realize that many medicines are poisons of one sort or another and today we are learning things about the 'double fatal' yew that the ancients may have known. Folklore often provides initial leads to scientists searching for anti-cancer compounds in plants. Those which were recorded in the lore as being used as arrow poisons or reported as toxic to man have provided the best prospects.[1]

Folklore may or may not have led scientists to the yew, but the genus *Taxus* has been much studied over the years. In 1856 an alkaloid called taxine was extracted from the European yew. Since 1856, forty taxanes, or compounds with similar skeletal structures, have been identified. In the early 1960's the National Cancer Institute (NCI) began an intensive screening of plant compounds for anti-cancer acitivity. They found taxol, the most complex taxane discovered to date, in the yew. Taxol is 'one of the most promising of more than 120,000 plant compounds tested for anti-cancer properties.'[2] Of all the species tested, only a few contained elements that inhibit cell growth and may have some promise in the fight against cancer.

In this context it is useful to remember that North American natives used yew as an abortifacient and against illnesses including bronchitis, scurvy and skin cancer. Taxol and other taxanes have been found in Pacific yew recently. James Duke notes that Canadian yew also contains taxol. He further tells us that the Japanese used yew leaves for an abortifacient and antidiabetic and that the Chinese have found:

> *Taxus* is showing good anti-cancer effects in animal trials, but the activity is not due to taxol, which has not shown too much promise. Until the Chinese isolate and name the new active principle, they will not take it into clinical trials.[3]

TAXOL MOLECULE ($C_{47}H_{51}NO_{14}$)

The only source of taxol to be developed intensively so far is the bark of Pacific yew. Dr. Matthew Suffness, a spokesperson for the National Cancer Institute reports why and how bark became the only approved source of taxol in a brief history presented to an NCI conference on taxol in the spring of 1990:

> *Taxus brevifolia* was first collected for the NCI program by a USDA team in Washington state in 1962. Confirmed activity against the KB cell line in tissue culture was noted in 1964 and isolation studies began in the laboratory of Dr. Monroe Wall at Research Triangle Institute in 1965. Pure taxol was first isolated in 1969 and the structure was published in 1971... A study of

abundance, distribution, and activity of *T. brevifolia* was carried out by the USDA in 1969. Results showed no major difference in bioactivity over the North-South range of the tree and that the plant part giving most consistent high level activity was the bark, followed by the roots... All further isolation was done from bark samples.

Suffness explains more of taxol's history:

In vivo activity against the standard leukemia models was not strong and the drug languished until 1974 when strong activity was seen against the B16 mouse melanoma tumor. Taxol was selected for preclinical development in 1977 and in 1978 good activity was found against the MX–1 human mammary xenograft which spurred further development efforts. Taxol is not remarkably active against...mouse tumors but did show activity against all three of the human tumor xenografts which were in use in the late 1970's. This may be a drug which is more effective in man than in mice.[4]

Dr. Robert Holton, who heads a research team at Florida State's Dittmer laboratories, elaborates on the complex nature of taxol:

Taxol is an important compound, not only because of its significant anti-cancer activity, but also because it exerts this activity in a new way. It has been found to act as an inhibitor of cell division, and to promote the formation of microtubules, rod-like structures that function as the cell skeleton. These structures are known to play an important role in cell division. Taxol has become a major research tool for those studying cell division.[5]

Suffness points out that the potential of taxol was not immediately recognized:

The difficulty in obtaining large amounts of the drug and the difficulty in formulation due to very limited solubility in aqueous systems slowed development. A major discovery in 1979 which stimulated interest in the drug was taxol's unique ability to stabilize microtubules and resist depolymerization to tubulin. An acceptable surfactant formulation was developed and taxol progressed to toxicology studies (1980). These studies were difficult due to toxicity from the administration vehicle. Taxol was approved by the NCI for Investigational New Drug Application filing with the FDA in 1982. Clinical trials began in 1983.[6]

CANCER

Holton gave an update on Phase II clinical trials in March of 1990:

> During the Phase I clinical trials, responses were seen in patients
> with non-small cell lung cancer, melanoma, head and neck
> carcinoma, gastric carcinoma, and ovarian carcinoma. Taxol was
> found to give the most promising results against ovarian cancer.
> It has now been in Phase II clinical trials for over three years.
> Phase II trials against ovarian cancer are the most advanced at this
> time, and in a recently completed Phase II clinical trial, approxi-
> mately a thirty percent objective response rate was observed in
> patients with relapsed or refractory ovarian cancer, a disease
> previously generally considered to be resistant to chemotherapy.[7]

More recently, Holton had this to say about the success of taxol
against several forms of cancer:

> Well it's really quite depressing when you think about it. I came
> to learn only within the last year that these anti-cancer drugs are
> really not very effective across the board. Against ovarian cancer
> taxol showed a response rate of over 30 percent; that means that
> a third of the patients either went into partial or complete
> remission. I thought it was remarkably low, but I came to learn
> that a new cancer drug is considered to be quite good if you see
> a response rate of 15–20 percent. The initial numbers that came
> back from one of the breast cancer trials were a 50 percent
> response rate. They have to do many trials and each trial has 40
> to 100 patients in it and so forth and so on; so it is not the bottom
> line yet. But the initial numbers were just astounding against
> breast cancer. They have got trials going against other cancer
> types now, lung cancer being one of them. What is encouraging
> about the ovarian cancer trials is that all of these trials were carried
> out with people who were absolutely hopeless, they had not
> responded to any other kind of chemotherapy and they had solid
> tumors, the hardest kind to treat.
>
>   I hate it when our media office puts out a press release, because
> most of the return that I get is people calling about their relatives
> who are dying of ovarian cancer. This is grim, I can't do anything
> except tell them the names of people who are carrying out the
> trials and see if they qualify. I think the future of this business
> revolves around finding the right cultivar and then finding a way
> to extract the correct material from it.[8]

Each new look at taxol seems more promising. According to the *New York Times*, recent studies indicate that taxol is:

...extraordinarily effective in treating advanced cases of breast cancer, which kills 45,000 women a year. And preliminary results from another small study show the drug is also active against lung cancer, which kills more than 100,000 people a year.[9]

More specifically, as reported from the University of Texas M.D. Anderson Cancer Center, Dr. Gabriel Hortobagyi:

...tested taxol in 25 women with advanced breast cancer that had spread through their bodies and was unresponsive to any other drug. 'We found that 52 percent had a major response,' he said. Their tumors shrank by more than 50 percent and in three of the women the tumors disappeared. Hortobagyi said his group has tested about 20 other drugs for breast cancer in the last two decades, but 'I don't remember a single drug that has been this effective.'[10]

According to the *Wall Street Journal*, one group at Columbia University would like to run clinical tests on taxol in combination with radiation on brain cancer:

Researchers studying brain cancer cells in the test tube reported 'a dramatic interaction between taxol and ionizing radiation,' offering a 'significant advantage' over either type of therapy used alone.[11]

One of the major problems is described by Dr.Sterling Ainsworth:

As has already been alluded to in the clinical data, the solubility of taxol is a real problem. What derivative or analogue is more soluble that can be administered to the patient is the question. The vehicle that the drug is presently being administered in is cremophor which is a very toxic material itself but it makes the taxol soluble. It causes many of the side-effects, and there are some side effects that are not desirable with taxol – polyneuropathy and milosuppression of the bone marrow. Perhaps a derivative or an analogue with some change in one small structure of the molecule will alleviate many of these side effects or diminish them somewhat, to a point where you don't have to pretreat the patient as we currently do in the clinical trials.[12]

An April article in the *Wall Street Journal* indicates that the demand for taxol far outstrips the supply already:

> But taxol is so tightly rationed that 50 of 65 proposed studies of its effect on human beings are on hold. Federal scientists say they need 10 times their current supply for so-called 'compassionate-use' treatment of the dying, and to complete research necessary for approval.[13]

Taxol has been going through clinical trials on humans since 1983 and has proven very promising in the treatment of ovarian cancer through three phases of clinical testing, so successful in fact that clinical testing has already begun in some other types of cancer: small-cell lung, melanoma, breast, colon, leukemia and head & neck and carcinoma.[14] Taxol is about to enter clinical tests in 31 types of cancer. Preliminary results are attracting attention. "It's the biggest blockbuster drug around," says one NCI researcher. "Doctors can't wait for it to go through the regulatory process and get it in their hands."[15]

If it proves to be as successful as it seems in treating other types of cancer, demand for it will increase geometrically, posing a difficult dilemma. How do we manage to provide taxol for persons already faced with cancer, guarantee a continuous source of it for clinical trials, and still assure the survival and integrity of the last significant population of native *Taxus* on earth?

The NCI is seriously concerned with the problem of immediate supply, and contingency plans are being formulated, as outlined by Dr. Kenneth Snader:

> In the development of taxol as a clinical candidate, the NCI has prepared 2.4 kilograms of pure compound between the years 1974 and 1989. The average yield has been 1 gram per 30 pounds of bark. Recent, positive clinical results indicate that a minimum of 24 kilograms per year will be needed once FDA approval is granted for the drug, which translates into 720,000 pounds of bark or 36,000 trees if harvesting from 'native' *T. brevifolia* continues to be the only source. For the 'short' term (1–2 years) this will be the major source of taxol and an ecologically protective plan is being used. For the 'medium' term (3–5 years), a combination of sources including harvest of 'native' *T. brevifolia*, semi-synthetic conversion of other taxane

analogs, and cultivation and harvest of other *Taxus* species and cultivars is planned. The magnitude and difficulties of each of these approaches is summarized in five topics:
 – lack of information about taxol content in various species.
 – limited abundance of *T. brevifolia*
 – ecological constraints to harvest of 'native' *Taxus*
 – difficulties with synthesis of taxanes
 – difficulties with cultivation of *Taxus* species.[16]

Dr. Cragg of NCI appraises taxol's prospects:

> The reason for wanting so much is that there is an increasing interest on the part of clinicians in trying the drug...If the initial promise of the drug holds up, then we are certainly going to need large supplies. In that case, we will certainly have to look at alternative sources. We are very aware of the potential environmental impact, and we want to keep that to a minimum...There have been a lot of attempts to synthesize the drug...Personally, I don't foresee a viable synthesis being developed in the near future. It's a very complex molecule.[17]

Dr. Samuel Broder, director of the NCI, was quoted in the *New York Times* as saying that taxol is, "the most important new drug we have had in cancer for 15 years." Dr. Bruce Chabner, also with NCI, says, "We can't possibly supply it. At times we have had shortages of other drugs, but nothing like this."[18] Officials at NCI are aware that bark cannot possibly supply the current growing demand for taxol.

According to recent information from NCI spokesperson Dr. Saul Shepartz, it costs about $300,000 per pound to extract taxol from dried bark, or $660 per gram. As reported, the current contract between Bristol-Myers and their extraction contractor (Hauser Chemical of Boulder, Colorado) is for 13.5 million dollars, or 45 pounds of taxol at $300,000 per pound. Shepartz also indicates that the average dose per treatment is two grams. Forty-five pounds (20,430 grams) of taxol would produce enough taxol for 10,215 treatments, considerably less than the number of projected annual terminal ovarian cancer cases.[19]

If taxol is allowed onto the commercial market, the rule of thumb in the industry is that the cost to produce the drug is 20 percent of the ultimate cost of the drug to the patient.[20] If, using the above figures, a dose of two grams would cost roughly $1,320 to produce, the cost to the consumer for the drug would be in the neighborhood of $6,600. This price may rise or fall depending on what happens in the near future concerning the availability of taxol and convertible taxanes from renewable resources.

Dr. Charles Bolsinger, who studies the range and distribution of Pacific yew in the Northwest, says:

> Continued or increased demand for yew bark for taxol production could substantially decrease a resource that has already been greatly reduced...The only known source of taxol now is yew bark. Taxol has been found in most of the several other species of *Taxus* that exist, but Pacific yew is the only one that is considered to be a practical source of quantities sufficient for clinical use.[21]

BARK

The bark of Pacific yew is less than an eighth of an inch thick, which means that no matter how many trees there are, the supply of pounds of bark is extremely limited. It is difficult to ascertain for sure what the average yield of dry bark per tree might be, because the estimates vary

"THE BARK OF PACIFIC YEW IS LESS . . .

. . . THAN AN EIGHTH OF AN INCH THICK."

from a low of three pounds per tree to a high of 25. Prudent estimates place the average yield of dried bark per tree at considerably less than half the recent estimates by scientists at NCI. Prudent observers also caution that the yield of pounds per tree will drop considerably as the harvest progresses, because the larger trees will invariably be taken first and yew grows very slowly. A 200 year old tree with a ten inch diameter, twelve feet long will yield six pounds of dried bark[22] which in turn will produce approximately one-fifth gram of taxol. A five inch diameter tree would produce three pounds of bark and a twenty inch tree twelve pounds. The average amount of taxol required to treat one patient is two grams.[23] It would require the bark of ten large trees to produce enough taxol to treat one patient.

The whole process of obtaining bark begins in the woods of the Northwest, where there happen to be many unemployed woodsworkers who know about yew trees. Until recently there were no apparent markets for yew wood; the trees were simply considered a nuisance.

Most yew trees of any size were felled or bulldozed onto the slashpile. Clear cut means what it says – when it's all over, what is left is a burned unit, exposed mineral soil ready for treeplanters to plant the next crop-tree seedlings in the ground. Some woodsworkers have turned into yew loggers with interests in marketing the wood as well as bark, stems and needles. Ray Eller describes bark-stripping in a news interview:

> "You've got to do this before the sap goes down and she starts to dry up in July and August." he explained as he tossed bark peelings on a growing pile. "Now, when it's slippin, you can pull the bark off as fast as you can pull your shirt off. But when she tightens up, you can get it, but you have to take it – she don't give it to you."
>
> The denuded tree, slippery and white like a naked body, lay among others under the dark forest canopy, to be retrieved later with a horse. The bark, as pliable as wet cardboard, goes to a warehouse or to Eller's back yard to be dried to a crisp.
>
> "In a way, it's a special job," he said. "I feel different about this job. I don't know how to describe it. Maybe it'll get somebody well, I don't know. But I'm no hero. It's a job. I'm gettin' paid."
>
> Eller said he agrees with environmentalists that the region's slow-growing yew resource should not be depleted – even for cancer research. He insists, however, that his crew will take relatively few trees, as much as possible from clear-cuts, where the yew would otherwise end up on the slash pile.
>
> "I'm tryin' to save all I can and still get the job done," he said. "I definitely don't want to see all the yew wood cut. I'm not out here to destroy yew wood. That would be stupid. It's a re-source."[24]

Dominic Daley collects yew bark for a reason. "If I can help with cancer research, I feel I could be making a small contribution. I explained to everyone who works for me why we are doing it, everyone has a good attitude about that, and we're making expenses." Daley and his crew collected bark for a Portland contractor for $1.50 per dry pound in 1987.[25]

In 1990 bark contractor Patrick Connolly paid his collectors $1.75 per pound for dry bark and $.50 per pound for limbs, although the extraction company quit buying limbs soon after. He paid $1.00 to the Forest Service for each tree and was required to remove it from public

PEELING YEW BARK

forest land. According to Connolly the price goes up from there. Hauser's predecessor, Polyscience, extracted taxol from Pacific yew bark for NCI and was paid $32 per dry pound, which if 30 pounds of bark yields one gram, would have made the cost of unextracted taxol about $960 per gram.[26]

News sources say that a bark collector can earn between $100 and $200 a day at $1 per pound of wet bark.[27] A bark stripper would have to find, cut, strip, sack and haul bark from 8.3 yew trees 10 inches in girth to earn $100 a day. The same treatment of 16.6 10-inch trees would net $200. The trouble is that there aren't very many large yew trees. Only 10 percent of the total population are 10 inches in girth or larger, the size preferred by bark collectors. Only 35 percent of the total yew population is over five inches in diameter and according to one account, some five-inch trees may well be over 200 years old.[28]

THE IMPACT OF DEMAND ON PACIFIC YEW

Dried bark weighs 50 percent of the wet weight and according to NCI sources, 30 pounds of dry bark is needed to produce one gram of taxol.[29] A treatment consists of approximately two grams of taxol and would require 60 pounds. If the average is six pounds of dry bark per tree then it would require ten large trees to produce one treatment of taxol. 150,000 treatments (enough to handle a year's combined ovarian, breast and lung cancer victims) would require the bark of 1.5 million trees. If Bolsinger is correct in his estimate that three to four million large yew trees remain on federal lands, then this demand could have serious consequences.

These numbers underscore the fact that there is a finite amount of bark to be had in the wild. If the current practice, which uses only bark in the production of taxol, is allowed to prevail, then we risk eradicating yew trees of any significant dimension within walking distance of roads and trails. A spring 1990 news article reports a request by NCI for 60,000 pounds of dried bark from the region's National Forests:

> Conservationists are nervous about the cancer institute's experiments. They say they support cancer research, but argue that 60,000 pounds of yew bark adds up to a lot of stripped trees. It won't take many more ambitious bark-collection efforts to rapidly use up the region's slow-growing yew resource...[30]

In August 1990, the Willamette National Forest, which produces the most timber of any National Forest in the country, estimated that it could furnish 10,000 pounds of dried yew bark toward the goal of

PACIFIC YEW OUTSIDE USUAL HABITAT

60,000 pounds and announced that it would issue permits for what is estimated at five pounds of bark per tree or about 2,000 trees. Bob Leonard, Timber Staff Officer with the Willamette National Forest asks:

> How often can you do that? If in fact they're going to be looking at doing this on a repeated basis, it's going to be necessary to look at some other way of creating the supply of bark. I'm not sure it exists in our natural stands at that level.[31]

There is now (summer of '91) a minimum annual goal of 750,000 pounds of dried yew bark and at least one Forest Service official "has placed a high priority on helping Bristol-Myers in every way we legally and environmentally can."[32] Current Forest Service policy allows yew bark to be harvested only in areas that are slated for logging, but in order to increase twelve-fold from 60,000 to 750,000 pounds, this policy will have to be changed and yew wood harvesters allowed to push further into the old-growth, habitat and wilderness areas, into the remaining pockets of forest whose timber has not yet been auctioned.

In an interview with documentary film maker David Heine, Dr. Bruce Mannheim, senior attorney and scientist for the Environmental Defense Fund, had this to say about the potential demand for millions of pounds of bark:

> I think that if they plan on meeting that level of demand in the form of bark from the yew tree then there is no doubt that the species will be in great jeopardy and that the ability to extract taxol from the needles of the tree will also be in great jeopardy.

Mannheim further explained that there are many types of restrictions on federal forest lands:

> There are wilderness areas, national parks, habitat conservation areas which are sites set aside to protect the spotted owl. There are areas within sale units, between some of the harvest units that are still old-growth. I think that in terms of the priority ranking of areas into which yew harvest should go, assuming you get all of the yew trees for those areas already up for sale, you would want to go then into fragmented areas, areas that are not old-growth forest.

He said of Dr. Bolsinger's data:

> I think that he generally has been the most credible and outspoken Forest Service official on this subject and we have no reason at all to question his predictions. We find his predictions frightening in the presence of the Forest Service and Bureau of Land Management policy that doesn't mandate an expeditious transition from bark to needles and that doesn't necessarily forbid burning of the areas that have been cut and may seek to regenerate themselves.[33]

Until recently, when demand for bark began to sky-rocket, most timber companies and governmental agencies had not considered the yew in their long-range plans or forest inventories. Bolsinger, putting it bluntly, says that the yew was considered to be a 'trash' tree. "It gets the same treatment as manzanita or vine maple. Nobody worries that most of the yew is being destroyed by logging operations. The yew tree population has been decimated over the years."[34] His candid opinions were given in an interview with David Heine:

> We have a statistical sample outside National Forests only in Oregon, Washington and California and there are similar statistical samples in Idaho and Montana, but not for all ownerships...There are huge areas that have never been covered in any kind of an inventory. But our statistical inventories show Pacific yew to be present on around a half million acres outside National Forest land. There are something like 12 to 13 million yew trees in this area. You would find it on about two out of a hundred acres. Of course it's not evenly distributed...there are vast areas in which yew is totally absent, then there are some areas where it's locally common to even abundant.

When asked about the impact of the harvest of 750,000 pounds of bark, Bolsinger said:

> If they actually collected that much they would be getting a noticeable portion of the larger accessible yew trees. To date most of the bark has been collected from the larger trees. Our data for outside the National Forest show that only 10 percent of the total number of trees are over 10 inches in diameter. That was the size of tree that bark collectors were targeting that first year. I suspect already they are taking the smaller trees more seriously.
>
> A very large number of yew trees are more accurately described as shrubs than trees. From that standpoint, I don't think it's possible to wipe the yew out. In some places it's like a brushfield. I've seen large areas that you could hardly walk through because of the yew shrubs. Only here and there would one reach tree size. To use bark for taxol is not in itself a threat to the species but it may be a threat to large yew trees. The larger trees are going to decrease in number, especially those that are near roads and trails. A lot of large yew trees are not near roads and trails and it will be cumbersome to go in and get the bark and pack it out. There is a built in safety factor there for the species, but still we can expect to see a great decrease in the larger yew trees in areas that are accessible. Already we have had reports of trespass and illegal yew-cutting by crooks in the night.[35]

A EUROPEAN LESSON

I see the yew tree as an indicator species for our own. We are inextricably bound together, having come hundreds of thousands of years down the same path. Yew has furnished our most highly prized wood for dependable tools and powerful weapons, implements which enabled us to compete for survival within the plant and animal kingdoms. Eventually, as we have seen, the yew tree came to be a symbol; Celtic tribes took it as their totem tree; Native Americans carved spirit and power poles out of it, and even today, in Japan, Buddhist toko poles are made of yew. All primitive cultures revered the tree because it served them well throughout their struggle. It was a tree of death, gateway to the afterlife and a favorite of Hecate. Today, surviving the kiss of myth and legend, the test of time and history and the grace of immortality in verse, each living yew is an icon to our own past whether it be a churchyard sentinal in Europe, a sacred entity in India, or facing the bark strippers' blade in the Pacific Northwest. There is a lesson here for us, a message from the yew tree, something it is trying to tell us.

All yew trees, no matter what species names we have given them, are descended from a common ancestor whose progeny began to spread over the earth 200,000,000 years ago, until the ice ages eventually confined them to the temperate zones of the Northern Hemisphere. Unfortunately for the yew, when we discovered its value as wood for weapons and a host of other articles, or as foliage and bark for poisons and medicines, we began a continuous deforestation project that left the crumbled dominions of Egypt, Greece and Rome bereft of natural yew groves by the time of Christ. It was gone from most of Europe, 'land of the yew', by the 17th century – used up mainly for armaments. In Poland, in 1423, King Wladyslaw Jagiello decreed:

> Should anyone, entering a forest, fell trees of great value, such as the yew or its like, he may be detained by the lord of the manor or the squire and put in the care of those who would pledge for him. This law on groves is to be observed where forests are scanty.[36]

What little yew remains in Europe today does not fare well. In

Poland, foresters and botanists are puzzled as to why the scant but protected natural yew population continues to shrink. According to Stanislaw Krol "the yew has retained great capacity for generative reproduction if conditions are favorable." But groves are dying out because "inadequate silviculture...has destroyed natural biotopes in the process."

The absence of young trees indicates that the future of yew in the old protected natural reservations is endangered since the total number of trees decreases every year. Many biologists suspect that the lowering of ground water, a loss of vitality by the species, unsatisfactory phyto-sociological conditions, excessive shade, microbiologically unsatisfactory soil communities and other causes are responsible. No definite answer to this question has been found yet. *T. baccata* is under careful protection in Poland and studies on its ecology continue.[37]

A DWINDLING RESOURCE IN THE UNITED STATES

Chances for wild yew's survival are tenuous at best, as, having suffered centuries of anonymous arboricide, it wanes toward extinction in Europe and Asia. This may be the fate of the Pacific yew as well; even now, as it is, with only small pockets of its natural habitat left unmolested. The Pacific yew is the last sizeable population of native yew trees left on earth, and now we have discovered in it the gift of a powerful anti-cancer compound. It is a sad commentary on our times that the only feasible way we have yet devised to acquire this gift is to kill mature yew trees for their five pounds of bark. This policy is not an answer to our dilemma, but only hastens the demise of Pacific yew by destroying precisely those trees which are the prime specimens and sources of seed.

Nevertheless, Bolsinger holds out some hope for Pacific yew:

> *T. brevifolia* is regenerating in some logged areas, but has diminished with the progress of timber harvesting from old-growth to second-growth timber. The broad range of sites on which *T. brevifolia* occurs, and its variable growth and repro-ductive traits suggest considerable genetic variability. Its absence from extensive areas suggests that it could grow on several million acres where it does not now exist. Sixty years of research

on Douglas fir have enabled foresters to increase productivity of that species, and offer some hope for *T. brevifolia*. Declining abundance of *T. brevifolia* in the face of increasing demand puts urgency on a research program for the species.[38]

Yew habitat is old-growth forest, and as that is removed the yew tree also declines. Dr. Stanley Scher and co-workers conducted a study of yew habitat in northern California forests and determined several reasons why *T. Brevifolia* is not populous in the Northwest:

On Six Rivers and Klamath National Forests, yew achieves its maximum development under the canopy of old-growth conifers. On sites with less than fifty percent canopy cover, Pacific yew shows evidence of foliage damage and morphological changes in response to direct sunlight. Studies of yew frequency of occurrence by landscape position, slope shape, proximity to water, and water holding capacity of forest soils support the view that moisture availability is a major determinant of its distribution.

It is also vulnerable to an often man-made affliction, wildfires:

Catastrophic disturbances such as wildfire periodically destroy Pacific yew. Fire risk decreases with overstory stand age; accordingly, yew is reported to be more common in old-growth forest than in younger stands. Integrating information from ecological studies may contribute to a better understanding of the environmental factors underlying the distribution of *Taxus* species.

Dr. Scher goes on to describe another nemesis, that the yew is highly susceptible to browsing by deer, elk, moose and other smaller forest animals:

Reports on wildlife feeding behavior indicate that yew foliage and fruit – a fleshy aril or berry – are important sources of forage for ungulates, small mammals and birds. Such observations suggest that the concentration of potentially toxic compounds in these tissues may be below the dose level to produce a detectable toxic reaction. Perhaps yew foraging species have evolved a mechanism to detoxify ingested taxol or other taxanes to harmless products. Where forest management practices have favored ungulate habitat, overbrowsing severely reduces yew abundance and skews population structure.[39]

FIRE-SWEPT YEWS NEAR FISH LAKE, SOUTHERN OREGON

But the primary reason that the yew is absent from much of the Northwest woods, as mentioned by several foresters, is that it depends on old-growth habitat for its survival. Bolsinger reiterates that severe stress has already been put on the species:

> On non-federal lands in California, Oregon, and Washington, where inventories have been made, there are an estimated 700,000 Pacific yew trees eleven inches (dbh) and larger, the size of most trees cut for bark collection. Almost all of the yew trees on non-federal lands are survivors of logging operations that removed the old-growth overstory. On federal lands where old-growth forests still exist, considerably more yew trees are thought to be present, but yew trees of the size needed to produce large quantities of bark are not abundant in most areas. An unknown but unquestionably significant percentage of the original yew resource has already been destroyed in logging operations. In the process of harvesting Douglas fir and other timber species, mostly by clearcutting, yew trees were either cut or knocked over and broken by machinery. Yew trees were seldom taken in primary logging operations, but some yew wood was later salvaged by firewood cutters and gleaners gathering wood for specialty products. By far the greatest portion of the yew trees

that existed in logged areas were burned in slash-disposal fires. In many logged areas, the rootstocks have survived and resprouted, so although the wood and bark of many yew trees were destroyed, there seems to have been little threat to the existence of the yew germ plasm. Continued or increased demand for yew bark for taxol production could substantially decrease a resource that has already been greatly reduced.[40]

In the meantime only bark is being utilized for taxol production while stems and needles that contain taxol are being wasted on the units. This destruction of a living, renewable source of taxol is questionable at best and negligent at worst, especially since processes, if not commercial production facilities, are available now to extract taxol or convertible congeners from foliage not only of Pacific yew but all species and cultivars of *Taxus* that have been tested to date. There are millions of pounds of foliage in as many as a half a billion yew shrubs, ornamental trees and hedges in urban and suburban America today. Annual trimmings from these plants could be used to alleviate the pressure on natural yew. But these potential sources of taxol are being wasted, and in order to bring them into production, new modes of cooperation between public and private interests must be devised.

At the very least, we should, during taxol extraction, be stabilizing all other taxol congeners and convertible taxanes from the extraction liquid. In addition, rather than wasting the limbs and foliage from trees killed in the bark harvest, they should be reclaimed and all taxol and other convertible taxanes should be (at least crudely) extracted and stablized into a 'mother liquor'[41] that could be kept until such time as an approved process is developed for the production of clinical taxol from such sources.

The switch from bark to foliage for taxol production will open up more sources of taxol. We need to remember that 90 percent of all Pacific yew is less than ten inches in diameter and 65 percent is less than five inches. Most Pacific yew is more aptly referred to as a shrub rather than a tree. We need to use and nurture this resource as well.

CHAPTER ELEVEN

DEALING WITH THE DILEMMA

FEDERAL ROLE

LTHOUGH perceptions of the Yew vary within the Forest Service, the dominant attitude – that the 'non-commercial' yew is a 'weed' or a 'trash' tree, not worth counting in the forest inventory – is changing. Almost all Pacific yew trees are in U. S. Forest Service Region Six, which is comprised of all National Forest land in Oregon, Washington, Idaho and Northern California. The Willamette National Forest in Oregon, the largest timber producing forest in the United States, lies mainly within Lane County. In 1984, concern for the fate of the yew tree and the loss of jobs was expressed to the Forest Service by Lane County Commissioner, Jerry Rust, who led his fellow board members to pass a resolution against exporting yew logs to overseas markets. This resolution proved to be helpful in stopping a major drive in the Oregon Legislature to allow exportation. At the same time, Rust, a former woodsworker himself, criticized the Forest Service, BLM and "the mindless monoculturists of the timber industry who want to turn the world into a Douglas fir garden at the expense of all the other species."

A Forest Service silviculturist acknowledged in 1984:

We do control the growth, in its early stages, for the most commercially viable crop. The yew has always been a specialty item. If the commercial demand for it changed, we'd change our management.[1]

In a more recent interview, John Lowe, Deputy Regional Forester for Region 6, described the role of the Forest Service in the management of public lands:

> Our primary role, within the confines of the legislation that we operate under, is to go through planning processes with the public, and sort out what kinds of things we ought to manage a particular piece of ground for. That depends on what the public demands are. What do they want to see happen to that land and what resource capability does that piece of land have? Some lands that don't have a lot of resource capability can't be managed for what the people want, because the capability is not there. We go through a planning process, then in the sense of timber sales we manage the selling, prepare the sales – the business end of doing the job.

Lowe confirmed that the yew was not high on the list of Forest Service priorities until recently:

> The yew is an understory part of the forest and our practice here in the west is to go in after harvest and clean up the ground. In a lot of cases we burn the area to get rid of the slash and reduce the fire hazard as well as to prepare the site for planting new trees. In most cases the yew has not been utilized for anything, but was just consumed in that process...In the not so distant past the yew was a weed species and had no real commercial value. To the best of my knowledge it never had really been associated as a viable part of any wildlife habitat either. So it really had no place in the world in terms of species.

According to Lowe the Forest Service is reacting to the dramatic change in the status of the Pacific yew:

> Now, with the high probability that the yew has a role to play in the cure for cancer, that of course is all changed. We have two concerns. One is the demand; how do we move it into the marketplace and help supply the demand? We have flexibility and rules and regulations set up for other species that have commercial value, which we can apply to the yew. We have been able to do that. The other issue that we have with any species out there, is to make sure that we do not eliminate the species from the system by some type of over-harvesting.

We are required under the National Forest Management Act to maintain the viability of all the species that presently exist, so we are not going to enter into any kind of program that would annihlate the yew from the system. If we do go into areas and harvest yew that are not in the scheduled timber sales, we will do that under a prescription that won't jeopardize the continuation of the plant in any way.[2]

Now that a commercial value has been found for the yew, the Forest Service is moving more quickly. Robert Lease, who represents the Forest Service concerning its yew management plans, says, "Yew trees probably will be depleted in some areas, but there are many other areas where there will always be plenty of yew." He also indicates that the conservation strategy "may not be as elaborate as some folks want to see it."[3] Other Forest Service officials espouse doing all they can to help bark collectors find and strip the bark from what they estimate to be 125,000 yew trees in order to produce 750,000 pounds of dried yew bark: "Women are dying every day of ovarian and breast cancer," said Dick Shaffer, Assistant Director of Timber Management for the Forest Service's regional office in Portland. "The Forest Service has placed a high priority on helping Bristol-Myers in every way we legally and environmentally can."[4]

THE YEW COUNT

Until now, Forest Service policy was that bark will only be taken from trees found on units that have just been or are ready to be logged. In other words, from only those units that were already documented, as required by the National Environmental Protection Act, as being under some sort of sales contract. Bark collectors are to be commended for their efforts to salvage taxol from this otherwise wasted resource, but the fact that these trees have been wasted and continue to be wasted is not mitigated by their efforts. Cutting down trees for five pounds of bark is not the answer. If they are able to get 750,000 or more pounds of bark in 1991, where will it come from next year or the year after, as timber harvest rates continue to slow down and the demand for taxol continues to rise?

It is clear that an accurate survey is needed if any large-scale harvest of yew trees is to be launched. At present no one knows how many trees are out there. John Lowe agrees:

> One of the things that we have to get a better handle on is the inventory. Are we looking in all of the right places? Do we have a handle on exactly how much there is?
> We are estimating right now, and it's a fairly rough estimate, that there are about 1.7 million acres of National Forest land that the yew is growing on. We are currently doing a little better inventory to find out how accurate that is, but that is our best guess at this point. That is less than ten percent of the National Forest lands.[5]

Bolsinger, with the Pacific Northwest Research Station, estimates that yew is present on 1.2 million acres of Forest Service land in Idaho, Montana, Washington, Oregon, and California.[6]

Jim Weir, of the Bureau of Land Management, says that his agency has yew trees on about 2 million acres as well.[7] Between the two agencies it is estimated that there are between 3.2 and 3.7 million acres of federal timberland upon which yew trees can be found. Estimates in the newspapers have run higher. The *Wall Street Journal* reported 4.3 million acres.[8]

Bruce Mannheim of the Environmental Defense Fund agrees with Bolsinger's estimate:

> The Forest Service and the Fish and Wildlife Service concluded that the yew tree occurs on 2.5 million acres of land in the Northwest. We estimated in our petition that it occurred on not more than 1.2 million acres. The discrepancy there is that the Forest Service considered areas that have already been cut, in other words in secondary or tertiary growth forest. We don't believe that the yew trees that occur on those lands are viable contributors to the species, because it takes at least 50 years for the yew tree to become reproductively viable. Many of these secondary or tertiary forests are in short rotation plans that call for cutting before the yew trees actually reach reproductive maturity. How can they possibly contribute to the perpetuation of the species if in fact they are going to be cut before they reach an age where they can produce seed?[9]

At this moment there is no accurate inventory of yew in general nor any differentiation between yew shrubs and yew trees. Only trees five inches in diameter or larger are suitable for bark stripping. And it is estimated that only 35 percent of all yews are five inches or more. No one really knows how much is out there, yet in the meantime bark-strippers are well into a full-scale harvest of yew and would like to harvest in areas not already scheduled to be logged. Any move to harvest yew outside areas with proper NEPA documentation will probably be challenged.

Despite the lack of any accurate inventory of yew, certain claims have been made by the Forest Service that there may be 130 million yew trees on federal lands. This 'fact' appears on a US Forest Service fact sheet designed to educate the public:

> Q: Are yew trees scarce and will taxol production push them to extinction?
>
> A: Yew trees are not scarce. There are an estimated 130 million on National Forest land. Yew management will be tied to Forest Plans, which provide for species retention. Research and a planned regional inventory will lead to a conservation plan. The NEPA process will be followed.[10]

Unfortunately this estimate does not differentiate between yew shrubs and trees, though it has been quoted by the *Wall Street Journal* and by National Cancer Institute officials as well.

Dave Barton, a longtime Oregon woodsworker, gave his appraisal of how much yew wood might be out there:

> If there are 130 million yew trees out there, only ten to fifteen percent would be larger than four inches in diameter. I haven't seen all of the woods, but in the areas that I have seen over the past twenty years, the yew tree is pretty spotty. Yew trees seem to prefer wet, south-slopes. They band together in clumps. If you find one, then there are usually more around. If you don't find one, it is likely that there aren't any for miles, but there are some good concentrations of it here and there. I have seen a few places where there are thousands of seedlings on an acre, but most of them will never reach maturity. If they don't even have the beginnings of an inventory, then it makes no sense to say that they have that many trees. I don't think that there are anywhere near that many, not with any size to them.[11]

THE OLD-GROWTH CONTROVERSY

The Pacific yew is becoming like the much heralded spotted owl, a major issue within the old-growth 'set-aside' controversy. The reason is that yew trees, spotted owls and old-growth forests are all found together. Since spotted owl set-aside has reduced the acreage of available timber sales, the amount of yew to be harvested (under the existing policy not to cut yew outside sale areas) is also reduced. Although John Lowe indicates that some activity is allowed inside set-aside areas,

> ...there is no question that there is probably a large amount of yew to be found inside habitat conservation areas. They are specifically off limits to logging and that sort of commercial venture. We have already had some questions like can you go in and cut Christmas trees or mushrooms. We are beginning to work through that and some of those things really are not critical to the maintenance of the owl habitat. We are allowing Christmas tree cutting in habitat conservation areas, although not commercial ventures. We don't see any reason that we should control mushroom picking.
>
> I think the yew question is one we will have to look at; is it or is it not compatible with the intent of why we set aside the conservation areas for spotted owl habitat? As the demand increases and we have to go to more and more parts of the forest to try to meet that demand then this controversy will get larger and larger.[12]

There are reasons to protect endangered species in the Northwest and in the Amazon Basin – wherever they may be threatened. Rust is worried that the yew tree issue might be used to assail the Endangered Species Act:

> One of the things that the timber industry always says when these species come up is, 'we don't have a spotted owl problem or a marbled murrelet problem, we don't have a yew problem, we've got an Endangered Species Act problem. It's the law that is the problem.' That isn't right. The problem is that some species are on the decline, going down hill – we are seeing fewer of them. Their habitat is eroded and they are in retreat, and *that* is the definition of an endangered species – one that has been pushed

to the point where it doesn't have the genetic biodiversity needed to survive. Each of these species is an indicator of the health of the ancient forest. These species range from Alaska to Northern California and their habitat has been cut down dramatically; something like ninety percent of it is gone.

A friend of mine calls spotted owls down from higher reaches of the canopy for the Forest Service, and five out of the last six pairs he has called down alighted in yew trees. That's not too hard to feature because yew trees are an understory tree, 20, 30, 40 feet high and tend to have strong big limbs, and in certain areas under the canopy, may be the only tree at that particular level and the owl swoops down onto the most natural perch of all.[13]

In 1987 the National Cancer Institute made eight million dollars available for a crash program to find and analyze plant and animal species for possible compounds useful against cancer. The reason for the world-wide crash program is given by Michael Balick of the New York Botanical Garden:

The problem is that rates of extinction are escalating so quickly that if one were to find a plant that displayed interesting bioactivity, it's quite possible to go back and find its habitat destroyed. It is a race against time.[14]

Our underlying concern should be the deterioration of species habitat and our greatest fear should be that the hard won restrictions on harvesting timber in spotted owl and marbled murrelet habitat, riparian zones or old-growth and wilderness set-aside areas, might somehow be jeopardized, somehow breached by the building pressure to harvest yew bark from wild Pacific yew trees.

NATIONAL CANCER INSTITUTE, BRISTOL-MYERS SQUIBB AND HAUSER CHEMICAL CO.

Since drugs like taxol occur naturally in plants and can therefore not be patented, no drug company will risk the investment in the research, development, clinical trials and FDA registration which are necessary to bring the drug to market, unless the drug company can be assured some degree of market exclusivity. Sometimes it is difficult to reconcile the company's need for profit with the public need for timely development of the product. It is especially difficult in the case of taxol because there are so many who might benefit from it yet there is so little of it. Many who clamor for it will not be able to get it because of its scarcity and its cost when refined only from bark.

The fate of Pacific yew as a natural species and the immediate fate of thousands of persons who will not get taxol until alternate sources are fully employed, hang together in the balance against the current drug-industry commercialization processes. The future looks grim for both, because the tortuous processes that attend development and commercialization of new drugs in the United States are probably hindering full development of taxol from renewable resources. Bear with me while we follow the string through the labyrinth.

Here for the moment are the major players and their roles. The National Institute of Health (NIH) and the National Cancer Institute (NCI), who did the initial studies and are monitoring the clinical trials. Bristol-Myers Squibb (Bristol), the drug company that was awarded the Collaborative Research and Development Agreement (CRADA), an arrangement which essentially gives Bristol exclusive rights to develop the compound's commercial potential, in exchange for a committment to finance and develop methods to get the drug to the patient. Under the CRADA, Bristol must supply NCI with taxol for further clinical testing and all data resulting from that testing will be given to Bristol when they seek Federal Food and Drug Administration approval to use taxol on other forms of cancer. Hauser Chemical Company is under contract with Bristol to extract taxol from bark. Hauser Chemical is provided bark by Hauser Northwest, a company which in turn contracts with individual contractors, who supply and organize labor to strip the trees and collect the bark. The bark collector, who has a contract with Hauser or Bristol, gets the bark from public forest land under special arrangement with the Forest Service or Bureau of Land Management, as explained by Jim Weir of BLM:

> The BLM makes yew trees available and Hauser has been the primary purchaser. We sell the yew trees by negotiated sale rather than advertised. A draft agreement between the BLM and Bristol-Myers Squibb Company is in the works that provides for all of the yew trees to be sold to them, except for *de minimis*

amounts. Bristol will furnish to us a list of names, addresses and locations, of contractors, subcontractors or agencies authorized to collect yew bark for them.

The BLM in Oregon was given a draft copy of the agreement from Washington, D.C. We were asked to make comments on it. There was a similar Forest Service agreement attached. The agreement is for five years.[15]

Because it is necessary that a drug company take certain precautions to insure that a new drug will be profitable before undertaking the task of developing it for the market, they are given a form of exclusivity called a Collaborative Research and Development Agreement (CRADA), as Dr. Saul Shephartz, an NCI spokesperson, explains in a recent interview:

The clinical work is continuing to look exceedingly promising, and as far as we're concerned, we have little doubt that we will get to the market and have a new drug application that will be approved by the FDA, at least for ovarian cancer, possibly for others as well, we don't know yet. That is still sometime off and this will then be handled by Bristol-Myers Squibb.

The procurement of material is being turned over to Bristol at this point. They have agreed to supply us with clinical material for further clinical studies, so they will be responsible for procurement of material for clinical trial and it will be their responsibility to pull together the data that are necessary and present their case to the FDA for marketing.

I'm carrying out various other activities in relation to procurement of alternate sources, in exchange for which they will have exclusive rights to clinical data that we generate. Since there is no patent on the material itself, this is the way that they are able to have exclusive rights to the compound, at least for a limited period of time. They are putting some millions of dollars into procurement and other aspects of the work. It's the way of giving them the exclusivity that they need to put in the investment.

Other companies can certainly carry out their own studies, although it's my understanding that Bristol-Myers had obtained orphan drug status for the compound, and under the legislation that provides for that, once they get an application approved, that in itself gives them seven years of exclusivity. Once they put it on the market, no one else can market that drug for seven years. That legislation went into effect some years back.[16]

According to Dr. Kenneth Snader, also with NCI:

> In order to prevent any misunderstanding, the CRADA covers all
> NCI clinical data. It is not limited to ovarian cancer...There will
> not be an additional CRADA for taxol. Under the existing
> CRADA, NCI will provide clinical data on taxol to Bristol-Myers
> Squibb exclusively. The FDA has awarded Bristol orphan drug
> status for taxol to be used for ovarian cancer. This will afford
> Bristol seven years of exclusivity once the New Drug Application
> is approved. There is no relationship between the FDA designa-
> tion and the CRADA.[17]

Regardless of exclusivity, there is no doubt that the shortage of taxol
is creating a crisis, and there is no doubt that in order to solve that crisis
other methods of taxol production are going to be needed. Dr. Holton
sums up the situation:

> So they are trying to collect 750,000 pounds of bark? That will
> give them, according to my calculations, about 30 kilograms of
> taxol. People at Bristol-Myers said once upon a time that before
> they went on the market with taxol they would want to have stock
> of 20 kilograms and that their projected first year sales would
> probably be in the range of 100 kilograms. So the amount that
> will come from 750,000 pounds of bark, based on those esti-
> mates would get them through about four months on the
> market. The NCI is scared to death of this because if taxol is on
> the market first for treatment of ovarian cancer, it would be
> unethical to withold taxol from that market. But if all the
> available taxol is supplied to treat those patients with ovarian
> cancer, that will prevent the NCI from doing trials against other
> cancer types. They are rushing right now to do as many clinical
> trials as they possibly can.[18]

ENVIRONMENTAL CONCERNS

As tree after tree is felled for its five pounds of bark, Pacific yew is
in jeopardy. Environmental groups are taking action to insure that
Pacific yew is not wasted or annihilated. Bruce Mannheim had this to
say about the concerns of the environmental community:

> The Environmental Defense Fund first became involved with
> this issue shortly following a conference that took place in

Washington in June 1990, which brought together scientists, lawyers and government officials to discuss the advancement of taxol. The principal conclusion of that conference was that clinical development of the drug has been slowed by its acute shortage. So we looked into the problems, the reasons for this shortage of the drug, and to our absolute amazement discovered that the species had received virtually no protection at all on federal, state or private land, that it was essentially treated as a weed species by the Forest Service and the Bureau of Land Management. As a result of that designation, it was essentially trashed and destroyed as part of the clear-cutting, broadcast burning operations taking place in the Pacific Northwest.

After drawing those conclusions and then evaluating the scientific information available about the yew tree, we decided to petition the U.S. Fish and Wildlife Service, specifically the Interior Secretary, to add the Pacific yew to the list of threatened plant species under the Endangered Species Act. On September 19th of last year we submitted that petition and unfortunately, about three months after that, the Interior Department denied the petition. We are currently studying the basis for the Fish and Wildlife Service's denial of our petition and we will soon decide whether to pursue judicial review of its determination that the Pacific yew tree is in fact not sufficiently threatened to warrant protection under the Endangered Species Act.

The Fish and Wildlife Service's assessment is based on material it received from the U.S. Forest Service and it is somewhat questionable, particularly since the U.S. Forest Service has never done an inventory for the Pacific yew tree. I guess my immediate response is, if Pacific yew trees are so widely available as some suggest, then why is there in fact a problem with getting to the tree and making the drug available. This is a tree that is principally, though not exclusively, restricted to old-growth forest. Many of those forests as you know have been cut and destroyed over the last century. The future of this forest now hangs in the balance and as those forests go, so will the Pacific yew tree.

Our legal recourse is to seek judicial review of the U.S. Fish and Wildlife Service's determination that the petition doesn't present sufficient evidence to even warrant an inventory or review of the status of the yew tree. In other words the U.S. Fish and Wildlife Service decided that this thing is so abundant that we don't even have to do the inventory that we have never done, which a court might take a second look at. How can a federal agency decide that a species which has these pressures on it is not in fact possibly threatened if it hasn't even done an inventory of individual areas, trees and diameter classes on their own land?

Our actions are completely consonant with those of the cancer research community. We are not by any means seeking to prevent or impede development of this drug; it's just the opposite. Two very prominent cancer researchers joined our petition to the government to protect the species. The same day we filed our petition the American Cancer Society also requested Interior Secretary Lujan to afford the species protection. In many ways the interests of the environmental community are completely consistent with those of the cancer research community. There may of course be some difference and some uncertainties about how orderly and expeditious a transition can be made from the bark of the yew tree to the needles, but I think that both the environmental and cancer research communities recognize the need to protect the species.

The first sentence of the petition says 'in order to insure continued availability of this drug we hereby petition you to designate this tree as threatened under the Endangered Species Act,' because that would give government adequate authority to establish a conservation program and to insure that other threats to the species are eliminated so that it can be used for this particular purpose.

If the agency was really serious about logging of the yew tree, it would in fact reserve those trees and insure that each ounce of bark, or each needle is in fact utilized for taxol. I think that ultimately the Forest Service and the Bureau of Land Management are going to have to recognize that protection of the yew tree and making that tree available for extraction of taxol will require constraints on timber operations in the Northwest.[19]

Rhoda Love, member of the Native Plant Society of Oregon, writes of specific concerns:

As far as the Native Plant Society has been able to learn, the U.S. Forest Service has written no Environmental Impact Statement describing the effects of this level of harvest on the Pacific yew. In addition, the Forest Service has not indicated how the harvest of yew bark will be spread over the various National Forests in this region. In fact, they have indicated that they do not know how many of the rather rare yew trees actually grow on our western forests.

NPSO has written to the Forest Service asking that it inventory yew trees throughout the region with special attention to geographical distribution, number and age of trees, distribution of male and female trees and analysis of the trees' genetic makeup. We have asked the Forest Service to begin replanting yews in logged areas. And we have asked that during replanting, efforts be made to use local genotypes and ensure a natural mix of male and female trees. And we have strongly recommended that Forest Service biologists write a long-term plan which will provide for a sustainable taxol harvest while at the same time preserving yews as part of the natural biodiversity of our forests.

The Native Plant Society of Oregon strongly believes that it is a serious mistake to rush to harvest hundreds of thousands of pounds of yew bark for experimental purposes, when knowledge of the numbers and natural distribution of the yew tree is virtually non-existent.

NPSO asks the Forest Service to issue only limited permits for yew bark harvest until the biology of the Pacific yew is better understood. Only when it is certain that a sustainable harvest can be maintained should the Forest Service, the guardian of our public lands, agree to provide the amount of bark requested by the huge drug companies. In the short run, a few more cancer deaths may be prevented by overharvesting now, but in the long run, many more lives can be saved by keeping yew trees alive and well, and reproducing in the Northwest woods as they have for over a hundred million years.[20]

Commissioner Rust's current concerns are that taxol and other congeners from the tree are being wasted and that government policies are doing little to help alleviate the impact of the incredible demand for yew bark on natural large yew trees, as a news article reports:

'Every time we take a tree down, we are taking down a life-saving factory,' said Rust.

The U.S. Forest Service has estimated there are about 130 million yews in the national forests of Oregon and Washington. But Rust and others say there are far less, perhaps only 1 million trees.

Rust said federal action is needed soon because in the next few months the National Cancer Institute may announce that taxol is effective in fighting lung and breast cancer. If that happens, he said, the demand for taxol will skyrocket.

'The race is on,' he said. 'The Japanese are after it and so are the Italians and the French.'

Rust said the Pacfic Northwest could become the world's main source of taxol, providing thousands of jobs in towns hard hit by the timber slump.

But Rust added those benefits would come about only if the federal government and pharmaceutical companies learn how to extract taxol from needles and develop a process for a renewable harvest of yews.

Rust said the Northwest should exploit its advantage, including a climate ideally suited to growing yews. In the right conditions, he said, yews can grow as fast as ten inches a year, compared to one or two inches a year in the wild.

'Right here in River City is where the game begins,' Rust said. 'We ought to be the leader.'[21]

Don Adams has made his living from the yew for over forty years. In a recent interview he had this to say about the current destruction of the yew:

Q: The National Cancer Institute keeps saying that there are twenty pounds of bark on an average yew tree.
A: First of all, I don't think that there are twenty pounds of bark on any yew tree. That bark is very, very thin.
Q: Do you think the yew is a prevalent species of tree? Do you see a lot to choose from?
A: No. No, as a matter of fact, about the only place you find any amount of yew wood is under the remaining old growth. If there are not old-growth firs around we don't even look – it's a waste of time. You might find a few. If it's second-growth timber it's been logged off and in my opinion the yew was knocked down back then. Whether it was used for bows I don't know, but it's gone. Maybe a little bit left along the creeks in the second-growth, such a small smattering that it isn't worth your time to go look at it. We take one out of three hundred trees and you have got to look at a lot of trees to find one bow stave. So we go into the old-growth fir only and there isn't that much old-growth fir left. So any abundance of yew has to be there. They are always crying about the old-growth being wiped out, well so was the yew. They have to grow back together, which will never happen as long as man is alive.
Q: So if you are in the bow business and most of the yew is harvested, how do you feel about that?

A: I'm out of business. I'm kind of like the Indian with no buffalo. If they cut it all down, then that's just another one of the old crafts that we can forget about – that's progress I guess.

To my mind, it's kind of like the buffalo laying out on the prairie rotting after they took the hides and the tongues. It seems like kind of a waste. I don't feel that the Good Lord put that resource on this earth to just let it sit there and rot. If they are going to cut down the tree and use the bark, that's wonderful, but I think that they should find an equitable usage for what's left, rather than just let it rot, because it's never going to come back. It's going to go so fast that you would never believe it and it's never going to return, not as long as people are cutting down fir trees for houses. I think it's very, very wasteful. Didn't we learn anything from the slaughter of the buffalo? Now we are trying to bolster the herds to keep them from becoming extinct. Well, we should have thought about that a hundred years ago.

The cancer cure is great, but is the cancer cure the great motive, or is it the possible profit for a drug company? I have mixed emotions here too. Maybe I'm getting too political, but we've always got to filter this god almighty dollar into the process.[22]

NATIVE YEW CONSERVATION COUNCIL

Since the NCI's conference on taxol in Bethesda, a group of concerned persons has formed the Native Yew Conservation Council (NYCC) with a goal of establishing guidelines for walking the high-wire between preserving the species and producing direly needed taxol. The NYCC is comprised of individuals representing all facets of the issue, including Forest Service and BLM officials, a dozen bark collection contractors from four states, extraction companies, federal, state and local government officials, environmental activists and international yew wood and taxol interests.

At their first official meeting in Eugene, Oregon, they toured a bark stripping operation to observe techniques and see first hand what it entailed – dead yew trees, peeled logs gleaming as they lay across the creek, a gruesome sight. After the bark stripping tour, group members met to produce an initial draft of goals and purposes, which included ten recommendations:

1. Because cancer is a major cause of death, and taxol is highly effective against ovarian and other cancers, the group calls for a policy that declares the yew tree a national strategic resource.

2. Because yews are a retreating species threatened with global extinction, and because the current demand for taxol places an additional burden upon this species, a concerted effort needs to be made, at all levels, to protect and manage yew populations.

3. The following programs need to be implemented:

– A sample-based inventory of yew abundance and distribution must be conducted.

– Preserves to protect genetically unique populations need to be established.

– Harvesting guidelines should be reviewed and implemented to assure a continued renewable supply of taxol. High priority should be given to insure that all taxol-containing tissues are utilized in an efficient manner.

– Trashing yew during commercial harvesting operations must be stopped.

4. A research program should be planned and carried out to better utilize the yew resource, including but not limited to:

– Studies of seasonal variation of taxol within the tree.

– Methods of stimulating increased taxol production.

– Investigating non-destructive methods for obtaining taxol.

5. Harvesting of yews from environmentally sensitive riparian zones should be limited according to state guidelines.

6. Forest practices should be encouraged that insure regeneration, for example: retaining stumps with adequate bark to promote resprouting; elimination of slash burning that destroys fire-sensitive yews.

7. Limit yew harvesting to trees of agreed upon minimum and maximum dbh (diameter at breast height) for genetic diversity.

8. Environmental assessments must be issued before harvesting genetically sensitive yew populations.

9. Given the inadequate and limited native resources, and the long time frames to cultivate sizable yews, efforts should begin now to establish means of effective propagation of yew species. Selection of individuals with high concentrations of taxol and faster growth rates for propagation could contribute significantly to cost-effective taxol production in nurseries, orchards and coppiced woodlots.

10. Since direct chemical synthesis and biotechnology are, at best, long-range approaches, native sources need our immediate attention.[23]

CUT AND STRIPPED YEW TREE

Since then, the group has held six meetings in various locations, with increasing attendance. They are incorporating as a non-profit corporation to pursue educating legislators, organizing an international symposium and publishing a newsletter representing all viewpoints.[25]

In a recent interview, Rust responded to criticism that environmentalists are denying yew bark to cancer victims:

> They will suggest that environmentalists are responsible for witholding this drug from dying women. No environmentalist has ever suggested that a single tree be saved for any reason nor has any sale or proposed unit been contested on any basis. As a matter of fact the NYCC has been responsible for bringing out knowledge that is boosting the yields significantly. We have contributed more to the taxol production effort in these Northwest forests than virtually anyone. To suggest that somehow environmentalists like myself are responsible for the withholding of the drug from dying patients is ironic and untrue.
>
> We proposed to the Forest Service and Bureau of Land Management a number of solutions to help conserve the yew and to stretch out the resource and provide more taxol. Among these were conservation measures such as leaving stumps unstripped for a minimum height, so they can resprout, and restricting the

burning of units and slashpiles wherever yew is present, as well as other management policies that they have partially adopted. In addition, we pointed out at a symposium of our own the following January, that yew bark (viable for up to ten years after cutting) was being left on the unit. I estimate that a hundred tons were collected from these old units which would have gone to waste, many of which would have been burned. In addition we pointed out in January, six months after the NCI taxol symposium, that there were methods of extracting taxol from needles.[24]

THE IMPLICATIONS OF FEDERAL POLICY

The Forest Service and BLM control access to yew trees on public lands. In November, 1990, the NYCC sent a query letter to Dale Robertson, Chief of the Forest Service, urging him to pay close attention to the situation. The response from his office assured that the Forest Service was taking 'several positive actions':

> The Pacific Northwest Region (Region 6) has developed interim Pacific yew guidelines that discuss collection permits, timber sales involving yew, site preparation techniques that allow yew to sprout, regeneration using seed and cuttings, and inventory assessments as part of the stand exam process. The objectives are to be responsive to the needs of the National Cancer Institute and to assure that Pacific yew remains a viable component of forest stands. This effort should go a long way to solving some of the short-term potential impacts on the species.
>
> The Forest Service, National Forest System, Timber Management has initiated a cooperative project with NCI that will provide data on genetic variation, high yielding genotypes, and lead to the 'domestication' of the species so it can be grown like an agricultural crop. The objective is to work towards a stable supply for the future that will not involve harvesting the raw material from trees growing in forest stands...Many significant steps have been taken during the past few months and more are to come. It is imperative that we all work together on this most important venture.[25]

John Lowe details what is currently happening from the Forest Service point of view:

The fact that one chemical company has been awarded the exclusive rights to do the research by NCI makes our primary objective at this point to insure that bark goes to their project. I think a lot of different folks can be involved in this by working through the chemical company that is doing the gathering and processing. We have timber operators who are working directly through that company to provide access to bark off of their units where they already have ownership rights under the normal timber sale contract.

As the demand continues, we are going to have to look at how we handle those areas where other people want to come in and get involved who are not associated with the NCI. We know that there are some foreign companies that are very heavily interested. There are other national companies that would also like to be involved. We realize that within the next three or four months this is probably going to become a bigger and bigger issue. It is a national issue; even though the yew is primarily found here in the northwest part of the United States, cancer is everywhere. We are beginning to get a lot of interest from people around Washington D.C., from the administration, from Congress, as to what really is going on.[26]

Everyone seems to realize that the rising demand for Pacific yew bark cannot possibly be met by bark taken only from clear cuts or units slated for clear cutting in the near future.

As of this writing, Hauser Northwest has established bark collection plants in Oregon, Washington, Idaho and British Columbia. Additional plants are to be opened in Montana and Northern California. The pressure is building to scrap the current Forest Service and BLM policy of only harvesting bark from areas already logged, being logged or under a sales contract to be logged. John Lowe ventures what the Forest Service might do to accommodate the demand:

The chemical companies are beginning to yell somewhat loud and clearly that they need to find another process for getting the bark out of the woods. So we are now looking at some other ways that we can go in and remove some of the yew, not necessarily after the timber sale, but maybe in front of the timber sale, maybe even in some areas where we don't have timber sales planned.

I'm sure that we have quite a bit of yew in wilderness areas which by law we are prohibited from going into. So regardless of the other things, there are always going to be some areas that won't be available to us for any kind of a commercial venture. I am very comfortable that we can get an answer to the question of finding an environmentally sound process of going ahead and trying to get as much as we can.[27]

To effect these policies:

A Cooperative Agreement between the government and Bristol-Myers Squibb has been signed which gives Bristol first rights of refusal on any yew product to be found on federal lands. The seven page agreement spells out the terms of harvest and calls for additional studies and an inventory of Pacific yew. Bristol will pay all government costs of the yew harvesting program.[28]

Bruce Mannheim appraised the agreement in its draft form:

What concerns me from this meeting today is learning of a draft agreement pending between that company and both the Forest Service and the Bureau of Land Management, which would give a private company authority to decide who takes yew trees, where those trees occur on federal land.[29]

Dave Barton had this to say about the agreement:

It is apparent to me that the whole deal with yew bark and needles in the woods is a conspiracy between the government and private industry. It puts people out of work and at the same time it jeopardizes lives and raises the prices of taxol to where people can't afford it. If there was a competitive market people could go out and work and gather up dried bark off of already harvested units and make the supply more plentiful. That stuff is rotting into the ground and they aren't getting it. They're only looking for the easy stuff. In the areas that I have seen, they are probably getting a third to two-thirds of the bark.

The biggest density and largest volume of yew trees that I've ever seen was up near the lookout on Little Cow Horn Mountain. I went up there last year to check it out, and it had all been burned. They cut the whole thing and then burned it. There were two and three foot yew trees standing all over the place, burned to death. There were also a lot of them down. I would say that there were twenty or thirty metric tons on the high shoulder of the one road that had been left over from post cutting and it's all gone now. Not a strip of bark was gotten off of about a hundred acres of units up there and there was probably a yew tree about every twenty feet and in some places they were every five feet – a great concentration of big ones and littles ones mixed. They're still up there, all over the place, but they are burnt to crispy critters.[30]

A news article recounts some effects of the draft agreement:

A cancer-fighting drug derived from the Pacific yew tree is at the heart of a controversy that put at least 50 Canyonville-based forest workers out of work this week.

The workers, collecting yew bark in the Tiller Ranger District of the Umpqua National Forest, were stopped from working because of an exclusive contract the federal government has granted to Hauser Northwest, a Cottage Grove company. Hauser has won the rights to be the sole collector of yew bark on behalf of the Bristol-Myers Squibb pharmaceutical company.

Bristol-Myers was granted exclusive rights by the National Cancer Institute to develop taxol, a yew bark derived drug that has shown promise in fighting ovarian cancer.

Ken Wright, who operates the Yew-Can company in Canyonville, has collected bark during the past two years. Wright said he was forced to lay off 50 workers this week, just as the collecting season was beginning.

'The Forest Service and the BLM can't issue any permits,' Wright said. 'Hauser took a total monopoly on the yew wood.'

Wright had been collecting bark on the forest floor, picking up pieces that remained from earlier clearcuts. 'There's lots of stuff that had been pushed over by cats and that bark is still good,' Wright said. 'The Hauser company said it's no good. Of course, I don't have the medical facts, but some companies will buy it.'

Wright thinks the monopoly will create a black market, since other contries will be willing to buy the material. 'There's people out there that will get it – I won't – but this country isn't the only one wanting this.'

Wright, who worked in the logging business for 25 years before turning to yew collection, said he had no ill feelings for the Hauser company. 'A lot of it is Bristol-Myers fault,' he said. 'I fought the spotted owl and now I've got to fight this. There's no end.'[31]

In fact there have already been incidents of yew tree theft and bark stripping in off-limit areas in several ranger districts. In one such incident in the Oakridge Ranger District of the Willamette National Forest, in a designated scenic area, 56 yew trees were stripped of their bark. The Forest Service has posted a $5,000 reward for information leading to the apprehension of the perpetrators.[32]

Rust calls for higher levels of protection for the Pacific yew:

> Because there's kind of a feeding frenzy going on with respect to the Pacific yew – there are bottom feeders, there are top feeders, there are sharks – it is germane to question the extent of a black market, both locally and overseas. I don't think that it is happening in a huge way, but there is no doubt that bags of yew bark go to places like Germany, Italy, France, China, Japan and England. This material is much sought after. We need to put some kind of a special protection on this tree and recognize its value, call it a strategic resource, call it a botanical treasure. At any rate it needs a higher level of protection. We should convert strictly to the needles and this tree should be carefully and selectively cut in the future.[33]

CONGRESSIONAL INVESTIGATION

All this moved Rust and others, in April 1991, to call for a congressional investigation into the federal policies on yew trees and yew bark harvest, as featured in several news articles:

> A Lane County commissioner and environmentalists called Wednesday for a congressional investigation into what they described as a Pacific yew monoply that jeopardizes the trees and their cancer-fighting future.
>
> The slow-growing trees, sought for the cancer-combating chemical called taxol that's found in their bark and needles, are in danger because the U.S. Forest Service and the Bureau of Land Management are allowing one company to cut them down for their bark, said Commissioner Jerry Rust and Wendell Wood of the Oregon Natural Resources Council.
>
> 'The Forest Service is wasting fully one-third of all the available taxol in the world because all the branches and needles are lost,' Rust said.
>
> Rust has asked U.S. Rep. John Dingell, D-Mich., who heads

the House subcommittee on oversight and investigations, to hold hearings to examine the relationships among the National Cancer Institute, Bristol-Myers Squibb, to which the Institute has given exclusive rights to develop taxol for use in ovarian cancer, and the two federal forest agencies.

The drug company, through harvester Hauser Northwest Inc. of Cottage Grove, now has exclusive rights to collect yew bark from public forests in order to process it for taxol, regional Forest Service official Fred Page said.

That amounts to giving the company a government-assisted monopoly that endangers the yew because the collectors cut down the trees for their bark, Rust said. Other companies are interested in harvesting just the needles and twigs, but they can't obtain the raw materials, he said.

Page said the drug company's process for isolating taxol is the only one so far approved by the U.S. Food and Drug Administration, but the agency is looking forward to a management plan for harvesting just needles as soon as technology allows.

Rust and Wood, however, said the technology exists now and could get FDA approval within months, but the drug product couldn't be sold in the United States because of the exclusive agreement the National Cancer Institute has with Bristol-Myers Squibb.

The National Audubon Society and Headwaters, a watershed conservation group, have joined the Oregon Natural Resources Council in asking for the preservation of yew trees for future harvesting, Wood said. They want immediate studies of the species with the goal of sustainable-harvest management of the trees, he said.

In the interim, the forest agencies must halt clear cutting around yew trees and the burning of ground where they grow, in order to enable stumps to resprout, Wood and Rust said.[34]

And in another article:

Rust believes that unless a way is found to extract taxol without killing so many yews, the Northwest is doomed to have yet another natural resource exploited by big corporations. Rust wants the trees selectively pruned of branches and needles, keeping the trees alive and sustaining the resource.

'We will get to be bark gatherers at $75 a day for five years, or we can position ourselves to be the taxol-producing region in the world,' said Rust, who envisions an industry in the Northwest that includes hundreds of bark and needles gatherers, yew tree farms and processing plants.

'We talk a lot about economic development, but when the best thing in decades comes along, we're out there hauling logs out of canyons for a few dollars,' said Rust. 'It's about as crude a form of economics as you can get.'[35]

The environmental community has been thwarted in its attempts to focus attention on the immensity of the yew harvest because accurate information is not forthcoming from government agencies or private companies. Rust characterized his frustrations:

It was right after the National Cancer Institute's symposium on taxol that Bristol-Myers, NCI, BLM and the Forest Service began a disinformation campaign which essentially said that there was no taxol in needles. Each time we had to go to them with information to the contrary, and they would grudgingly change their statement. First there was no taxol in needles. Then they said, well it's not economically feasible to get it out of the needles. Then along comes David Carver and others with viable processes to extract taxol from needles. Then they said, well there is no GMP, 'good manufacturing process,' approved by the FDA and it takes three to five years to get that approval. But the FDA says it can be approved in six months with the proper cooperation. Then there is the exclusive deal between Bristol-Myers and the government: NCI, BLM, Forest Service. Their whole disinformation campaign has been to keep moving the target in order to confuse rather than resolve these questions. The process has been secretive, manipulative and the government has been there to protect a monopoly, for whatever reason.

The establishment, if we can call it that, meaning the Forest Service, the Bush administration, the Department of the Interior, the Department of Agriculture, NCI and certainly Bristol-Myers are engaged in a disinformation campaign. We have already seen evidence that the Forest Service, NCI and others are going to blame, point the finger at, environmentalists, are going to use the spotted owl crisis and use the yew and dying women as tools to try to gut the Endangered Species Act. The opening rounds have already been fired. Some people have been fooled, including a *New York Times* columnist, largely as a result of a *Wall Street Journal* article[36] which implied that environmentalists were denying cancer victims the drug, which of course is not true at all. In fact the opposite is true. Environmentalists have helped increase the supply of taxol. Nevertheless this campaign to win the hearts and minds of Americans to sanction the repeal of the Endangered Species Act has begun, and I think the owl and the yew and the salmon and the murrelet crises will be used to fuel the fire. The patterns are real clear.

It was on the basis of all these questions and concerns that I called for a Congressional investigation. It is my feeling that only through that process, where records and witnesses can be subpoenaed and people are under scrutiny and oath, can the light of day be shed on this, so we can get to the bottom of it.[37]

"WILL NO ONE UNTIE US?"

Despite the expressed desire to cooperate, obstacles arise in the intricate maze of process between government regulatory and resource management agencies and the entire spectrum of private sector operations, bark collectors and contractors, loggers and private timber companies, chemical extraction plants, drug companies and the public, hospitals, doctors and patients involved in clinical trials and those who are anxiously awaiting clinical trials in 30 other types of cancer. Interaction between these public and private entities has not yet yielded an earnest implementation of programs to get taxol from renewable resources. The need, in a free enterprise economy, for immediate corporate profits has to be, in this case, tempered with caution, for the prime specimens of the last natural stand of yew on earth hangs in the balance along with hundreds of thousands of people who will face certain types of cancer over the next five to ten years.

What we are doing at the moment in the face of this dilemma, ours and the yew's, may well be the worst possible alternative, because it leads to the eradication of prime specimens of a waning species, and for what – only enough taxol to barely whet the appetite of those in need of it, only a fraction of the amount required if we are to test and use taxol to its full potential. The 750,000 pounds of bark that Bristol-Myers Squibb wants to collect this year will effectively wipe out over 250,000 prime yew trees 5 inches in diameter or larger, anywhere near road or trail, severely limiting public access to yew trees.

By conservative estimates, 750,000 pounds of bark could be converted into 25 kilograms of taxol, enough, at 2 grams per treatment, for 12,500 patients. Unfortunately this is also the number of women who die annually from ovarian cancer. What about the advanced clinical trials in lung, breast and colon cancer or the three phases of clinical trials on 25 other types of cancer? It is not prudent for us to waste any material that may contain taxol, or convertible taxanes. To destroy trees capable of producing tons of foliage, over the long haul, for a mere five pounds of bark is to steal from the future. The consequences, in terms of lost lives, trees and opportunities, are unacceptable.

Some expectations are voiced that there might be 10,000,000 pounds of bark out there to get, which might supply 735 pounds of taxol, enough to provide 166,666 treatments (which is one year's deaths from ovarian, lung and breast cancer), but by most counts this is not feasible and it seems to me that the attempt to fulfill it, futile as it may be, puts an unnecessary bounty on large yew trees that could provide a renewable source of taxol. If harvest of bark is allowed from areas that are not clear cut or scheduled to be clear cut, then areas which are protected from clear cutting by legislation may also be pillaged, leaving the skinned yew logs where they fall, unused, beside the wasted limbs and needles.

There is little leeway for error here. What about the other taxanes and compounds that we have yet to discover in this tree? What other types of cancer or disease can be cured? We must stop destroying options now, which may later help to solve the taxol dilemma before we sacrifice yet another species for the blessings it has to offer us.

CHAPTER TWELVE

RENEWABLE SOURCES OF TAXOL

NEED FOR ALTERNATIVES

ALTERNATIVES to bark as a source of taxol should be close at hand, as we shall see, but to develop them will require time and commitment – time, which is running out for the natural species as well as for cancer patients, and the commitment of capital and skill to wage an extensive effort to develop these methods of taxol production from sustainable resources. In order to establish alternatives quickly enough to prevent the destruction of hundred of thousands of large yew trees, certain factors must be brought into play. The most conspicuously absent of these is an open cooperation between public and private interests which would enhance rather than impede coordination between various scientific approaches. In order to develop an adequate taxol production program certain alternatives should be implemented as soon as humanly possible.

Dr. Sterling Ainsworth describes how he thinks the production of cancer treatment drugs from taxanes will ultimately evolve:

> We are in our infancy in all this. This is a rapidly expanding market and there is a lot of room for growth. All that people are talking about at this point is just one taxane, taxol. Yet baccatin III, 10 deacetyl baccatin III, and a number of glycosides could be reduced to baccatin III type compounds. There are many roads that this will take; rarely does the first drug of discovery remain

the most active over the long run in the pharmaceutical field. Usually there is an analogue or derivative of the parent drug that proves to be much more potent and less toxic.

There are seventeen different compounds in bark, most of which can be used in some manner or another because they have the taxane ring. They can be reduced or added to, or the side chain can be cleaved and other side chains can be added. There are a variety of these combinations. An untold amount of work is to be done in the future with analogues. This is just in its infancy, so it's a huge expanding market and it is not time for a monopoly, but just the converse. This is an important drug. Let's expand this. Let's get it into other people's hands and get more companies involved. Let's get universities involved, get the institutes involved, because there is where you expand your knowledge base instantly to help develop an overall process and further scientific understanding.[1]

In the meantime, returning to the dilemma of Pacific yew, many obstacles have arisen to hamper the creation of a coherent taxol production plan. The greatest obstacle is the veil of secrecy, woven by the drives for profit, which makes some who are searching for alternative methods wary of sharing their knowledge. The other major components of a comprehensive taxol production plan are left undone because, for a variety of reasons, the necessary capital resources and corporate commitment has not been forthcoming. Everyone agrees that eventually taxol will be produced from renewable resources (foliage) or by total synthesis, which is still years if not decades away. But the need is urgent, the questions are immediate: what new methods of obtaining taxol will be implemented and when, and what is happening right now to the native Pacific yew trees? The future of a species as well as the future of persons facing cancer hang in the balance. The way we solve this dilemma, if we do, may help us attend to other environmental and social catastrophes that are rising before us now at an alarming rate.

Commissioner Rust sees a continuous resource in the yew tree:

I look at the yew tree as a kind of wondrous, almost magical factory producing at least four taxanes, all of which can be converted into cancer-fighting drugs. The way you obtain these boons from a slow-growing tree like the yew is not to cut it down and remove its thin layer of bark, but to prune its needles in perpetuity. The yew is a prolific resprouter; it will yield dozens of pounds each year. A good big tree will yield some number of dozens of pounds per year. The cumulative harvest of needles from our native stands of Pacific yew could fill the shortfall in foliage resource between now and the time when fast growing, high yield varieties currently being planted begin to produce. Facilities which utilize foliage could be sustained by this natural resource until the cultivated resource comes on line.[2]

PLANTING YEW TREES

The notion of managing yew trees or planting them for practical reasons most likely commenced with primitive humans when they pollarded trees for spears or bow-staves or transported the sacred yews with them as they migrated from place to place. Founders of churches planted yew trees during the dark ages, and medieval reforestation projects began in England when William the Conqueror created the New Forest and the Forest of Dean by decree; both forests have yew trees growing in them today. Monarchs from Henry to Elizabeth commanded that they be planted in churchyards and other public places for a multiplicity of reasons. Dense yew forests such as the one at Kingley Vale or Bow's Hill were planted by archers in the 15th century to provide bow staves for future battles.

As long ago as 1842 John Selby recommended it for reforestation:

> The great value and durable properties of its wood ought also to favour its introduction into our mixed plantations, even where profit is the chief object in view, and we should like to see it supplanting a certain portion of the evergreen coniferae, generally associated with the deciduous trees; for though its progress is slower and a longer time would necessarily be required to bring it to a useful and marketable size, the additional value of its wood, in a great measure, would compensate for the tardiness of its growth. We may further remark that the Yew, thus situated and fostered by the shelter of surrounding trees, would be drawn up and grow much more rapidly and with a cleaner stem than when isolated or standing exposed, and that much also might be effected towards a quicker growth by training the plants when young to a single stem, by eradicating supernumerary leaders, and shortening in the side branches where they appear to be too

rampant or to detract from the nourishment that ought to go to the central stem. When thus planted, with a view to its timber, the yew and the oak, as longest in attaining maturity, ought to remain as the ultimate crop upon the soil, such intermediate occupants as it might be thought necessary to plant along with them, whether consisting entirely of the coniferae or of a mixture of these with other deciduous trees, being gradually thinned out to give sufficient room and air to the survivors. Planted and treated in this way, the number of Yew plants required per acre would be comparatively few, and their cost (a matter of considerable importance when planting upon an extensive scale) moderate, as it would not be necessary to place them nearer to each other than from thirty to forty feet.[3]

If planting yew for reasons of its value as timber seemed feasible in 1842, planting it now by reason of its value as timber and taxol producing foliage would seem to be even more prudent. Although no commercial facility yet exists to extract either taxol or taxanes which are convertible to taxol from foliage, scientists have done it in the laboratory. A switch to foliage would make most Forest Service personnel happier. As expressed by one supervisor:

We strongly support such research, especially if the chemical can be extracted from twigs and needles, rather than having to strip bark from the trees, which obviously kills the tree. With yew being a minor component of the forest, it is easy to envision eradication of the species if the tree has to be killed to produce a few milligrams of taxol. On the other hand, trimming of branchlets will probably stimulate growth of foliage, allowing a continuing and potentially increasing supply of raw material.[4]

ALTERNATIVES TO BARK

Some researchers believe that complete synthesis of taxol will be possible; there are varying estimates of how long that may take, and then how long it would take to scale up from laboratory to commercial production. A news article reports:

Given the scarcity of Pacific yews, [Dr. Bruce] Chabner said, 'the ultimate answer to this is to synthesize taxol.' But the taxol molecule is complex. Intrigued by it as a challenge in organic chemistry, scientists have been trying to synthesize it for 15 years.

But Dr. Charles Swindell, an organic chemist at Bryn Mawr College who has worked on the synthesis, says that molecules just as intricate have recently been synthesized and that he believed taxol would be too.

Even so, the drug would have to be produced in bulk, which would require a variation of the methods used in the laboratory. Taxol, according to Chabner, "is not going to be commercially available through the synthetic route for a while."[5]

French scientist, Dr. Jean-Noel Denis, describes the efforts being mounted:

> The structural novelty of this complex, highly functionalized diterpene together with its exciting therapeutic potential has engendered worldwide a prodigious effort toward its total synthesis. Taxol is quite possibly the number one target today of synthetic organic chemists. The various strategies revealed to date appear, however, to be of little practical value in that even if successful they would probably be incapable of furnishing the natural product in more than trace amounts.[6]

Dr. Robert Holton explains:

> Since 1982, we have been working to develop a synthesis of the taxanes, particularly taxol, and this work has been funded by a grant from the NCI. We reported a short synthesis of the taxane ring system in 1984. In 1988, we reported the total synthesis of taxusin, the simplest member of the taxane family. This is the only total synthesis of any of the taxane natural products. Unfortunately, taxusin does not possess anti-tumor activity.
>
> We are continuing to mount an all out effort, funded by our current National Institute of Health grant, to develop a total synthesis of taxol. Taxol is much more complex than taxusin, and there are several problems which must be solved before the total synthesis of taxol can be realized. It is unlikely that a solution to the short-term (5–10 years) taxol supply problem will be forthcoming in the form of a total synthesis of taxol. It is likely that our total synthesis effort will, in time, provide new taxol-like antitumor agents and a method for their preparation. However, taxol has now undergone at least six years of clinical study and development, and any taxol mimics that would be developed as a result

of our synthetic effort will also have to go through the rigors of the full range of clinical trials and drug development.[7]

There is some activity on other fronts as well, but it is not expected to produce much in the short run unless efforts are stepped up considerably. One program, conducted by Dr. James Linden at Colorado State University, is investigating the possibility of growing taxol-producing *Taxus* cells in fermenters or other biomass reactors.[8]

Donna Gibson and other researchers at the Department of Agriculture's Plant Technology Research Laboratory in New Orleans, have filed for a patent on a technique to grow *Taxus* cells in petri dishes. Now efforts will focus on how to speed up the process by determining optimum growing conditions.[9]

TAXOL FROM NEEDLES

Nearly everyone agrees that the answer to the taxol supply problem for the short-term is to switch to needles. The question is how long are we going to wait and how many yew trees in prime habitat will be cut down in the interim? Scientists have already developed ways to get taxol from needles in the laboratory, as G.I. Kingston and others attest:

> Our approach to the study of taxol has been driven by the concept that its development as a routinely useful drug will require either an improved source of taxol or a simpler but effective analogue. The total synthesis of taxol is a formidable task, and in spite of some outstanding synthetic work, most notably by Holton and his co-workers, it remains an as-yet-unattained goal. The partial synthesis of taxol from the simpler diterpenoid baccatin III has been reported, however, and this approach thus offers in principle a source of taxol from the renewable resource of yew leaves as opposed to yew bark.[10]

Dr. Denis agrees that partial synthesis is a likely solution to the taxol supply problem:

> In the context of a more modest, but potentially quite rewarding program, directed toward a partial synthesis of taxol as well as the preparation of some analogues of taxol, we have developed a highly efficient synthesis of the taxol side chain.[11]

T.BREVIFOLIA NEEDLES

He further describes in another journal:

An efficient partial synthesis of taxol from an easily and permanently accessible taxol congener would provide an attractive solution to this serious supply problem. We report in this communication a direct synthesis of taxol through the successful implementation of such an approach.

10-deacetyl baccatin III can be readily extracted in high yield from the leaves of *Taxus baccata*. It is important to recognize that the yew leaves are quickly regenerated, hence through prudent harvesting large amounts of 10-deacetyl baccatin III can be continually supplied with negligible effect on the yew population. The structural similarity of 10-deacetyl baccatin III to taxol belies, however, the difficulty of effecting the desired conversion.[12]

Taxol and convertible taxanes are not peculiar to the Pacific yew, but have also been found in the following species and varieties that have been tested so far:

T. baccata	T. baccata cv fructoluteo
T. baccata cv barroni	T. baccata cv repandens
T. baccata cv fastigiata	T. baccata cv fastigiata

T. brevifolia	T. mairei
T. canadensis	T. media
T. chinensis	T. media cv densiformis
T. cuspidata	T. media cv hicksii
T. cuspidata cv capitata	T. speciosa
T. cuspidata cv nana	T. wallichiana[13]
T. floridana	

Each of these species or cultivars contains some of the desired substances, many in significant quantities when measured against the amount of taxol which can be extracted currently from bark. To my knowledge, commercial bark extraction processes are not now extracting and stabilizing any of the taxanes that could conceivably be converted to taxol.

Dr. Holton and his team of researchers have found a key to shifting from bark to foliage in the production of taxol; one which may work with other varieties of Taxus, as he explains:

> The partial synthesis of taxol, i.e., conversion of other naturally-occurring taxanes to taxol, does now provide a solution to the short term (5–10 year) taxol supply problem. A French research group has found that the taxol congener 10-baccatin III can be isolated from the leaves of *Taxus baccata* (English Yew) in a yield of 1 gram/kilo. of wet leaves (0.1 percent). This is approximately ten times the yield of taxol isolated from *Taxus brevifolia* [bark]. Yew leaves can be quickly regenerated, and through carefully controlled harvesting, a large and continuous supply of this material will be available.
>
> We have discovered a method for the conversion of 10-deacetyl baccatin III into taxol in approximately 70 percent yield, and this is the subject of patent applications filed by Florida State University since June, 1989. Furthermore, we have demonstrated that a variety of other taxol congeners (cephalomannine, 10-deacetyl cephalomannine, baccatin III, and 10-deacetyl taxol) can be converted to taxol using the method we have discovered. Therefore, it is likely that a crude extraction mixture containing several taxol congeners could be completely converted to taxol, resulting in a highly cost-efficient method for obtaining the drug.
>
> Bristol-Myers Squibb has estimated that the commercial demand for taxol will be in the range of 50–200 kg (110–440 pounds) per year. To obtain this amount of taxol, 1.1–4.4 million

pounds of bark would be needed each year. Obviously, this quantity of taxol cannot be obtained from bark harvests. Alternatively, at the currently estimated yield, this amount of taxol could be obtained from 160,000–640,000 pounds of yew leaves using our process. This assumes that only 10-deacetyl baccatin III would be converted to taxol. We need to seriously explore the practicality of taking a crude extraction mixture and converting a number of the taxol congeners contained therein into taxol. This should reduce the amount of leaves required substantially, and is most likely to provide the ultimate solution to the taxol supply problem.[14]

Dr. Holton elucidates further in a recent interview:

Q: Is the taxol you can produce the same as the taxol they have used against ovarian cancer?
A: Identical, you can't tell them apart.
Q: Is the process that you're using one that can be adapted to commercial production?
A: We hope so, and it looks feasible at this stage. Of course we're in the discovery end; we do very small scale stuff in the lab. Based on what we've done it looks like it should be amenable to commercial production, but that's in the hands of the drug company or a drug company partner.
Q: You do a hand off to Bristol-Myers?
A: That is correct.
Q: And Bristol-Myers in turn allocates someone like Hauser to start gathering samples for them and distilling it?
A: It is their responsibility to allocate somebody to find the best source of the baccatin III and of course then their scale-up development people must develop the synthesis of the other piece and the chemistry for re-attachment on a large scale, with our consultation of course.
Q: Why is it better to use the English yew as opposed to the Pacific yew?
A: I don't think anybody has analyzed *T. brevifolia* for baccatin III. I know some people who have analyzed the bark and I have heard reports that there is no baccatin III in the bark. In terms of the needles, I have not heard precisely what the analysis of the needles is, in terms of baccatin III or taxol content.
Q: How long do you think your process is from achieving commercial viability?

A: I don't know. I can't even guess because that depends on what Bristol-Myers does. Their off-the-cuff estimates are that right up front about 50 percent of the taxol will probably come from this process and 50 percent may come from bark initially, because when they go to market they are going to have to get taxol every way they can. One way is to take the bark and isolate taxol, but in the process of doing that you have stuff left over that has other things in it, which can be chemically converted into baccatin III. So with a little chemistry, baccatin III can be a side-product of the bark extraction and then it can be converted into taxol. That is what they are thinking about in terms of 50 percent initially.

Q: NCI is calling for 750,000 pounds of bark initially for their first introduction, about a year from now.

A: They are not going to make it. Economics are going to drive the search for taxol in the direction of partial synthesis. There's another aspect, and that is that it's been forecast for a long time that taxol is not unique in its properties and that there are probably many other chemicals which will do the same thing, mimic taxol. This really hasn't been investigated because there hasn't been a good way to investigate it. You have to be able to make things that might mimic taxol before you can investigate it. That's one thing our process allows us to do, because as you can synthesize one piece and stick it on to baccatin III to make taxol, you can synthesize similar pieces and stick them on to baccatin III and make things that aren't taxol, but which are similar and as a matter of fact the French group has done this. Their method of putting the pieces together is not good, but they have done it and the French drug company Rhône Poulenc has a compound, which they claim is better than taxol; they call it taxotere.[15]

If it requires 60 pounds of bark to produce two grams, or an average treatment of taxol, then with Holton's process it would require only nine pounds of foliage, which could be taken annually from one tree instead of killing a dozen. According to Holton, it might be possible to develop a process to convert many of the taxanes found in yew needles into taxol, further increasing the yield.[16]

Scientists have isolated several compounds from the bark and needles of the previously named species which can be converted to taxol. Crudely, the method is to extract the baccatin III molecule from these other taxanes, or congeners, and then attach the taxol sidechain

STRIPPED YEW LOGS

to it, forming taxol through partial synthesis.

Some of those convertible taxanes, or taxol congeners, are cephalomannine, baccatin III, 10-deacetyl baccatin III, 10-deacetyl cephalomannine and 10-deacetyl taxol.[17] At this moment these compounds and other taxanes are being wasted; they are not being extracted in the bark extraction process, and the Pacific yew needles are not being gathered from the trees killed for bark.

Bark extraction people claim that it will take up to five years before the conversion to needles can take place, for several reasons, as Neil Jans of Hauser Northwest points out:

> Everyone shares the knowledge and the interest in getting out of bark as soon as possible and into a renewable resource for taxol. We all know that the supply of drugs for ovarian cancer is going to take an awful lot of trees. There are a lot of trees out there, so the near term is not a problem, it's the long term... Bark gives the only source of taxol now for the drug. Basically there are two issues: one is technical, how you actually produce the drug, the other is regulatory, because producing a chemical and a drug are two different things.

There is a range of questions and variables that you have to integrate before you switch to different materials. You have to characterize what your raw material is. How do the growing conditions, genetic variety, variability of the individual trees and season effect the level of taxol. Do you have to freeze it right away to preserve a high level of taxol? The other major question is where do you get your raw material? If you get it from the wild, are there only certain geographic areas, just the south slopes or down by the water? Can you farm to get the material or grow nursery plants and hedges? Do you have to extract right away? You have to be careful, there is a range of issues that needs to be solved in order to change raw materials.

On the technology side, we have to develop a process based on the raw material. What is the composition of the raw material? What is the amount of taxol in it? What is the size of needle that we are looking for?

We can look at the extraction process and the amount of variables in that, the methods we use, the solvents we use and then the downstream processing. The Hauser process uses sixty-eight steps. And at each step you have to tweak and adjust to get maximum yield.

Then once we have got a laboratory to make taxol then we have to get bigger and bigger until we can make kilos of it...you just can't go from a little bit to 20 kilos a month. As you get into large equipment some of the processes used in the laboratory can't be used in larger scale. Sometimes you have to change the process to fit the larger scale.

The drug taxol has got to have a stack of documentation that says it was made by an approved process for producing taxol that the FDA recognizes. It has got to have documentation of the source of raw material, how you clean the room, literally an assay of all the raw materials, the solvents used, what batch, the analytical results; all these things are required. The drug also requires a certain impurity profile...and that profile must be the same, batch after batch after batch. If you go from bark to green stuff, chances are the impurity profile is going to be different and won't match.[18]

NaPro, a new company comprised of a joint venture between Pacific Biotechnology of Seattle and MediMolecules of Boulder, has expressed its intention of building an extraction plant in Oregon which would use needles. Dr. David Carver, president of MediMolecules and CEO of NaPro, commented on the differences in getting taxol from needles rather than bark:

> We isolate substantial quantities of taxol from the leaves and stems at reasonable cost and in good yield. This will provide a renewable supply of taxol.
>
> Our findings have been based strictly on the content of taxol in the leaves and stems. The content of taxol in the leaf does vary significantly depending upon its location and other factors. However, this is true of the bark also. We have found that if you have a tree that has a high content of taxol, then you will have leaf material that is also high in taxol. The converse is also true. One thing that should be noted is that the content of taxol in the leaf is generally around twenty percent or less of the content in the bark. The leaf is a 'lower' grade source of taxol. But, be that as it may, there is still enough taxol in the leaf to isolate it in economical yield. Another factor that needs to be considered is that the impurities that will remain in the leaf taxol at a ninety-nine percent purity level may be different from that found in the bark taxol at its ninety-nine percent purity level. Because of this possibility, the FDA considers the taxols to be different until proven otherwise. In the worst case scenario, the one percent of impurities in the unproven leaf taxol could be extremely toxic and could cause increased deaths when used as a drug. The chances of there being a highly potent poison in the leaf taxol that is not present in the impurity profile of the bark taxol is extremely slight. However, the FDA must consider the worst case, and the leaf taxol will be considered guilty until proven innocent. To prove the leaf taxol safe, there have to be trials and testing performed. Until the results of those trials are finished, the leaf taxol is not considered taxol, the anti-cancer drug.[19]

VARIETAL DIFFERENCES AND CULTIVATION

We know that certain varieties of yew grow faster or larger; some may be hardier and others may produce higher levels of taxol. The task is to find which varieties provide the desired balance of necessary characteristics. In fact, efforts are being made today to investigate the potential of yew plantations in the industrial forest and elsewhere. To this end there are people searching for the right combination of varietal characteristics that can produce taxol or convertible congeners in trees which grow hardily and quickly. In fact most varieties sold in nurseries have been developed from species that are known to contain taxol; it stands to reason that most cultivars would then also contain it. We need to investigate the abundance of ornamental *Taxus* and quantify the tons of foliage that may be available from it. Tests should be run to find out what the yield of taxol might be.

In order to gain some knowledge about the various genotypes of Pacific yew and other *Taxus* species the federal government is beginning to take cuttings and seeds from different locations throughout the region. A recent news article outlines the Forest Service program:

> A Forest Service team headed by forester Jim McGrath is seeking ways to propagate more of the slow-growing yew trees.
>
> No one knows with certainty how much yew is available, but Forest Service managers say the demand will quickly exceed the supply unless taxol can be extracted from other parts of the yew or a synthetic drug can be developed.
>
> In the meantime, McGrath has collected 3,400 yew cuttings from 51 districts in 15 different national forests in the Northwest and planted them in special beds sheltered from the direct sunlight. Each was treated with a special hormone to promote root growth.
>
> 'None of them has sprouted roots yet,' McGrath said. 'But it has been a long cold winter and spring. Roots should begin to form when the days grow longer. But we don't know what to expect. No one in the Forest Service has yet succeeded in propagating yew from cuttings so far as we know.'[20]

Nicholas Wheeler, of Weyerhauser Corporation, outlined the steps he thought were necessary:

> Improving productivity of valued taxanes in *Taxus* species, using traditional plant breeding techniques, requires that the traits of interest are heritable, that variation in these traits occurs amongst populations and/or individuals, that selected individuals can be easily mass propagated and cultivated, and that genotype by environment interactions are understood. Relatively little is known about any of these requirements, but prospects are good that significant improvement opportunities exist. Short-term

improvement approaches concentrate on selection within wild populations or existing cultivars and mass propagation for domesticated cultivation. Long-term approaches relying on breeding and testing procedures would likely reduce risk and increase gain but require more time. Parallel development of both approaches is recommended.[21]

Wheeler suggests that selection within wild populations would be an important factor in producing an optimum cultivar that would grow quickly, hardily and yield high levels of taxol and convertible taxanes. In a recent publication from the Pacific Northwest Research Station:

> Several companies, like Weyerhauser, have taken an interest in marketing the yew. 'For the past three years we have been looking at marketing and producing the yew, 'says Nicholas Wheeler, a geneticist with Weyerhauser. 'We are still determining if it makes sense to pursue commercial production of this tree. We are concerned with producing sustainable quantities of the tree so we don't destroy the stands already thriving.'[22]

Apparently Weyerhauser Company has found reason to continue with their yew project as indicated by Mark Hehnen in a recent news article:

> The Weyerhauser Co., anticipating a need for taxol, began attempts to mass-produce yew four years ago. The idea is to grow the trees as a crop specifically for taxol production.
> Only a few cuttings are taken from wild Pacific yew. The rest are from other varieties, including ornamentals.
> 'We may have to wait another four years for final answers,' Hehnen said, 'but the results so far are encouraging.'
> Hehnen also has had good results with yew seed. About 25,000 seedlings have been produced from seed of the wild Pacific yew in the past year, he reported.
> 'Years ago we saw the dilemma we would all be in,' Hehnen said. 'The supply of Pacific yew is relatively scarce and should be protected. We saw the need to develop domesticated yew plants to meet the demand for yew bark.'[23]

Yet at the moment we are out there cutting down the prime specimens of the wild population. Not only are we destroying the possibilities with every tree that falls, but we are also drastically reducing the amount of available yew foliage, when the time comes for needles. Sixty-five percent of Pacific yews are less than five inches in diameter and more properly called a shrub than a tree. These plants would also be available for taxol production if a switch to needles were made.

BRISTOL-MYERS SQUIBB

Bristol-Myers Squibb indicated at a recent press conference that they want to keep cutting down trees for bark until 1998. They say that they are actively investigating alternative sources and methods to develop additional taxol. Bristol-Myers Squibb issued a statement to the press in late June, 1990, entitled *Taxol Q and A*. In it they attempted to mitigate the impact of cutting millions of yew trees over the next seven years by giving a wildly optimistic estimate in answer to the question of how many yew trees exist in the United States:

> While the exact number of Pacific yew is not known, the United States Fish and Wildlife Service estimates that there are more than 130 million trees in National Forests and large numbers on other public and private lands. Bristol-Myers Squibb is funding a major species inventory survey, as part of its obligations under its Cooperative Agreements with the Forest Service and Bureau of Land Management.

Bristol-Myers Squibb also volunteered an answer to whether widescale harvesting of yew trees might threaten the spotted owl:

> Bristol-Myers Squibb supports efforts to ensure the continued survival of the northern spotted owl. Yew collecting is typically conducted utilizing low-impact methods such as hand-peeling and selective harvesting. Such methods would not normally destroy nor adversely modify the spotted owl's critical habitat.[24]

Critical habitat set-aside areas have a lot of yew trees in them and Bristol-Myers would like to harvest bark there. When asked, they would not say where they got this specious information about the relationship between the northern spotted owl and the yew. In order to obtain a million or more pounds of bark per year for the next five to ten years, they will need access to every yew tree in the Northwest that is over five inches in diameter. At the moment the Forest Service and BLM are proud of the fact that all yew trees are being salvaged from pre-existing timber sales covered by NEPA documentation, but when the pressure builds for more bark, critical habitat areas will be the first place they will look.

Commissioner Rust suggests that Bristol-Myers has been dragging its feet when it comes to developing alternatives:

> Remember the story of the gas company that bought up the carburetor that could get a hundred miles to the gallon? The same thing applies to Bristol-Myers, who has been sitting for at least the last six months on advanced technology which could dramatically increase the supplies of taxol, which could ease the environmental burden on the Pacific yew and which could save thousands upon thousands of lives. But, the manipulation of the market and the suppression of competition is the governing force in this corporation's current policies, and they are acting very rationally from a profit maximization point of view. Unfortunately everyone else is getting hurt.[25]

It does indeed seem that Bristol-Myers has the major elements in its control: the right of first refusal on all yew products (bark and needles) on federal lands, the exclusive right to develop taxol for the commercial market, exclusive access to all NCI clinical data on taxol, patents on partial synthesis and cell culture – all guaranteed by contract with public agencies. Because of this government assisted exclusivity, they control the pace of development as well. Dr. Ainsworth is hopeful, but like the rest of us is watching with a wary eye:

> Others say it appears to be a monopoly, but in effect there may be several reasons why Bristol has chosen to go the way they are now going. We are discussing things with Bristol. We are corresponding with them in hopes that Bristol will work with us. They are working with Polyscience as of a month ago. They are asking for proposals outside of the Hauser connection. It is obvious that there is no exclusivity. Bristol would never, as large as they are, I don't believe, ever get hooked on one supplier. Why? It wouldn't make good business sense. It is certainly not the way large drug companies work.
>
> We want to be part of the American program. We do not want to be part of a monopoly, or even have to fight a monopoly.

That's not ideal, and in fact I don't believe that is NCI's intention. I think it has appeared that way thus far, but I think that there is a lot of alignment. Hopefully that is not the intention. It may be, but we don't know what the CRADA says. Once people understand the CRADA and the legalese, then we will understand why the attitudes have prevailed the way they have.

I could say negative things about the way I see it, but I don't think I should until we see the CRADA. Under the Freedom of Information Act the legislators in Washington will get a copy of it. Congress will get interested in this, because obviously the last thing the government does is to form a monopoly. It's difficult to believe that that is what Bristol-Myers Squibb is doing.[26]

There are definitely other sources of foliage available which are not being utilized. The most promising may be Canadian yew, which grows in the north central and northeastern United States and in Quebec, Manitoba and Alberta. Canadian yew is a hardy shrublike species that produces an abundance of leaves. Its range is larger than that of Pacific yew. I do not know the abundance or distribution of Canadian yew throughout its range, but it is known that taxol and other valued taxanes have been found in it.

URBAN AND SUBURBAN YEWS

There are sources outside the forest as well. A potentially formidable supply of taxol is from the millions of yew bushes, ornamental trees and hedges that grow throughout urban and suburban America. Excerpts from a *New York Times* article hint at the dimensions:

> Early every spring, when it is time to trim back the yews that a previous owner planted to corset the foundation of my house, I rejoice that years ago I ripped many of them out and lament not having exterminated more of them. A basic but neglected principle of gardening is that no garden should have more than one yew, and that it should be placed at a distance from the house and allowed to grow into a handsome tree.
>
> Yews planted as a hedge near windows require regular trimming twice a year, at least. If the chore is neglected, downstairs rooms will be plunged in a twilight gloom all day long. But the chore can be a nasty one. Sometimes a ladder is needed, and there

is always the risk of disturbing a nest of wasps or hornets.

My hometown has not, to my knowledge, adopted an official plant, but if it did it would probably be the yew. English yews, Japanese yews and a multitude of hybrids grow all through the neighborhood. In the spring, yews arrive at the nearest garden center by the truckload. The yew seems to be the emblem of American suburbia, certainly in the Northeast.[27]

Recently quoted in the *Wall Street Journal*, botanist Dr. Ed Croom of the University of Mississippi says:

U.S. commercial nurseries now house some 20 million ornamental yew shrubs, some of which produce taxol in their needles equal to the amounts in *brevifolia* bark.[28]

Many towns on the west coast reveal tendencies similar to the east. Eugene, Seattle, Portland and San Francisco have large populations of urban and residential yews firmly established; in block after block every other house has one or more 30, 40, 50, 75 year old Japanese, Irish, English or some other yew in the front yard, or a hedge or shrub of one or another of over 200 cultivars. Public places, universities, government facilities and especially churches abound with yew trees, hedges and bushes. A nationwide survey should be taken to see how much yew is growing there in urban and suburban America. The cultivated yew population might match, if not surpass, that of the native population. If taxol or convertible taxanes are found in all parts of all species, then surely this resource must be utilized if we are to provide enough taxol to meet the projected need for it. It seems that a way could be found to derive taxol from every bit of yew foliage collected in an annual harvest from a renewable urban and suburban resource.

Dr. Croom, who is currently involved in determining the potential of ornamental *Taxus* cultivars for clinical taxol supplies, summarized his views for a conference on taxol held in Bethesda, Maryland in spring 1990:

American nurseries have propagated and cultivated *Taxus* for landscape use for many years. The genetic parentage of most ornamental *Taxus* in America is *T. baccata*, *T. cuspidata* and the hybrid of these two species *T. x media*. The original report of the biological activity and structure of taxol noted the compound's

T. BACCATA AT THE UNIVERSITY OF OREGON MUSEUM

presence in *T. baccata* and *T. cuspidata* as well as *T. brevifolia*. In addition, the efficient synthesis of taxol from precursors such as 10-deacetyl baccatin III has been reported from the leaves of ornamental *T. baccata*. Clinical supplies must be based on a reliable, sustainable, abundant and economical source. The American nursery industry is the only proven sustainable large scale source of *Taxus*.[29]

The point here is that the amount of taxol that is not being extracted from wasted needles is unacceptable because of the high demand and its extreme scarcity. Every ornamental yew tree, bush or hedge should be considered a living manufacturer of taxol or convertible taxanes. In some ornamental varieties the ratio of leaf material to total mass is ten times greater than in the natural species *T. baccata*, *T. brevifolia* and *T. cuspidata*.

Urban and suburban yews are easily accessible, not in the farthest reaches of the woods, in deep canyons nor on steep mountain sides. They are here among us, where we live; beside a sidewalk, at the end of a driveway, telephone or letter. People, if asked or paid, would give their yew trimmings to help fight cancer. Yew bushes and hedges have to be trimmed at least twice a year and either burned or taken to the dump anyway. If these trimmings were given or sold to foliage

T. BREVIFOLIA IN AN URBAN PARK

collectors on a twice-a-year basis, a large renewable resource could be developed.

We could also plant more yew trees. We've had victory gardens before, why not healing gardens, with yew shrubs, bushes, trees and hedges now? To achieve this and help resolve the current dilemma would demand an unusual level of cooperation between such diverse interests as city, county and state governments, local and national media, service organizations and private enterprise (nurseries, timber companies, foliage collectors, extraction facilities, shipping companies and Bristol-Myers Squibb); also national cooperation between the Bush Administration, Congress, the Departments of Agriculture and Interior, National Institute of Health, National Cancer Institute, hospitals, doctors and patients. As citizens we can further this cooperation, by observing carefully what is going on in the public forests and by working together to stop the killing of yew trees for their five pounds of bark. We can urge all parties, government agencies as well as private enterprise, to get on with the business of obtaining taxol from renewable resources immediately.

Have we lost sight of the future as we spin away from the past? No shamans exchange the eternal yew wood digging stick to insure the abundance of camas for our tribe, no common understanding nor tradition links us with the past. We have grown estranged, have forgotten our tens of thousands of years of reverence for the yew. We have lost our way between hunger and satiety and fallen into avarice. The yew was and is the most significant tree in our culture whether we be Asian, European, or North American, but over the past 150 years this significance has eluded us. The tree has not changed, it is we who have changed, if nothing else in our ability to cut down huge tracts of forest efficiently and on a massive worldwide scale. During our historically brief lapse of consciousness we decimated the Pacific yew population ninefold because it stood in the way of the fir, hemlock, cedar, redwood, spruce and pine harvests. Now it comes back into our consciousness offering yet another crucial tool like a stick to dig camas, or a spear to harvest salmon, or a bow to bring down game or keep an enemy at bay, another tool suited to our times to help us in our struggle to keep death a little further from the door. Our ancestors revered this tree above all others in the forest. Current events would imply that they had good reason; certainly English poets from Chaucer to Eliot thought so.

YEW PROTECTING URBAN PORTAL

PART VI

THE METAPHORICAL YEW

For most of us this is the aim
Never here to be realized;
Who are only undefeated
Because we have gone on trying
We, content at last
If our temporal reversion nourish
(Not too far from the yew tree)
The life of significant soil.

               – T. S. Eliot

CHAPTER THIRTEEN

POETIC IMAGE

OETRY connects all who participate in it through language and time, and through language and time the yew tree eventually came to represent a visual and sensual icon of eternal time. In oral myth and legend, the yew was a prime symbol and metaphor – gleemen, minstrels and bards borrowed its somber visage or funereal tones to bolster the impact of their own songs and rhymes with primal associations of death, mourning and the grave.

Yew trees growing in England amidst churchyard graves were alive long before any of the poets whose images are to be considered here and, in that sense, its very longevity is perhaps its most significant attribute. Allusions to the yew by poets from Chaucer to Eliot have rendered an entire poetic image, drawn from each physical aspect, each use and association. They had much to draw from the yew tree's appearance, which became a paradigm of holy tree. Some focused on its physical characteristics: slow growth, gnarly red trunk and limbs, evergreen boughs, red berries and gold anthers. Others noted its utility, its superiority as wood for longbows, magic wands and rods upon which poems were carved in runic script. Still others mentioned it as poison or its association with funeral rites and graveside offerings, its connection with dead bodies buried at its roots, or ghosts meeting at midnight or sounds of voices leaping from the foliage. Great poets lent genius to the yew's image with flashes from their own visions of immortality.

EUROPEAN OR COMMON YEW

By the 14th century the distinctive yew was an integral part of the churchyard but was declining in the countryside . Geoffrey Chaucer (1340–1400) simply noted the yew's presence in the forest in *Canterbury Tales*, in a list with twenty other forest trees. Eleven of the trees Chaucer mentions are represented in the Irish version of the Celtic Tree Alphabet. The firre was 'ailm', the vowel 'a', which Chaucer places near the beginning of his list. Ew was 'idho', the vowel 'i', which he places near the end of his list. In the order of letters in the Tree Alphabet, fir/ailm/A was first of the vowels and yew/idho/I was the last, but they shared the same station of the year, the winter solstice.

> Ne eek the names that the trees highte,
> As ook, firre, birch, asp, alder, holm, popler,
> Wylugh, elm, plane, ash, box, chasteyn, lynde, laurel,
> Mapul, thorn, bech, hasel, ew, whippel-tree...[1]

Chaucer may have been as interested as his Celtic forebears in the order of trees and the relationships between them. Since the yew was both a vowel tree in the alphabet, and a Chieftain Tree in the annals of Brehon law, it is not surprising that Chaucer mentions it in its proper order. In *Romaunt Of The Rose*, each of the deciduous trees he mentions is included in the Tree Alphabet; ewe is the only evergreen:

> There were elmes greate and stronge,
> Maples, asshe, oke, asp, planes longe,
> Fyne ewe, popler and lindes fayre,
> What sholde I tel you more of it?[2]

DARK APPEARANCE

The yew's distinctive physical features made it an ideal mood enhancer for poetry. Centuries after Chaucer, Abraham Cowley (1618–1667), wrote of the yew tree's mien:

> Beneath a bow'r for sorrow made
> Th' uncomfortable Shade,
> Of the black Yew's unlucky green[3]

Matthew Prior (1664–1721) mentions its evergreen qualities:

> Why the changing Oak should shed,
> The yearly honour of his stately head;
> Whils't the distinguished yew is ever seen
> Unchanged his branch and permanent his green.[4]

William Wordsworth (1770–1850) spent most of his life in Cumbria where yew trees once grew profusely. To this day the yew is still a symbol of the district. Wordsworth, Poet Laureate of England, features several of the yew tree's aspects:

> There is a Yew tree, pride of Lorton Vale,
> Which to this day stands single, in the midst
> Of its own darkness, as it stood of yore:
> Not loath to furnish weapons for the bands
> Of Umfraville or Percy ere they marched
> To Scotland's heaths; or those that crossed the sea
> And drew their sounding bows at Azincour,
> Perhaps at earlier Crecy, or Poictiers.

> Of vast circumference and gloom profound
> This solitary Tree! A living thing
> Produced too slowly ever to decay;
> Of form and aspect too magnificent
> To be destroyed. But worthier still of note
> Are those fraternal Four of Barrowdale,
> Joined in one solemn and capacious grove;
> Huge trunks! And each particular trunk a growth
> Of intertwisted fibres serpentine
> Up-coiling, and inveterately convolved.[5]

The Lorton Vale yew still lives, without its top, which it unfortunately lost in a storm during Wordsworth's lifetime. The citizens of Lorton Vale made a chair from some of the wood from its broken top and presented it to Wordsworth. It sits today as the chairperson's chair in the Cockersmouth Council meeting room.

Of the Four of Barrrowdale John Lowe wrote in 1897:

> This grove of yews in Barrowdale, 'fraternal four', – 'a brotherhood of venerable trees', remained uninjured till 1883 – a natural temple, or, as described by Mr. Stopford Brooke, an 'ideal grove', in which the ghostly masters of mankind meet, sleep, and offer worship to the destiny that abides above them, while the mountain flood, as if from another world, makes music to which they dimly listen. But in the great gale of December 1883, one of them was uprooted; leading branches of the others were wrenched from the main stem, and although three still remain the solemn majesty of the grove is gone.[6]

I went in search of the 'Fraternal Four', but could find neither them nor anyone who knew about them until I came across an octogenarian, long-time resident of Barrowdale, who told me that the 'Four Brethren' as he called them, were finished off by strong winds and high waters in the early 20th century.

Wordsworth blows a soft wind through a forsaken yew to good effect:

> Nay, Traveller! rest. This lonely Yew tree stands
> Far from all human dwelling: what if here
> No Sparkling rivulet spread the verdant herb?
> What if the bee love not these barren boughs?

THE 'FRATERNAL FOUR' OF BARROWDALE

> Yet, if the wind breathe soft, the curling waves,
> That break against the shore, shall lull thy mind
> By one soft impulse saved from vacancy.[7]

Wordsworth suggests that the yew might lend some significance to the breathing wind, that the tree, even though barren and forsaken by bees, might still have some influence on the 'one soft impulse saved from vacancy,' in the mind of the poet.

Samuel Taylor Coleridge (1772–1834) was Wordsworth's friend and spent much time strolling through the yew studded, rocky hills and crags of the Cumbrian countryside where he learned to appreciate the striking appearance of the twisted yew. He hints of ancient altars:

> The Yew tree bursts! Beneath its dark green boughs
> (Mid which the May-thorn blends its blossoms white)
> Where broad smooth stones jut out in mossy seats,
> I rest:—and now have gain'd the topmost site.[8]

Sir Walter Scott (1771–1832), a Scotsman, describes a yew grove which stood near his home:

> But here 'twixt rock and river grew
> A dismal grove of sable yew,
> With whose sad tints were mingled seen
> The blighted fir's sepulchral green:

Seem'd that the trees their shadows cast
The earth that nourished them to blast,
For never knew that swarthy grove
The verdant hue that fairies love;
Nor wilding green, nor woodland flower,
Arose within its baleful bower.
The dark and sable earth receives
Its only carpet from the leaves
that from the withering branches cast,
Bestrew'd the ground with every blast.[10]

Alfred Lord Tennyson (1809–1892) was Poet Laureate of England for over 20 years and enjoyed great popularity in his lifetime. Tennyson studied the yew closely and throughout his work constructed a whole image, one aspect of which was its ominous appearance. From *In Memoriam:*

O not for thee the glow, the bloom,
    Who changest not in any gale,
    Nor branding summer suns avail
To touch thy thousand years of gloom.

Again, in *The Letters*, 'A black yew gloom'd the stagnant air.' In *Orcana*, again the gloom, 'In the yew wood black as night.' In *Amphion* a macabre dance:

Came wet-shot alder from the wave,
    Came yews, a dismal coterie,
Each pluck'd his one foot from the grave,
    Poussetting with a sloe-tree.

SEXUAL CHARACTERISTICS

A more colorful facet of the yew's visage is its sexual characteristics: male and female strobili are usually found on different trees, rarely on the same specimen. John Keats (1795–1828) asks:

Where shall our dwelling be? Under the brow
Of some steep mossy hill, where Ivy Dun
Would hide us up, although spring leaves were none:
And where dark Yew Trees, as we rustle through
Will drop their scarlet berry cups of dew?[11]

Richard Mant (1776–1848), Bishop of the Anglican Church in Ireland for thirty years, minutely describes the yew tree's springtime sexual characteristics, when golden swirls of pollen are blown from the male tree while the female buds are small and green, not to become bright red berries until late summer:

> Nor less curious the mountain yew,
> Which, 'mid its leaves of solemn hue,
> Its sulphur-coloured anthers now,
> In clusters on the dark green bough;
> Here void of cup or blossom fair,
> Exhibits; and at distance there
> Its verdant chalices minute,
> The embryos of its scarlet fruit.[12]

Tennyson evokes the male 'smoke' in *The Holy Grail:*

> Beneath a world-old yew tree, darkening half
> The cloisters, on a gustful April morn,
> That puff'd the swaying branches into smoke.[13]

And in *In Memoriam* he adds the possibility of 'whispers' being 'kindled at the tips' to disturb the imposing gloom, if only for a moment:

> Old warder of these buried bones,
>   And answering now may random smoke,
> Dark yew, that graspest at the stones
>
> And dippest toward the dreamless head,
> To thee too comes the golden hour
>   When flower is feeling after flower;
> But sorrow fixed upon the dead,
> And darkening the dark graves of men –
>   What whispers from her dying lip?
>   Thy gloom is kindled at the tips,
> And passes into gloom again[14]

In another stanza, he empathizes with the fate of female yews beyond the range of distant males:

> Old sisters of a day gone by,
> Gray nurses loving nothing new;

> Why should they miss their yearly due
> Before their time? They too must die.[15]

Matthew Arnold (1822–1888), mentions the berry, 'Under a dark-red-fruited yew tree's shade,'[16] as does George Meredith (1828–1909), 'Threading it with color, like yew berries the yew.'[17]

LONGBOW

The yew is depicted as an imposing presence, sometimes solitary, either male or female, usually old and often associated with rocks, churchyards and graves. Just as in myth and legend, these characteristics were complemented in the poetic image with allusions to the yew tree's utility to man as a wood for weapons, especially the longbow. Chaucer, who lived in the years between the major battles of the Hundred Years War, mentions the 'shetere ew'[18] referring to the longbow, which by his time had come to be a major factor in English warfare.

Between Chaucer and Spenser lay nearly two centuries of struggle between kings with armies armed with yew wood longbows. There was little poetry written down during those centuries, but Edmund Spenser (1552–1599) picked up the theme with a Chaucerian list, 'the Eugh obedient to the benders will,' and testimony to its strength, 'so farre as Ewghen bow a shaft may send'[19] and 'his stiffe armes to stretch with eughen bow.'[20]

Son of a yeoman, William Shakespeare (1554–1616) grew up in a house near the river in Stratford-on-Avon. There is a yew tree there today in the back yard. It is said that a poaching incident provided the impetus for him to flee Stratford for London, where he began his illustrious career. If the tale is true, then he certainly would have known the value of a good yew wood bow.

His references dramatize the many faceted associations the yew held for the Elizabethans. One Shakespearian jewel combines the deadly power of yew as longbow with the poisonous essence of crushed yew leaves smeared on arrow-tips. King Richard II, on the verge of losing the kingdom he had usurped, receives a grim report of general revolt:

Thy very beadsmen learn to bend their bows
Of double-fatal yew against thy state;
Yea, distaff-women manage rusty bills
Against thy seat: both young and old rebel,
And all goes worse than I have power to tell.[21]

Shakespeare further describes yew poison in *Hamlet* when the murdered king's ghost speaks of the part 'cursed hebona' played in his death. Shakespeare, like Marlowe before him in *The Jew of Malta*, called yew poison, 'hebona':

Upon my secure hour thy uncle stole
With juice of cursed hebona in a vial,
And in the porches of my ears did pour
The leperous distilment, whose effect
Holds such an enmity with blood of man
That swift as quicksilver it courses through
The natural gates and alleys of the body,
And with a sudden vigor it doth posset
And curd, like eager droppings into milk,
The thin and wholesome blood. So did it mine,
And a most instant tetter barked about
Most lazar-like with vile and loathsome crust
All my smooth body.[22]

Michael Drayton (1563–1631) continues with the longbow, alluding to its scarcity in England in the early 15th century.

The English archery
     Stuck the French horses
With Spanish yew so strong,
Arrows a cloth-yard long,
That like to serpents stung,
     Piercing the weather:
None from his fellow starts,
But playing manly parts,
And like true English hearts,
     Stuck close together.[23]

Drayton elaborates further, in *The Battle Of Agincourt*, setting the archer's awesome range at 240 yards:

> And boy, quoth he, I have heard thy grandsire say,
> That once he did an English archer see,
> Who shooting at a French twelve score away,
> Quite through the body stuck him to a tree.

Sir Thomas Browne (1605–1682) knew the yew's place in England's history.

> The warlike yewgh, by which, more than the lance,
> The strong-armed English spirits conquered France.[24]

Even peaceful Keats mentions selecting a bowstave:

> Again I'll poll
> The fair-grown yew tree for a chosen bow.[25]

Much later, Arthur Conan Doyle (1859–1930), creator of Sherlock Holmes, reflecting nostalgically on the diminishing size of the British Empire, asks:

> What of the bow?
> The bow was made in England;
> Of true wood, of yew wood,
> The wood of English bows;
> So men who are free
> Love the old yew tree,
> And the land where the yew tree grows.[26]

FUNERAL RITES

Turning to another traditional use of the yew, its evergreen sprigs have been used since the beginning of western civilization in mourning rituals and funeral rites. Beaumont and Fletcher compiled a book of popular songs in 1609 containing, 'Lay a garland on my hearse/Of the dismal yew'[27] Shakespeare mentions yew sprigs, 'My shroud of white, struck all with yew.'[28] John Dryden (1631–1700) paraphrases Chaucer's 'shetere yew' with 'mourner-yew.'[29] Alexander Pope (1688–1744) writes 'With all the mournful family of yews.'[30] William Blake (1757–1827) notes its funereal significance, 'And mournful lean Despair/ Brings me yew to deck my grave.'[31]

Britons, in Druid times, placed the day of the yew on the winter solstice because it was considered one of the most hallowed of trees, and because it was associated with death, an attribute shared with winter. In more recent Christian times, yew boughs were substituted for the biblical palm tree in Palm Sunday processions; ashes remaining from the burned Palm Sunday boughs were used to mark crosses on the foreheads of the penitent on the ensuing Ash Wednesday. Robert Herrick (1591–1674) fixed the day of the yew to be on Easter:

> Let Box now domineer,
> Until the dancing Easter-day,
>   Or Easter's Eve appear.
> Then youthful Box which now did grace,
>   Your houses to renew;
> Grown old, surrender must his place,
>   Unto the crisped Yew.
> When Yew is out, then Birch comes in,
>   And many Flowers beside.[32]

Herrick connects ghosts and yew:

> But now 'tis known. Behold; behold, I bring
> Unto thy Ghost, the 'enfused Offering:'
> And look, what Smallage, Night-shade, Cypress, Yew,
> Unto the shades have been or now are due.[33]

THE GODALMING YEW

Keats warns, 'Make not your rosary with yew berries.'[34] And
Swinburne (1837–1909) mourns for Charles Baudelaire, finding yew
leaves little consolation to the living.

> It is enough; the end and the beginning
>> Are one thing to thee, who art past the end.
> O hand unclasped of unbeholden friend,
> For thee no fruits to pluck, no palms for winning,
>> No triumph and no labor and no lust,
>> Only dead yew leaves and a little dust.[35]

NUMINOUS INTONATIONS

Just as the yew tree grew more complex as a symbol in myth and
legend, so did its poetic image, with the passage of time, become
something larger than the sum total of its many aspects. The yew tree
took on the role of interlocutor between man's incarnate state of being
and the other states to which his imagination might at times be drawn:
his buried body, gray ghost, or wind-blown secrets and immortal soul.
Poison is an aspect of the yew with an obvious relationship to death.
Other associated potions and brews lead through supernatural territory into the province of witches and other beings.

Shakespeare shows a broad knowledge of man's associations with
the yew tree and in *Macbeth* he subtly combines some of its various
nuances. The symbol of the House of Ross is the yew tree. A sprig of
it attached by brooch to the clan hat is an obligatory part of their
uniform. It is Lord Ross who bears the message from his ill-fated king
to Macbeth that he (Macbeth) is to become Thane of Cawdor. But
Macbeth has already received this information by forecast of three
witches. Hecate, Queen of Witches, chides her minions for not
including her more directly in the manipulation of Macbeth's affairs in
order that she might 'show the glory of our art,' which the witches
demonstrate, stirring into their boiling cauldron:

> Gall of goat, and slips of yew
> Sliver'd in the Moon's eclipse.[36]

In *Romeo and Juliet*, the yew tree provokes a dream of the future,
intimating the yew's function in offering a certain permeability in the
sensory wall between time present and time future.

As I did sleep under this yew tree here,
I dreamt my master and another fought,
And that my master slew him.[37]

Others besides Shakespeare sprinkled their poems with magical intonations. Michael Drayton refers to the folk belief that the shade of a yew is poisonous and that in fact few plants grow beneath it. Its associations with the moon, fairies and midnight, sacred to Hecate, must have accorded it great power in potions.

Then sprinkles she the juice of rue
That groweth underneath the yew,
With nine drops of the midnight dew,
    From lunary distilling.[38]

Over a century later, Shelley joins elements sacred to Hecate:

As two gibbering night-birds flit
    From their bowers of deadly yew
Through the night to frighten it,
When the moon is in a fit,
    And the stars are none, or few.[39]

Keats alludes to a fatal but not necessarily poisonous occurrence, perhaps at least a deadly omen.

How a ring-dove
Let fall a sprig of yew tree in his path;
And how he died.[40]

GRAVEYARD YEW

Another aspect or association that underscores the eerier side of the yew's poetic image is its physical attachment to the grave, where our entire western culture has planted it. Shakespeare ties it there in *Romeo and Juliet*:

Under yon yew tree lay thee all along
Holding thine ear close to the hollow ground;
So shall my foot upon the churchyard tread
(Being loose, infirm, with digging up of graves)
But thou shall hear it.[41]

And in *Titus Andronicus*:

> But straight they told me they would bind me here
> Unto the body of a dismal yew.[42]

One venerable yew tree, magnificent even in Shakespeare's time, lives to this day in the churchyard at Stokes Poges in Buckinghamshire. This tree inspired Thomas Gray (1716–1771), poet and history professor at Cambridge, to write these lines:

> Beneath those rugged elms, that yew tree's shade,
> Where heaves the turf in many a mouldering heap,
> Each in his narrow cell for ever laid,
> The rude Forefathers of the hamlet sleep.[43]

Robert Blair (1699–1746) muses on the yew's choice of company in *The Grave*:

> Well do I know thee by thy trusty yew;
> Cheerless, unsocial plant, that loves to dwell
> 'Midst skulls and coffins, epitaphs and worms;
> Where light-heel'd ghosts and visionary shades,
> Beneath the wan cold moon (so fame reports),
> Embodied thick, perform their mystic rounds;
> No other merriment, dull tree, is thine.[44]

William Blake engraved an edition of Blair's poem, in which he featured the 'trusty yew.' Although Blake only mentioned the yew tree by name once in his poetry, his work is filled with gnarly trees, some 'of blackest leaf' and 'berries red.'[45]

Maria Gisborne (1770–1836) reflects on the 'reverend yew' and a thousand burials:

> Nor shall the reverend yew, the sire who held
> His sceptre verdant through the changeful years,
> Unnoticed stand, he has beheld
> Thousands entombed within his shadows;
> For ages past the sobs, the far-fetched groans
> Of parting anguish ere the grave was closed,
> And drunk the mourners tears.[46]

John Webster (1580–1625) was one of the first to point out that the yew might have made corporal gains through its association with the grave – how many bones have these consecrated yews been fed?

> Like the black and melancholy Yew Tree,
> dost think to root thyself in dead men's graves,
> And yet to prosper?[47]

This very physical facet of the yew tree's image reflects the Celtic folktale about the roots growing into the throats of the buried dead to dredge up untold secrets. A recent event in England lends credence to the myth. The Selborne Yew was blown over in a wind storm in January of 1990. In an effort to replant the 1,800 year old tree, citizens of Selborne carefully excavated the hole around its roots in order to trim it of broken parts without causing damage to the graves all around it. Seven sets of bones were partially exposed in the process, the oldest dating back to the 12th century.[48] Occurrences of old yews blowing down like this over the years may have given rise to the folktales and other imaginative embodiments of the 'rude forefathers of the hamlet.' Thus, in the strictly physical sense, each tree does indeed contain parts of the departed buried beneath it. Is it macabre to note that the yew 'has high requirements with regard to mineral nutrition, above all such elements as potassium, phosphorus and calcium'[49] which are, of course, major components of flesh, blood and bones.

CHAPTER FOURTEEN

IMMORTALITY

EMBODIMENT

HE yew tree's fatal applications and its grim but evergreen visage led to its associations with death, graves, ghosts, deities and rituals, until ultimately it became, through a metamorphosis of imagination, a living, working symbol of man's aspirations toward immortality. This function of the yew's poetic image developed through time as poets came to understand what Greek, Roman and Celt took for granted, that the yew was both symbolically and physically connected with the afterlife. Jonathan Swift (1667–1745) describes:

> Description would but tire my muse:
> In short they both were turned to yews.
> Old Goodman Dobson of the Green
> Remembers he the trees has seen.
> On Sundays after evening prayer,
> He gathers all the parish there;
> Points out the place of either yew,
> Here Baucis, there Philemon grew.
> Till once the parson of our town,
> To mend his barn cut Baucis down;
> At which 'tis hard to be believed
> How much the other tree was grieved,
> Grew scrubbed, died a-top, was stunted
> So the next parson stubb'd and burnt it.[1]

Thomas Hardy (1840–1928), who is buried beside a yew tree in Stinsford, Dorset, personalizes the transformation:

> Portion of this yew
> Is a man my grandsire knew,
> Bosomed here at its foot:
> This branch may be his wife,
> A ruddy human life
> Now turned to a green shoot.[2]

And, Hardy again:

> I, these berries of juice and gloss,
>   Sir or Madam,
> Am clean forgotten as Thomas Voss;
> Thin-urned, I have burrowed away from the moss
> That covers my sod, and have entered this yew,
> And turned to clusters ruddy of view,
>   All day cheerily,
>   All night eerily![3]

THE HAUNTED YEW

With these images in mind, it takes only a short mental leap to conjure a world of ghosts gathering around yew trees with dreams and voices rising from the foliage like a thousand whispers.

Ben Jonson (1573–1637) recalls a folk belief that death comes to those who dare to pluck a branch of sacred yew:

> What gentle Ghost besprent with April deaw,
> Hayles me, so solemnly, to yonder Yewgh?
> And beckoning wooes me, from the fatall tree
> To pluck a Garland, fore her selfe, or mee?[4]

Thomas Parnell (1679–1717) animates a yew amidst ravens sacred to Hecate:

> Now from yon black and fun'ral yew,
> That bathes the charnel house with dew,
> Methinks I hear a voice begin;
> (Ye Ravens, cease your croaking din,
> Ye tolling Clocks, no time resound
> O'er the long lake and midnight ground)

THE SHORNE YEW. "WHAT GENTLE GHOST...HAYLES ME...TO YONDER YEWGH?"

It sends a peal of hollow groans,
Thus speaking from among the bones.[5]

Wordsworth raises ominous beings:

Nor uniformed with Phantasy, and looks
That threaten the profane; a pillared shade,
Upon whose grassless floor of red-brown hue,
By sheddings from the pining umbrage tinged
Perennially—beneath whose sable roof
Of boughs, as if for festal purpose decked
With unrejoicing berries—ghostly Shapes
May meet at noontide; Fear and trembling Hope,

> Silence and Foresight; Death the Skeleton
> And Time the Shadow;—there to celebrate,
> As in a natural temple scattered o'er
> With altars undisturbed of mossy stone,
> United worship; or in mute repose
> To lie, and listen to the mountain flood
> Murmuring from Glaramara's inmost caves.[6]

Dr. Leyden implies a sensate being which draws his consciousness closer:

> Now, more I love thee melancholy yew!
> Whose still green leaves in solemn silence wave
> Above the peasants' red unhonoured grave,
> Which oft thou moistened with the morning dew.
> To thee the sad, to thee the weary fly;
> They rest in peace beneath thy sacred gloom,
> Thou sole companion of the lowly tomb!
> No leaves but thine in pity o'er them sigh,
> Lo! now, to fancy's gaze thou seem'st to spread
> Thy shadowy boughs to shroud me with the dead.[7]

INTIMATIONS OF IMMORTALITY

Tennyson harkens to the same sense. Planting the yew trees firmly amongst the dead, he takes a further step and the yew becomes an interlocutor between man's incarnate state of being and other states, of corpse and ghost, to which his imagination might wander:

> Old yew, which graspest at the stones
>   That name the underlying dead,
>   Thy fibers net the dreamless head,
> Thy roots are wrapped about the bones.
>
> The seasons bring the flower again,
>   And bring the firstling to the flock;
>   And in the dusk of thee the clock
> Beats out the little lives of men.
>
> O not for thee the glow, the bloom,
>   Who changest not in any gale,
>   Nor branding summer suns avail
> To touch thy thousand years of gloom;

"THY ROOTS ARE WRAPPED ABOUT THE BONES"

And gazing on thee, sullen tree,
    Sick for thy stubborn hardihood,
    I seem to fail from out my blood
And grow incorporate in thee.[8]

Musing on graves, bones, gloom and his own mortality, the poet feels an impulse to 'grow incorporate' in the tree and, through the tree, in the bones around which its roots wrap. Although Tennyson speaks of a 'dreamless head,' perhaps the impulse that he feels rises from the dead who are connected to the tree. The yew tree's long-lived presence in the churchyard, with its roots curling amongst the dead enables it to be, within the poetic image, a conduit between dead and living.

Thomas Hood (1799–1845) poses a conditional immortality – a tree nymph whose spirit is sustained by a living tree:

Where is the Dryad's immortality?
Gone into mournful cypress and dark yew,
Or wearing the long gloomy winter through
In the smooth hollow's green eternity.[9]

W.B. Yeats (1856–1939) was particularly interested in the relationship between yew, apple trees and immortality. One of his favorite legends was of Baile and Aillinn, lovers deceived by Aengus, God of Love and Poetry. Aengus wanted them to be happy with him in the hereafter, so he tricked each into thinking that the other had already died; heart-broken, they both died:

And poets found, old writers say,
A yew tree where his body lay;
But a wild apple hid the grass
With its sweet blossom where hers was;
And being in good heart, because
A better time had come again
After the deaths of many men,
And that long fighting at the ford,
They wrote on tablets of thin board,
Made of the apple and the yew,
All the love stories that they knew.[10]

Legend tells that the two trees grew entwined together, each top assuming the shape of its respective lover's head. Ages ago the magical trees were cut down by poets and made into sacred wands, upon which all of the love songs of the Irish were carved and taken to the Hill of Tara.[11] Legend also says that branches of the fallen trees jumped immediately together and were inseparable; likewise boards made of their wood clung together. Yeats elaborates:

> Of Baile and Aillinn you need not speak,
> All know their tale, all know what leaf and twig,
> What juncture of the apple and the yew,
> Surmount their bones; but speak what none have heard.
>
> The miracle that gave them such a death
> Transfigured to pure substance what had once
> Been bone and sinew; when such bodies join
> There is no touching here, nor touching there,
> Nor straining joy, but whole is joined to whole;
> for the intercourse of angels is a light
> Where for its moment both seem lost, consumed.
>
> Here in the pitch-dark atmosphere above
> The trembling of the apple and the yew,
> Here on the anniversary of their death,
> The anniversary of their first embrace,
> Those lovers, purified by tragedy,
> Hurry into each other's arms; these eyes,
> By water, herb and solitary prayer
> Made aquiline, are open to that light.
> Though somewhat broken by the leaves, that light
> Lies in a circle on the grass; therein
> I turn the pages of my holy book.[12]

Like dryads, the lovers became trees and when poets felled the trees and inscribed sacred songs on wands cut from them, through a mystical interplay of yew, apple, bones, sinew and language, another aspect of the multi-faceted metaphor for immortality takes shape. Words transmitted through the sacred alphabet, whether communicated by ogham script carved on rods of yew, or letters written on a page, provide the medium through which the 'holy book' carries the undying image of Baile and Aillinn to the poet and through his poem to us.

YEW IN THE WORK OF T. S. ELIOT

The 19th century gave way to an uncertain age; poets, while watching the erosion of empire and the horrors of world war, strove to invent tangible new metaphors for life. Despite the stark horizon and loss of innocence, the yew tree's poetic image continued to evolve. T.S. Eliot (1888–1965) finished *The Wasteland* in 1922. Barren of trees and hope, it set a backdrop of desolation against which the rest of his poetry limned man's struggle for salvation. He made the yew a central figure in his work.

Eliot often continues to develop a metaphor or poetic allusion from one poem to the next. Several of his works, for instance, contain children's hidden laughter or voices rising from the foliage. The rose and the rose garden are also featured with some frequency. Eliot first invokes the yew in *Ash Wednesday*, written in 1930. He had by this time converted to anglo-catholicism. Many critics say that *Ash Wednesday* is a Christian poem, which it probably is, but for Eliot, religion reaches beyond or behind Christianity:

> The silent sister veiled in white and blue
> Between the yews, behind the garden god,
> Whose flute is breathless, bent her head
>   and signed but
>   spoke no word
>
> But the fountain sprang up and the bird sang down
> Redeem the time, redeem the dream
>
> The token of the word unheard, unspoken
>   Till the wind shake a thousand whispers from
>   the yew
> And after this our exile.[13]

The 'silent sister' calls to mind several feminine entities. Dante directs his supplications to Beatrice. The Virgin Mary's colors are white and blue. But 'bent her head and signed,' evokes a Druid priestess, perhaps even Sulis, a local Celtic semi-deity associated with the springs at Bath. Blue was a color sacred to the Druids and they were adept at sign language. 'The garden god' is an incarnation of the sun-king, Pan or Priapus, whose silent flute is breathless, which may mean, no longer

"THE SILENT SISTER BENT HER HEAD AND SIGNED"

effective. The silent sister, whether Mary, Beatrice or Sulis is ultimately an incarnation of the Great Goddess whom Eliot places 'behind the garden god,' because she came so long before him. Later in *Ash Wednesday,* Eliot stations her between the yews again and asks:

> Will the veiled sister between the slender
> Yew trees pray for those who offend her
> And are terrified and cannot surrender
> And affirm before the world and deny between the rocks
> The desert in the garden the garden in the desert
> Of drouth, spitting from the mouth the withered apple-seed
> O my people.[14]

The silent or veiled sister stands between the yews, where the mystical, yet significant action of the present moment, the conduction of the message or impulse from consciousness to consciousness, must take place. If the present moment 'between the slender yew trees' is the plane of life and 'Till the wind shake a thousand whispers from the yew' is the span of it, then the silent or veiled sister must indeed be standing in the field of life. Each yew then would define the limits of life on earth, but each would also be an entry into what lies beyond life; one into the past; the other, through death, into the future. Religion, born of experience at that fateful moment in the first garden, had become for Eliot and the modern masses a 'withered apple-seed,' which he contrasts here with living yew trees and all that they represent. Eliot, according to his biographer, Peter Ackroyd, confided to John Haywood in 1930 that 'the yew trees of the poem were in fact remnants from two or three of his dreams:'[15]

> This is the time of tension between dying and birth
> The place of solitude where three dreams cross
> Between the blue rocks
> But when the voices shaken from the
>   Yew tree drift away
> Let the other yew be shaken and reply.[16]

'Between dying and birth' is after or before life, on the other side of the yew trees rather than between them. This is the province of Hecate, who can be called from her dominion beyond human ken to places

"BUT WHEN THE VOICES SHAKEN FROM THE YEW TREE DRIFT AWAY..."

where three roads cross. Yew trees are her temples. The profound hope expressed in this plea, the dynamic action requested, is that the silent sister cause 'the other yew' to 'be shaken and reply.' This is what the poet, supplicant, pleads for – that there be communication between the yews, not only exchanges of whispers in the plane of life or present moment, but also between what is on the other side of each yew, past and future moments.

Eliot took up the yew again in *Four Quartets,* published in 1943. Although each *Quartet* was written and published separately, they were, it occurred to him, meant to go together.[17] *Four Quartets* pictures an intimate juncture between the yew and the mortal body based on images rooted deeply in the past. Each poem takes its title from a physical place; each is relevant to a particular way of looking at time passing. The yew imagery begun in *Ash Wednesday* is more fully established in *Four Quartets* and indeed helps Eliot to utter his final poetic statement on human mortality and what may lie beyond. The yew appears, obliquely unnamed, in *Burnt Norton,* the first *Quartet,* written in 1935:

> The dance along the artery
> The circulation of the lymph
> Are figured in the drift of stars
> Ascend to summer in the tree
> We move above the moving tree
> In light upon the figured leaf
> And hear upon the sodden floor
> Below, the boarhound and the boar
> Pursue their pattern as before
> But reconciled among the stars.[18]

The 'We' that moves is the entire human experience including the collected whispers of the dead mentioned in *Ash Wednesday.* The 'moving tree' of *Burnt Norton* is above 'the boarhound and the boar.' In an earlier poem, *Animula,* we find 'Floret, by the boarhound slain between the yew trees,' which would seem to indicate that 'the moving tree' might be thought of as a yew.[19] In *Burnt Norton* 'We' are situated above the 'moving tree' looking down on what is happening to Floret, who, like the 'silent sister' of *Ash Wednesday,* is found on the ground between the yew trees. This affirms what Eliot began with the yew trees in *Ash Wednesday,* that 'between the yews' represents life in the here and now. Floret lost his life 'between the yews,' but while the 'silent sister' is there 'between the yews' the living poet can reach her with his supplications and, more importantly, the dead (through the yew trees) can also reach her, and through her the connection with past and future is made in the present.

Further in *Burnt Norton,* Eliot establishes a direct connection, as have other poets, between the yew tree and those of 'us' buried beneath it:

> Time and the bell have buried the day,
> The black cloud carries the sun away.
> Will the sunflower turn to us, will the clematis
> Stray down, bend to us; tendril and spray
> Clutch and cling:
> Chill
> Fingers of yew be curled
> Down on us? After the kingfisher's wing
> Has answered light to light, and is silent, the light
>   is still
> At the still point of the turning world.[20]

The action shifts from the tendril and spray above ground, through the incantatory magic of the one-word line, 'Chill,' to 'Fingers of yew,' cold roots 'curled down' into the throats of 'us.' These lines are not cheerful but they hold a glimmer of hope compared to the utterly hopeless lines written eighteen years earlier in *The Wasteland*:

> What are the roots that clutch, what branches grow
> Out of this stony rubbish? Son of man,
> You cannot say, or guess, for you know only
> A heap of broken images, where the sun beats,
> And the dead tree gives no shelter, the cricket no relief,
> And the dry stone no sound of water.[21]

Or these chilling lines from the *Fire Sermon,* also from *The Wasteland*:

> The river's tent is broken: the last fingers of leaf
> Clutch and sink into the wet bank. The wind
> Crosses the brown land, unheard. The nymphs are departed.[22]

Then, the nymphs or dryads were gone, the trees were broken, the brown land uninhabited and no whispers were in the wind. Against this devastation, the alternative that living 'fingers of yew' could 'curl down on us,' 'at the still point of the turning world,' hints of possibilities, connections. In the final section of *Burnt Norton*, Eliot glimpses or hears the other end of the process:

> Sudden in a shaft of sunlight
> Even while the dust moves
> There rises the hidden laughter
> Of children in the foliage
> Quick now, here, now, always –
> Ridiculous the waste sad time
> Stretching before and after.[23]

Throughout Eliot's work children's voices rise up out of time past through the foliage into time present. To coax the whispers from the past into the present is a function of the yew within the poetic image of immortality. By curling its roots down into the throats of the past to retrieve the whispers and then by bringing them up through the trunks into the limbs and the foliage, the yew makes it possible for the whispers to be shaken loose for those with ears to hear. Through the silent sister's grace and the wind which blows from yew to yew, the buried dead are connected, not only with each other in the past, but with the present and future as well.

In *East Coker*, the second of the *Four Quartets*, written in 1940, Eliot incorporates a personal association by using the words of his ancestor, Sir Thomas Elyot, who lived in East Coker, Somerset, in the 16th century:

> In that open field
> If you do not come too close, if you do not come to close,
> On a summer midnight, you can hear the music
> Of the weak pipe and the little drum
> And see them dancing around the bonfire
> The association of man and woman
> In daunsinge, signifying matrimonie—
> A dignified and commodious sacrament.
> Two and two, necessarye coniunction,
> Holding eche other by the hand or the arm

> Which betokeneth concorde. Round and round the fire
> Leaping through the flames, or joined in circles
>
> Rustically solemn or in rustic laughter
> Lifting heavy feet in clumsy shoes,
> Earth feet, loam feet, lifted in country mirth
> Mirth of those long since under earth nourishing
> the corn.[24]

Eliot's evocation of ancestral words demonstrates the immortality of literature, which works in much the same way as the yew tree to keep words and whispers from the past alive. It was from East Coker that Andrew Eliot departed for America in the late 17th century, and it was to East Coker that T.S. Eliot returned, once in 1937 and for good in 1965.[25] At his request his ashes were interred in the Parish of St. Michael's Church in East Coker, Somerset. His epitaph is: 'In my beginning is my end' and 'In my end is my beginning,' the opening and closing lines of *East Coker*. The village of East Coker in Somerset is very near the headwaters of the Yeo River, two miles south of Yeovil.

If there were left any doubt about the yew tree's role in Eliot's work as the connection between the individual and immortality, it is dispelled with lines from *Dry Salvages*, the third *Quartet*, written in 1941:

> For most of us this is the aim
> Never here to be realized;
> Who are only undefeated
> Because we have gone on trying
> We, content at last
> If our temporal reversion nourish
> (Not too far from the yew tree)
> The life of significant soil.[26]

The body or ashes begin transformation into dust within range of the roots. The poet is content for his temporal remains to be buried near a yew tree in consecrated ground, as any Christian might, but in the framework of his poetic image the yew tree's consecration runs much deeper than that, and would also embrace a desire, a hope that his whispers too would be brought up through the yew to be blown by the wind to another yew and that indeed, the other yew would be shaken and reply.

THE YEW AND THE ROSE

Eliot's last incorporation of the yew into his design of immortality
is a reconciliation between the fleeting moment of the rose and the
long-lived yew, often contrasted by other poets. Henry Vaughan
(1622–1695) knew the time of the yew to be winter and the time of the
rose to be spring:

> Twist not my cypresse with your bays,
>   Or roses with my yewgh;
>
> Go, go seek out some greener thing,
>   It snows and freezeth here;
> Let nightingales attend the spring,
>   Winter is all my year.[27]

Matthew Arnold epitomizes the funereal aspects of the yew, opposite red roses and lilies:

> Pluck no more red roses, maidens,
> Leave the lilies in their dew –
> Pluck, pluck cypress, O pale maidens
> Dusk, oh, dusk the hall with yew![28]

And from Arnold the opposite plea:

> Strew on her roses, roses.
>   And never a spray of yew!
> In quiet she reposes;
>   Ah, would that I did too![29]

Eliot names the last of the *Four Quartets* after a utopian religious
community to which Charles I retired briefly after losing in battle to
Cromwell in the English Civil War. Soon after, Charles was captured
and beheaded. The community of Little Giddings was decimated by
the victorious Roundheads but was rebuilt in the 19th century. Eliot
made a pilgrimage there in the spring of 1936.[30] In *Little Gidding*,
written in 1942, he mentions the long-lived yew for the last time:

> The moment of the rose and the moment of the yew tree
> Are of equal duration. A people without history
> Is not redeemed from time, for history is a pattern
> Of timeless moments. So, while the light fails

On a winter's afternoon, in a secluded chapel
History is now and England.[31]

With his words and art, Eliot comes close to creating a symbol of our human desire for salvation by declaring the 'moment of the rose and the moment of the yew tree are of equal duration.' He bends the arc into a circle, spinning at once through past, present and future. Like a master ollave he uses the strength of the yew tree's mythic and poetic associations to enliven his own design of immortality, polishing images from impulses more rudely struck in the days before ever a poem was carved on wands of yew.

THE YEW AND THE ROSE

Dylan Thomas (1914–1953) takes up the rose and, casting an aye for Eliot's notion, states the conviction that he, as man or poet, depends on roots:

> The force that through the green fuse drives the flower
> Drives my green age; that blasts the roots of trees
> Is my destroyer.
> And I am dumb to tell the crooked rose
> My youth is bent by the same wintry fever.[32]

More recently, Sylvia Plath (1932–1963) voices a view contrary to Eliot:

> The yew tree points up. It has a Gothic shape.
> The eyes lift after it and find the moon.
> The moon is my mother. She is not sweet like Mary.
> Her blue garments unloose small bats and owls.
>
> I have fallen a long way. Clouds are flowering
> Blue and mystical over the face of the stars.
> Inside the church, the saints will be all blue,
> Floating on their delicate feet over the cold pews,
> Their hands and faces stiff with holiness.
> The moon sees nothing of this. She is bald and wild.
> And the message of the yew tree is blackness—
> blackness and silence.[33]

In another work, Plath hears and sees more specific silences:

> The yew's black fingers wag;
> Cold clouds go over.
> So the deaf and dumb
> Signal the blind, and are ignored...
>
> ...He could hear Beethoven:
> Black yew, white cloud,
> The horrific complications.
> Finger-traps—a tumult of keys.
>
> Empty and silly as plates,
> so the blind smile.
> I envy the big noises,
> The yew hedge of the Grosse Fuge.

Deafness is something else.
Such a dark funnel, my father!
I see your voice
Black and leafy, as in my childhood,

A yew hedge of orders,
Gothic and barbarous, pure German.
Dead men cry from it.
I am guilty of nothing.

The yew my Christ, then.
Is it not as tortured?[34]

Perhaps for Plath neither the yew nor Christ could serve as a path to immortality. There are no roses here, no whispers in the 'silence' of the yew, but only a sense of impending doom.

Robert Graves (1895–1985) tells much about the yew tree's associations with other trees, the alphabet and the Goddess herself. His perception of the yew as an image of immortality depends on its ancient relationship with the fir, where in the Celtic Tree Alphabet, they share the winter solstice as their station of the year. Together, fir, tree of birth, and yew, tree of death, form a metaphor for immortality:

Fir, the womb of silver pain,
Yew, tomb of leaden grief—
Viragoes of one vein,
alike in leaf—
With arms up flung
Taunt us in the same tongue:
'Here Jove's own coffin-cradle swung.'[35]

Just as 'the moment of the yew and the moment of the rose are of equal duration,' so are the yew and the fir necessary for 'Jove's own coffin-cradle' to swing, remaining an appropriate symbol for us, who created Jove, to contemplate today. In the widening spiral of environmental degradation that threatens our very existence today, the yew tree stands out as a symbol of the past errors we have made as well as of the choices we must make for the future. What more apt symbol could there be than a 200,000,000 year old species of tree, sacred to the earliest civilizations both east and west which continues even to this day to help us battle our greatest enemies.

AFTERWORD

by Jerry Rust

I distinctly remember, as a treeplanter, walking across units where oftentimes there would be a big long yew tree lying across a swale and it was handy to walk on the yew log to get across. The yew bark would sometimes slip off, but when it was a nice gray buckskin yew log you could just sink your caulks right into it and walk across. It would always be solid no matter how old it was. That was when I began wondering about the utter waste of these two or three hundred year old trees.

Then later on I went directly from treeplanting into politics, using slices of yew branches as campaign buttons in 1976 and 1982. In 1984, I called for an end to the export of raw yew logs, and then in 1990 I helped start the Native Yew Conservation Council (NYCC). That effort was a direct response to the National Cancer Institute's symposium on taxol in June 1990, in which it became very apparent that none of the alternatives for developing taxol was going to be assertively pursued. I called for the formation of the NYCC at that time because it was clear to me that if making taxol out of yew bark was to be the only game in town, then the Pacific yew was going to take a terrific beating.

It still is.

I regret having to confine my comments on the yew tree to its current political situation in the Northwest, when in fact I have a feeling for the yew tree's mythical and historical connections, for Robin Hood, Merlin, T.S. Eliot, and am a student of its use as wood for utensils and sculpture, and its long medical tradition with our forebears. These antecedents point us in the direction of a solution to the modern conflict over its use.

The first thing I think we need to realize is that the yew tree dilemma is bound up in the ancient forest issue of the Northwest. The dominant management policy of the federal government and industrial forestry is clear-cutting. This is anathema to not only the yew tree, but at least also to the spotted owl, the marbled murelette and the salmon, all of which have been proposed for listing as threatened or endangered species in the Northwest. All are sensitive species. The web of life in the Northwest is starting to come unravelled, as some have predicted. If we want to reverse the process we are going to have to move to selective harvesting. It will take a lot of restorative forestry to allow these forests to grow back their canopy. The yew has been forced to retreat so dramatically; we ought to propagate and plant a hundred million yew trees in the riparian zones and on the edges of riparian zones and wherever there are residual populations of yew. We have got to have a commitment to that.

The second thing we have to do is construct appropriate socio-political policies. We need to force the Forest Service, Bureau of Land Management, Bristol-Myers Squibb and the National Cancer Institute into a rapid transition before the last of the sexually mature Pacific yews are eliminated. We have to force them to utilize needles instead of bark. This is an economic and political issue. There are no technological barriers to making this transition. The economic benefits of switching to needles can hardly be overestimated; it will create many immediate and long-term jobs in pruning trees and bushes, collecting foliage for taxol recovery, collecting berries and cuttings for propagation, raising seedlings in nurseries and ultimately planting them in the forest.

The third thing we need to do is develop market niches for the yew wood itself. As it's being cut down, we have seen deplorable situations in which most of the last prime stands of yew trees are being wasted and left to burn or eventually rot. The logs are not being sawn and coated on the ends to prevent cracking. In addition there has been very little work done in the way of developing markets for it. It is prime wood for musical instruments like lutes, flutes, guitars, violins, specialty items like bows, both the longbow and reproductions of the Native American bows, and for other uses such as carving and sculpture. This is a world class sculpture wood, some say it is the finest. It has always been a great mystery and disappointment to me that we have not developed this wood as we have done with myrtlewood, especially on the southwestern Oregon coast. Myrtlewood products are recognized throughout the world.

Finally, the fame of the yew tree is again being spread far and wide. Why not promote the mystical, spiritual qualities of the ancient forest and the ancient yew trees, so that people will come to see our old groves and famous yew trees, as they do in England?

YEW TREES LARGER THAN 20 FEET IN CIRCUMFERENCE IN ENGLAND AND WALES

In 1664 John Evelyn wrote a tract on forests and in it mentioned several ancient yews, all of which have disappeared. In 1897 John Lowe compiled a list of yew trees in Britain which were on record as being over ten feet in girth. Of those more than 300 yews thirty were larger than thirty feet. In 1946 Vaughan Cornish published a book which updated and added to Lowe's list. In 1983 I travelled to England and saw several of these old trees for myself. In 1990 I corresponded with a number of individuals throughout Great Britain and managed to get updates on 75 trees which were on Lowe's original list. There are today several hundred venerable old trees found primarily in churchyards throughout England and Wales. For perspective, although not extremely accurate, size can be a measure of age. It seems reasonable to me to consider a yew tree twenty feet in girth to be approximately 1400 years of age. This places the time of birth of such a tree within a couple of centuries of the Romans' departure from Britain. Christianity had been introduced, but the remnants of the old Druid ways were abundant. Trees that are thirty feet in girth and larger, by my estimate would be 2200 years old, which means of course that they preceded the churchyards that they now grace.

PLACE	TOWN	SIZE/STATUS	REFERENCE*
	BERKESHIRE		
St. Michael, All Angels	Sunninghill	Fluted trunk a wreck	C
	Hampstead Marshall	47' at ground in 1897. Gone	L
St. Mary	Bucklebury	27' at 3'	L,C
	BUCKINGHAM		
Saint Nicolas Church	Hedsor	27' at 3' in 1897	L,C
	CARNARVON		
St. Judclyd	Penmachno	Great yew now gone	C
	DENBIGH, WALES		
All Saints	Gresford	29' 6" in 1961. 2000 years	S,L,C,B
	CUMBRIA		
Four Brethren	Barrowdale	Gone. Immortalized by Wordsworth 1803	L

* BOOKS: B – Berral; C – Cornish; Ce – Cecil; H – Hadfield; L – Lowe; T – Thomas; W – Wright; Y – Hartzell & Rust. CORRESPONDENCE: 1 – Ron George; 2 – John Allen, Vicar of Sidbury, retired; 3 – Rev. J.W. Hurrell; 4 – C.H. Gilson; 5 – Sir Guy Fison; 6 – Peter Ryan; 7 – J. Rennie; 8 – Rev. M. Coppen; 9 – Rev. G.B. Waghorn; 10 – Prebendary John Davies; 11 – E.A. Bateson; 12 – Rev. J.G. Williams; 13 – E.H.T. Ridger; 14 – Mrs. S.A. Darke; 15 – George Dockrell; 16 – Rev. Tim Hatwell; 17 – Rev. David Clark; 18 – Lt. Col. J.R.V. Thompson; 19 – P.E. Norton; 20 – Rev. G.B. Waghorn; 21 – Rev. Peter Judd; 22 – Co, John Elgar; 23 – Rev. M.K. Sparrow; 24 – Rev. G.C.H. Watson; 25 – Richard Macdonnell; 26 – J.W. Fryer Churchwarden; 27 – Rev. Hugh Pruen; 28 – Rector Canon David Partridge; 29 – Rev. Roger Hodgson; 30 – Rev. J.G. Collins; 31 – Rev. Donald A. Johnson; 32 – Jill and Peter Drury; 33 – John F. Smith. YTC – The Yew Tree Campaign (England).

PLACE	TOWN	SIZE/STATUS	REFERENCE*
St. Cuthbert	Lorton Vale	23' 10" in 1897 Immortalized by Wordsworth	L,C,W,1
St. Ninian	Brougham	Cut down recently	C
Holy Trinity	Mardale	Church surrounded by old yews	C
DERBYSHIRE			
St. Helen	Darley Dale	32' 10" at 5' in 1897 2,000 years, female	L,C,B
St. Edmund	Allestree	27' in 1946	L,C
DEVON			
All Saints	Budleigh East	There in 1686	C
St. John, Wilderness	Withycombe	30' at ground, a stock in 1946	L,C
St. Peter and St. Giles	Sidbury		C, 2
	Dartington	25' in 1946	C
DORSET			
	Woolland	31' 4" in 1936	C,B
GLOUCESTER			
St. Mary Virgin	Forthampton	26' in 1839. Gone in great gale of Jan. 1839	C, 3
St. Thomas à Becket	Moreton-in-Marsh	20' 6" at 5'	C,4
WALES			
St. Michael & All Angels Tintern Abbey	Gwent	18' in 1946	L,C
HAMPSHIRE			
All Saints	Dibdin	30 feet at 3' 1897. Gone	L,C
St. Botolph	Hardham	21 feet in 1835. Gone	L,C
All Saints	Farringdon	30 feet, a ruinous tree	C
St. Mary	Newton Valence	Hollow tree in '46	C
St. Mary	South Hayling	33' 6" in 1961 Over 1,000 years	L,C,B,W
St. Mary	Breamore	30' in 1897	L,C
All Saints	Long Sutton	26' in 1946	L,C,5
St. James	Woodcott	28 feet	C
St. Mary	Selborne	27' 9" in 1965. Blown over and replanted in 1990	L,C,B,W,6
St. Thomas	Bedhampton	20' 4" at 3' in 1897. (2) each 20'	L,C,7
All Saints	Steep	19' 8" in 1897. 1,000 years	L,C
St.Peter	St. Mary Bourne	21' in 1990. Several yews	C,8
Holy Cross	Durley	1,500 years (YTC)	C,9

PLACE	TOWN	SIZE/STATUS	REFERENCE*
	HEREFORD		
	Kyre Park	30' in 1897	L
St. Peter	Peterchurch	31'	C,10
St. James	Stanford Bishop	31' at 7'. St. Augustine sat beneath it	C,W,11
St. James	Cradley	(2) each 26' in 1946. 1200 years (YTC)	C, 12
St. Mary	Cusop	31' in 1990. 1,000 years	C,13
St. Mary Magdalene	Hereford	Fine hollow yew in 1946	C
St. Bartholomew	Marcle Much	1,500 years. Hollow	C,W,12
	HERTFORD		
St. Augustine	Broxbourne	19' 3" at ground in 1897	L,C
	KENT		
	Harrietsham	30 feet at 3' in 1897. Gone	L, 14
St. Mary Blessed Virgin	Brabourn	58' 6" in 1664 . Gone	E,L,C
All Saints	Ulcombe	35' 2" at 3' in 1897	L,C,B
St. Nicholas	Leeds, Maidstone	30' 9" in 1961. A shell	L,C,B
St. Andrew	Buckland-in-Dover	24' in 1897. Moved, 1880	S,L,C,W,9
St. Mary	Thurnham	24' in 1946	L,C
St. Peter	Bredhurst	21' 6" at 3' in 1897	L,C
St. Mary Virgin	Stowting	(2) 20' and 22' in 1946	L,C
St. Mary Blessed Virgin	Lamberhurst	24' in 1897	L,C
St. Peter and St. Paul	Shorne	17' in 1897. (2)	L,C,15
St. Mary Virgin	Speldhurst	18' 6" in 1897. Top broken	L,C
St. Martin	Detling	19' in 1946	L,C
St. Peter and St. Paul	Cudham	(2) 30' female and 26 '10" male in 1990. 2,000 years	L,C,B,16
St. Mary Virgin	Stanstead	26' in 1946	L,C,17
	Petham	23' 1" in 1897. Hollow	L,18
Capel Churchyard	Tudeley	24' at 2' in 1990. Barely alive	L,W,19
St. Mary	Northiam	18' 6" at 3' in 1897. Hollow	L,C
	MIDDLESEX		
St. Mary Blessed Virgin	Staines	30' 9" at 3'. Gone "Ankerwyke Yew"	L
Parish Church	Harlington	24' in 1990 Damaged in 1959	S,L,D,C, 20
	MONMOUTHSHIRE		
	Bettws Newydd	30' 6" in 1897	L,C
St. Peter	Goytre	(2) largest 32' 4" in 1897	L,C
St. Faith	Llanfoist	(2) largest 32' in 1897	L,C
St. David	Llanthewy Bach	34' in 1946, hollow	L,C
St. Iltyd	Mamhilad	31' in 1959	S,L,C,B

PLACE	TOWN	SIZE/STATUS	REFERENCE*
	MONTGOMERY		
St. Cadfan	Llangadfan	Gone	C
	MERIONETHSHIRE		
St. Illtyd	Llanelltyd	(2) Largest 21' in 1946	C
	OXFORDSHIRE		
St. Mary Virgin	Iffley	25' at ground in 1897 Trunk a shell	S,L,C, 21
St. Mary Virgin	Adderbury	Mentioned in 1656. Still there	C
	SHROPSHIRE		
Church Preen	Wantock Abbey	40' 5" at ground in 1897 1,000 years. Druid site	L,C,B,W
St. Mary	Ashford Carbonell	(5) over 20'	C
St. John the Baptist	Hope Bagot	24' in 1990. 1,600 years (YTC) Well cures sore eyes	C, 22
Norbury Park	Norbury	Druids grove	L
	SOMERSET		
St. Michael & All Angels	Dinder	31' at 3'	L,C
Holy Trinity	Abbots Leigh	27' at 3' in 1946	L,C
St. Andrew	Compton Dundon	1,000 years	C
St. John the Baptist	Midsomer-Norton	Branches form 145' circle	C, 23
St. Augustine	Monkton West	(2) Largest 24' in 1946	C
Kingston St. Mary	Broomfield	24' 4" in 1897. Damaged 1990	L,C,24
St. Michael	Creech St. Michael	18' 10" at 3' in 1897	L,C
St. Mary Virgin	Portbury	(3) Largest 20' in 1946	L,C
St. John the Baptist	Churchill	Large ancient yew	C, 25
St. Leonard	Marston Bigott	23' in 1946	C
	STAFFORDSHIRE		
St. Michael & All Saints	Trentham	33' 6" at ground in 1897	L,C
	SURREY		
St. George	Crowhurst	30' 3" in 1959 Hollow 4,000 years (YTC)	
	L,C,B,W		
St. Peter	Hambledon	31 in 1959, hollow	L,C,B
St. Peter	Tandridge	33' 3" in 1959. Widest umbrage in England	L,C,B
St. Peter and St. Paul	Albury	22' at 3' in 1897	L,C
St. Giles	Ashstead	18' at ground in 1897	L,C
St. Mary Blessed Virgin	Addington	18' 6" in 1913	L,C
St. Margaret	Chipstead	1,000 years	C
St. Michael & All Saints	Dunsfold	23' in 1946	C, 26

PLACE	TOWN	SIZE/STATUS	REFERENCE*
	SUSSEX		
	Bognor Regis	Gone in gale of Oct. 1987	
		600 years old	C,27
St. Thomas à Becket	Warblington	30' at ground in 1897	L,C,28
All Saints	Hurstmonceau	30' at 3'. Compound tree	L,C
St. Giles	Cold Waltham	31' 3" at 3' hollow but vigorous	L,C,29
St. Margaret, Queen	Buxted	31' at five feet. 1,000 years	L,C,
St. George	Crowhurst	27' 9"in 1965. Fine female tree	L,C,B,W
St. James	Stedham, Midhurst	28' in 1946. 2,500 years (YTC)	L,C,30
St. Nicholas	Icklesham	(3) largest 19' in 1946	L, C
St. Mary and St. Peter	Wilmington	22' in 1946	L,C
St. Mary Assumption			
& St. Nicholas	Etchingham	18' at 3' in 1897	L,C
St. Mary	Funtington	21' in 1946	C, 31
St. Mary Magdalene	Bersted	900 years	C
	WILTSHIRE		
St. John the Baptist	Tisbury	32' in 1959	
		4,000 years (YTC)	S,L,C,B,W,G,32
	WORCESTERSHIRE		
St. James	Staunton	33' in 1946	L,C
St. Michael	Bockleton	21' in 1946	C
St. Bartholomew	Tardebigge	(2) largest 18' 6" in 1897	L,C,33
St. Leonard	Ribbesford	(2) largest 17' in 1897	S,L,C
	YORKSHIRE		
Fountains Abbey	Ripon	26' 6" in 1897. Gone	S,L

NOTABLE ENGLISH TOPIARY AND HEDGES ARRANGED BY COUNTY

There are many fine examples of topiary and hedges in Britain, mainly in England where they were integral components of formal gardens. I have assembled a list from a variety of authorities as cited below. This list in by no means exhaustive, but from afar I am fairly certain that the following ornamental yews continue to delight.

NAME	TOWN	TYPE	REFERENCE
	LONDON		
Hampton Court Palace	London	H and T*	A,B, L,C,Be**
	BUCKINGHAMSHIRE		
Chenies Manor		H and T	A
Dorney Court	Dorney	H and T	A
Waddesdon Manor	Aylesbury	H	A
Chicheley Hall	Newport Pagnell	H	A
	CUMBRIA		
Levens Hall	Kendal	T	A,B,Be, L,T,W
	DERBYSHIRE		
	Darby-in-the-Dale	H	A
Risley Hall		H, (2) doves	T
Chatsworth	Bakewell	H	A
	DEVONSHIRE		
Bickleigh Castle	Tiverton	H and T	A
Cadhay House	Ottery St. Mary	H	A
Knighthayes Court	Tiverton	H	A,H
Tapely Park	Instow	H	A
Castle Drogo		H	H
Coryton Park	Coryton	H	L
Dartington Hall	Dartington	T	A,H
	GLOUCESTERSHIRE		
Hidcote Manor	Chipping Campden	H	A,H
Westbury Court Garden	Westbury-on-Severn	H	A
Sudeley Castle	Winchcombe	H	A,Be
St. Mary Virgin	Painswick	99 clipped yews	L
Rodmarton Manor Gdn.	Cirencester	H and T	A

*H – hedge; T – topiary.
**A – Alcock; B – Beaumont; Be – Berral; C – Cecil; H – Hartzell & Rust; Hu – Hunt & Willis; L – Lowe; T – Thomas; W – Wright.

NAME	TOWN	TYPE	REFERENCE
	Cleeve Prior	T	L
Misarden Park Garden	Stroud	H and T	A,Hu
	HAMPSHIRE		
Highclere Castle	Newbury	T	Capability Brown
Jenkyn Place Garden	Bentley	H	A
	HEREFORDSHIRE		
Brobury Gdn. & Gallery	Brobury	H	A
Hill Court Gardens	Ross-on-Wye	H, Yew walk	A
	HERTFORDSHIRE		
	Ashridge	H	L
Hadham Palace	Hadham	H	L
	KENT		
Doddington Place Gdn.	Sittingbourne	H	A
Chartwell	Westerham	H	A
Penshurst Place	Tunbridge Wells	H	L
Mereworth Castle	Mereworth	H	H
Hever Castle and Gdns.	Edenbridge	T, maze	Be
	NORFOLK		
Blickling Hall	Aylsham	H and T	A
	OXFORDSHIRE		
Kingston Lisle Park	Wantage	T	A
	SHROPSHIRE		
Erbistock		H	C
Benthall Hall	Broseley	H and T	A
	SOMERSET		
Milton Lodge Garden	Wells	H	A
Montacute House	Yeovil	H and T	L,H
Midelney Manor	Drayton	T	A
Manor Cleeve		T	H
	SUFFOLK		
Helmingham Hall Gdn.	Ipswich	T	A
Ickworth	Suffolk		A
Nymans Garden	Handcross	H	A
	SUSSEX		
Bateman's	Burwash	H	A
Great Dixter	Northiam	T	Y
St. Mary's	Bramber	T	

NAME	TOWN	TYPE	REFERENCE
	WARWICKSHIRE		
Warwick Castle	Warwick	H	A,H
Compton Wynyates	Warwick	T, Chessboard	A,Be
	Bilton	H	L
Packwood House	Hockley Heath	T, Apostles	A,L,T,H
New place	Stratford-upon-Avon	T	S, H
Wightwick Manor	Wolverhampton	T	A,H
	WILTSHIRE		
Helmarton Lodge	Calne	H	L
Avebury Manor	Avebury	T	A
	WORCESTERSHIRE		
St. Michael	South Littleton	H	C
	Holme Lacy, Worcester	H	L

YEW SPECIES AND CULTIVARS

There are many cultivars of yew that have been developed for special characteristics: ornamental column beside the door, lush hedges of any height and a multitude of variation in coloration. For the following list I am indebted to P. Den Ouden and B. K. Boom who supplied the bulk of it in his *Manual of Cultivated Conifers* and to Murray Hornibrook for many additions. Once again the list is not exhaustive but does provide a broad survey of the types of Taxus available.

T. BACCATA*	European Yew.
T. baccata adpressa	A shrub with short leaves that spread in all directions.
T. b. adpressa aurea	Female with golden-yellow leaves at the tips and edges, which turn green in the second year.
T. b. adpressa erecta	Female with leaves green on top and light green beneath.
T. b. adpressa pendula	Long slender branches.
T. b. adpressa pyramidalis	Like erecta, upright branches.
T. b. adpressa variegata	Slender branches, leaves variegated yellow and gold.
T. b. albo-variegata	Clusters of white leaves grow in with the normal green foliage.
T. b. aldenhamensis	Brilliant variegated leaves.
T. b. amersfoort	Pyramidal shrub, leaves dark green on top, pale green beneath.
T. b. aurea	Both male and female; young leaves are often gold colored.
T. b. aureovariegata	Golden leaves.
T. b. backhousii	Crowded branchlets, leaves dull green on top and dull light green beneath.
T. b. barronii*	Rich orange shoots, leaves change to a coppery color with age.
T. b. beteramsii	Columnar shrub, young branches white then change to dark green with age.
T. b. brevifolia	Small bush with short dense branchlets and dense leaves which turn copper colored in winter.
T. b. buxtonensis	Dwarf shrub, leaves dark green on top and light green beneath.
T. b. cappenberg	Compact bush, short glossy green leaves.
T. b. carona	Broad bush.

* These species, the only ones tested to date, have been found to contain taxol or convertible taxanes.

T. b. cavendishii	Dwarf prostrate shrub, leaves blue-green on top and light green beneath.
T. b. cheshuntensis	A low-growing form. Discovered in 1862.
T. b. columnaris	Leaves variegated green with gold edges.
T. b. compacta	Dwarf, compact, conical bush; sickle-shaped leaves shiny green on top, duller beneath; since 1910.
T. b. compressa	Dwarf compact conical, short pale green leaves.
T. b. conica	Pyramidal shape.
T. b. contorta	Contorted branches, branchlets and leaves.
T. b. contortifolia	Crumpled leaves.
T. b. crowderi	Pyramidal compact.
T. b. davidiana	Fastigate, leaves yellow.
T. b. davisi	Conical, erect branchlets, crowded thin green leaves.
T. b. decora	Dwarf prostrate shrub, leaves dark green on top and light green beneath, turning to copper in winter.
T. b. dovastonia	Pendulous candelabra branches, black-green leaves.
T. b. dovastonia aurea	Pendulous candelabra branches, leaves golden on top and yellow-green beneath.
T. b. dwarf white	Drooping branchlets, leaves have white tinge in springtime.
T. b. elegantissima	Wide-spreading shrub with horizontal branches; leaves striped white and green.
T. b. Elvastonensis	Pyramidal shrub, orange branchlets, leaves golden yellow or orange in winter.
T. b. epacrioides	Dwarf shrub, slender curved branchlets; narrow, dull-green leaves.
T. b. erecta	Broad shrub, raised from seed of Irish yew.
T. b. erecta aurea	Broad shrub, golden leaves.
T. b. erecta aureovariegata	Broad shrub, leaves variegated green and gold.
T. b. ericoides	Dwarf spreading shrub; small leaves are bronze to purple in winter; three feet high.
T. b. expansa	Dwarf, bushy, large leaves, dark green on top and light green underneath.
T. b. fastigiata*	Irish yew
T. b. fastigiata aurea	Golden Irish yew.
T. b. fastigiata aureomarginata	Male Irish yew, new leaves edged with bright yellow on top.
T. b. fastigiata aureovariegata	Irish yew, leaves golden variegated.
T. b. fastigiata nova	Narrow growing Irish yew, fast growing.
T. b. fastigiata robusta	Irish yew, light green spreading leaves.
T. b. fastigiata variegata	Irish yew leaves variegated white and green.
T. b. fastigiata viridis*	Irish yew, densely set soft leaves, shiny green on top

	and pale green beneath.
T. b. fisheri	Spreading shrub with no dominant leader; some leaves green, some yellow.
T. b. fructoluteo	Yellow aril.
T. b. glauca	Robust shrub, blue green leaves.
T. b. gracilis pendula	Robust shrub, distinct erect leader.
T. b. handsworthiana	Upright form, leaves dark green on top and light green beneath.
T. b. hessei	Upright form, dense branches, leaves dark green on top and light green beneath.
T. b. horizontalis	Tree form with tiered, horizontal, wide-spreading branches; no leader.
T. b. horizontalis elegantissima	Tree form with horizontal branches, leaves golden when young.
T. b. imperialis	Erect compact shrub with ascending branches, thin dark green leaves.
T. b. intermedia	Candelabra branches, leaves green with a reddish point.
T. b. jacksonii	Horizontal, pendulous branches with shiny light green leaves.
T. b. kadett	Pyramidal shape, upright branchlets, thin dark green leaves.
T. b. knirps	Dwarf, irregular bush; narrow, dark green leaves.
T. b. laevigata	Golden variegated leaves.
T. b. linearis	Long spreading branches, long narrow yellow-green leaves.
T. b. longifolia	Pyramidal form, leaves yellow-green.
T. b. lutea	Broad shrub, light yellow aril, dark green leaves; since 1817.
T. b. macnabiana	Ascending form, dense foliage.
T. b. macrocarpa	Yellow aril.
T. b. michelii	Broad shrub, dark green leaves.
T. b. miniata	Dwarf, short leaves are scarce.
T. b. moll	Dwarf, short leaves are scarce.
T. b. monstrosa	Spreading branches, fastigate leaves.
T. b. nana	Dwarf, wide-spreading shrub; short dark green leaves; under six feet tall.
T. b. nidpathensis	Columnar shape with vigorous ascending branches; dark green leaves.
T. b. nigra	Upright form, black-green leaves.
T. b. nutans	Dwarf bush with sparse ascending branches; leaves dark green on top and pale green beneath.
T. b. overeynderi	Broad, pyramidal shrub, leaves green on top and dull green beneath.

T. b. page	Small, neat, dense variety, light green leaves.
T. b. parvula	Dwarf shrub, branches spread horizontally, long narrow leaves.
T. b. paulina	Dwarf conical bush, leaves dark green to bronze-brown.
T. b. pendula	Pendulous branches, green leaves.
T. b. pendula graciosa	Pendulous branches, long contorted branchlets
T. b. pendula variegata	Pendulous branches, variegated leaves.
T. b. praesident	Broad bush, stout dark green leaves.
T. b. procumbens	Broad bush, branches at right angle to stem, bright green leaves.
T. b. prostrata	Dwarf ground-hugging bush.
T. b. pseudoprocumbens	Dwarf shrub, long thick branches, long light green leaves.
T. b. pumila aurea	Dwarf bush, golden yellow leaves.
T. b. pygmatea	Dwarf conical bush, leaves shiny light green; smallest of the yews.
T. b. pyramidalis	Pyramidal form, erect branches, crowded leaves.
T. b. pyramidalis aureomarginata	Pyramidal form, erect branches, crowded leaves with yellow margins.
T. b. pyramidalis variegata	Pyramidal form, leaves golden variegated.
T. b. recurvata	Wide spreading branches, recurved leaves.
T. b. regent	Broad bush, fine dark green leaves.
T. b. repandens*	Dwarf spreading bush, flat sickle-shaped leaves blue-green on top, dull green beneath.
T. b. repandens aurea	A variant with golden-yellow leaves.
T. b. semperaurea	Male shrub, crowded branchlets, short yellow-brown leaves.
T. b. severin	Pyramidal form, dark green leaves.
T. b. sieboldii	Broad female shrub.
T. b. silver green	Compact bushy form, leaves deep green with a silver sheen.
T. b. standishii	Compact fastigate, leaves golden on top and yellow beneath.
T. b. thomsen	Broad pyramidal form, dark green leaves.
T. b. variegata	Large shrub, leaves green with white borders.
T. b. washingtonii	Loose broad shrub, short branchlets, yellow-green leaves.
T. b. william barron	Pyramidal compact form, long pointed orange leaves.
T. b. wintonensis	Dwarf upright form.
T. BREVIFOLIA*	Pacific yew, tree or bush form, yellow-green leaves.
T. CANADENSIS*	Canadian yew, low-growing shrub, leaves with a reddish tinge.

T. c. aurea	Low-growing bush; leaves striped with yellow.
T. c. pyramidalis	Bush with stiff, upright branches.
T. CHINENSIS*	Chinese yew, tree or shrub, leaves dark green on top and gray-green beneath.
T. CUSPIDATA*	Japanese yew, tree and shrub form, lustrous green leaves.
T. c. aurescens	Compact shrub, leaves deep yellow changing to green with age.
T. c. brevifolia	Forms a tall hedge.
T. c. brevifolia compacta	Forms a dwarf hedge.
T. c. brownii	Forms a low, dense hedge.
T. c. canadensis stricta	Forms a low, dense hedge.
T. c. capitata*	Upright form, green leaves.
T. c. columnaris	Dwarf, columnar form, dark green leaves.
T. c. contorta	Dwarf shrub, contorted branchlets.
T. c. densa	Dwarf shrub, crowded branches, leaves dark green; less than four feet tall.
T. c. densiformis	Forms a low, dense hedge.
T. c. erecta	Upright form, dense green leaves.
T. c. expansa	Broad shrub with wide-spreading, ascending branches, dark green leaves.
T. c. hatfieldii	Forms a tall hedge; good for topiary.
T. c. intermedia	Dwarf shrub, densely set deep green leaves; American clone.
T. c. latifolia	Bushy shrub, dense green leaves.
T. c. luteobaccata	Yellow aril.
T. c. minima	Dwarf shrub, dark green leaves; less than eight inches tall.
T. c. nana*	Dwarf, wide-spreading shrub, leaves light green on top and dark green beneath; less than six feet tall.
T. c. ovata	Female upright bush, vertical branches, dark green leaves.
T. c. prostrata	Male low-growing shrub, horizontal branches, dark green leaves on top, olive green beneath; origin in Connecticut.
T. c. pygmaea	Miniature shrub, erect branches and branchlets, short leaves.
T. c. pyramidalis	Pyramidal shape, dark green leaves.
T. c. robusta	Narrow upright form, dark green leaves.
T. c. stovekenii	Male, pyramidal shape, leaves glossy dark green on top, green beneath.
T. c. thayerae	Wide-spreading, low-growing female with leafy branches; light green leaves.

T. FLORIDANA*	Florida yew, small tree or shrub form, sickle shaped dark green leaves.
T. hunnewelliana	*Hybrid* – T. cuspidata and T. canadensis; leaves yellow-green with reddish tinge in winter.
T. media*	*Hybrid* – T. cuspidata and T. baccata; broad pyramidal shape, olive colored branchlets, leaves lustrous green on top and pale green beneath.
T. m. andora	Conical bush with fastigate branches; green leaves on top, olive-green underneath.
T. m. anthony wayne	Narrow pyramidal form, yellow-green leaves.
T. m. brevicata	Male, spreading compact form.
T. m. brownii	Compact, broad columnar male, sickle-shaped dark green leaves.
T. m. cliftonii	Female bush form, short bright green twigs.
T. m. cole	Conical bush, dark green leaves.
T. m. densiformis*	Dense shrub, bright green leaves.
T. m. dutweilleri	Irregular bush, dark green leaves.
T. m. farmen	Smaller than T. cuspidata, sickle-shaped dark green leaves.
T. m. halloriana	Broad compact bush, erect branches and branchlets, short densely set dark green leaves.
T. m. hatfieldii	Compact, conical shrub, erect branches, dark green leaves.
T. m. henryi	Shrub form.
T. m. hicksii*	Columnar shaped bush, leaves dark green on top, light green with dark green margins beneath.
T. m. kelseyi	Female, compact tall bush, densely set dark green leaves on top, light green beneath.
T. m. nanagrand	Narrow leaves.
T. m. nidiformis	Compact with horizontal branches, dark green leaves.
T. m. nigra	Compact bush with exceptionally dark green leaves.
T. m. pyramidalis	Forms a tall hedge.
T. m. robusta	Female; erect bush with curved dark green leaves.
T. m. skalborg	Dense compact form, short sickle-shaped green leaves.
T. m. stovekeni	Broad, columnar shrub; red-orange leaders.
T. m. thayerae	Broad shrub, horizontal branches, lustrous green leaves; forms a tall hedge.
T. m. vermeuleni	Dense, columnar shape; straight leaves glossy green on top and gray beneath.
T. m. wardii	Fine dark green leaves.
T. m. wellesleyana	Male columnar in shape, olive-green branches, dark green leaves.
T. SUMATRANA*	Southeast Asian Yew.
T. WALLICHIANA*	Himalayan Yew.

CHAPTER NOTES

CHAPTER ONE

1. From text of plaque in Fortingall Church.
2. Dr. Neill in the Edinburgh Philosophical Journal 1833, as cited in *A History of British Forest-Trees, Indigenous and Introduced* (London: John Van Voorst, 1842), p. 379.
3. *Trees of the British Isles in History and Legend* (London: Frederick Muller Ltd., 1972), p. 101. (Wilks)
4. William Dallimore, *Holly, Yew and Box* (London: John Lane, 1908), p. 187.
5. John Lowe, *The Yew-Trees of Great Britain and Ireland* (London: MacMillan and Company Ltd., 1897) p. 85.
6. As cited in D. Voliotis, 'Historical and Environmental Significance of the Yew (Taxus Baccata L.)' *Israel Journal of Botany*, 35, 1986, p. 4.
7. Plinie XVI. x.
8. As cited in Voliotis, p. 47.
9. *The White Goddess* (New York: Farrar, Straus and Giroux, 1948), p. 26. (Graves *Goddess*)
10. From 'The Madness of Suibne' as cited in Graves, p. 451.
11. From 'The Madness of Suibne' as cited in Graves, p. 453.
12. From an old English folk saying as cited in Graves, p. 268.
13. Charles Coltman Rogers *Conifers and Their Characteristics* (London: John Murray, 1920), p. 257.
14. Seamus MacManus, *The Story of the Irish Race* 2nd. ed., Vol. 2, 1921, p. 22.
15. Jonathan Bell in *A Social History of Ireland*, ed. P.W. Joyce, 2nd ed. v. 2 (Dublin: Gresham, 1910), pp. 287, 311.
16. Jennifer Westwood *Albion: A Guide to Legendary Britain* (London: Granada Publishing, 1985), p. 256.
17. Graves *Goddess*, p. 194.
18. *Iliad* xiii. 746.
19. *Georgics* ii. 48.
20. *Aeneid* Lib. xi.
21. Prologue to *Canterbury Tales* lines 103-8.
22. 'Robin and the Monk' ver. 86 in *A Selection of Traditional British Ballads* ed. B.J. Whiting (New York: Appleton Century Crofts, 1955), p. 110.
23. *Foresters*
24. L. C. Wimberly 'Death and Burial Lore in the English and Scottish Popular Ballads' no. 8 in *University of Nebraska Studies In Language, Literature, and Criticism* (Lincoln: University of Nebraska, 1927), p. 126.
25. As cited in Charles M. Skinner *Myths and Legends of Flowers, Trees, Fruits and Plants* (London and Philadelphia: J.B. Lippincott Company, 1911), p. 300.
26. Wilks, p. 245.
27. Dallimore, p. 181-2.
28. As cited in Dallimore, p. 168.
29. *Georgics* iv. As cited in Lowe, p. 155.
30. Plinie XVI. x.
31. As cited in Lowe, p. 136.

CHAPTER TWO

1. Graves *Goddess*, p. 193.
2. Graves *Goddess*, p. 193.
3. *The Oxford Companion to Classical Literature* ed. Sir Paul Harvey (Oxford: Clarendon Press, 1962), pp. 195-6.
4. Robert Graves *The Greek Myths* revised (Harmondsworth: Penguin Books Ltd., 1960), p. 125. (Graves *Myths*)
5. 'The Yew,' *House and Garden*, Jan. 1923, p. 102.
6. J.A. MacCulloch *The Religion of the Ancient Celts* (Edinburgh: T. and T. Clark, 1911), p. 198.
7. MacCulloch, p. 202.
8. MacCulloch, pp. 201-2.
9. VI. xxxi. Cited in Lowe, p. 136.
10. Henri Hubert *The History of Civilization: The Rise of the Celts* (NY: Dorset Press, 1988), p. 125.
11. As cited in Graves *Goddess*, p. 304.
12. As cited in Dallimore, p. 164-5.
13. As cited in Leo Grinden *Trees of Old England* (London: n.p., 1868), p. 68.
14. Stuart Piggott *The Druids* (New York: Thames and Hudson Inc., 1987), p. 80.
15. Piggott, p. 80.
16. MacCulloch, p. 201.
17. MacCulloch, pp. 201-2.
18. Patricia Monaghan *Book of Goddesses and Heroines* (New York: Dutton, 1981), p. 108.
19. MacCulloch, p. 203.
20. Eugene O'Curry *On the Manners and Customs of the Ancient Irish* v. 2 (London: Williams and Norgate, 1973), p. 194.
21. From Collinson 'History of Somerset.' As cited in *Oral Folk-Tales of Wessex* ed. Kingsley Palmer (Newton Abbot: David and Charles ltd., 1973), p. 61. (Palmer)
22. Marjorie Rowling *The Folklore of the Lake District* (Totowa: Rowman & Little Field, 1976), p. 137.
23. Susan Drury 'Customs and Beliefs Associated with Christmas Evergreens,' *Folklore*, 98 no. 2 (1987), p. 196.
24. Drury, p. 195.
25. Dallimore, pp. 169-70.
26. *Man, Myth and Magic* ed. Richard Cavendish (New York: M. Cavendish, 1970), p. 3070. (Cavendish)
27. Cavendish, p. 3070.
28. Rowling, p. 96.
29. Letter received from Rev. J.G. Collins, Aug. 1, 1990.
30. From O'Keefe 'Recollections.' As cited in Lowe, p. 106.
31. *Arbres Remarquables de Belgique* (Brabant: Administration des Eaux et Forets, n.d.) p. 226.
32. Letter received from Kristina Lindell, March 12, 1990.
33. Letter received from Pete Oppliger, June 11, 1990.
34. K. Partsch 'Wurde der alteste Baum Deutschlands entdeckt?' *Mitteilungen der Deutschen Dendrologischen Gesellschaft* 69 (Stuttgart: Ulmer, 1977), pp. 7-9.
35. *Handworterbuch Des Deutschen Aberglaubens* Band II (Berlin: Walter De Gruyter and Co., 1930), p. 1467.
36. Interview with Sabina Wilke.
37. 'Die Eibe - charakteristischer Waldbaum des Werralandes,' p. 152. ('Die Eibe')
38. *Deutschen Aberglaubens*, p. 1100.
39. 'Die Eibe,' p. 153.
40. From *The Elder Edda: A Selection* trans. W. H. Auden (NY: Vintage Books, 1970), p. 62.
41. Graves *Goddess*, p. 165.
42. Graves *Myths* p. 183-4 and Graves *Goddess*, p. 194.
43. Graves *Goddess*, p. 198.
44. Graves *Goddess*, p. 457.
45. Lowe, p. 137.
46. Lowe, p. 22.

CHAPTER THREE

1. Lowe, p. 111.
2. Lowe, p. 111.
3. Wilks, p. 102.
4. *Trees and Shrubs Hardy in the British Isles* (London: John Murray Ltd., 1970), pp. 561-2. (Bean)
5. Lowe, pp. 33-4.
6. Letter received from P.E. Norton, November 4, 1990.
7. Gibbon ch. lix.
8. Lowe, p. 113.
9. Lowe, p. 85.
10. *The Romance of Our Trees* (Garden City: Doubleday, Page and Company, 1920), p. 102. (Wilson *Trees*)
11. From an untitled poem by Fitzgerald as cited in Lowe, p. 181 and Dallimore, pp. 187-8.
12. Dallimore, p. 180.
13. Dallimore, p. 179.
14. Lowe, pp. 118-9.
15. Lowe, p. 121.
16. Hal Hartzell and Jerry Rust *Yew* (Eugene: Hartzell and Rust, 1983) p. 84.
17. Dallimore, p. 178.
18. Dallimore, p. 176.
19. Lowe, p. 120.
20. *Chronicles*. Cited in Lowe, p. 116.
21. Dallimore, p. 178.
22. Dallimore, p. 182.
23. Lowe, p. 105.
24. *Henry V* III, i, 25-36.
25. Roger Ascham *Toxophilus, The Schoole of Shooting* 1545. As cited in Dallimore, p. 178.
26. Ascham. Cited in Dallimore, p.178.
27. Lowe, p. 121.
28. Lowe, p. 121.
29. Fitzgerald as cited in Lowe, p. 181 and Dallimore, pp. 187-8.
30. Richard Williamson *The Great Yew Forest* (London: MacMillan London Ltd., 1978), p. 40.
31. Lowe, p. 122.
32. Ascham. Cited in Dallimore, p.177.
33. Ascham. Cited in Lowe, pp. 131-2.
34. Margaret Rule 'Mary Rose' *National Geographic* 163, May 1983, p. 654.
35. Rule, p. 664.
36. Rule, pp. 665-7.
37. As cited in Lowe, p. 122.
38. As cited in Williamson, p. 40.
39. Lowe, p. 125.
40. Lowe, p. 130.
41. Lowe, p. 103.
42. A. Czartoryski 'Yew in the Past,' *Cis Pospolity* vol. 3, ed. Stefan Bialobak (Kornik: Polish Academy of Sciences Institute of Dendrology, 1975), p. 113 and Robert Lundberg interviewed by David Heine, Jan. 1991.
43. From Stowe's *Survey of London*, 1598. As cited in Lowe p. 128.
44. Letter received from Rev. G.B. Waghorn, March 22, 1990.

CHAPTER FOUR

1. Louis Emberger *Les Plantes Fossiles* (Paris: Masson and Cie, '68), p583.
2. Emberger, p. 583.
3. A. Srodon 'History of the Yew in Poland,' *Cis Pospolity*, pp. 5-12 and S. Krol 'An Outline of Ecology,' *Cis Pospolity*, p. 75.
4. *Ancient Woodland: Its History, Vegetation and Uses in England* (London: Edward Arnold Ltd., 1980), p. 103.
5. Srodon, pp. 7-9.
6. W. Bugala 'Systematics and Variability,' *Cis Pospolity*, p. 15.
7. Charles Bolsinger and Annabelle E. Jaramillo 'Taxus Brevifolia Nutt. Pacific Yew,' *Silvics of Forest Trees of North America* (rev.), (Portland: Pacific Northwest Research Station, 1990), p. 17.
8. Voliotis, p. 48.
9. As cited in L. Pammel *A Manual of Poisonous Plants* (Cedar Rapids: The Torch Press, 1911), p. 328.
10. James Duke *Handbook of North-eastern Indian Medicinal Plants* (Lincoln: Quarterman Publications Inc., 1986), p. 156.

11. Robert K. Godfrey *Trees, Shrubs and Woody Vines of Northern Florida and Adjacent Georgia and Alabama* (Athens: University of Georgia Press, 1988), p. 59.
12. Keith Rushforth *Gazeteer of Conifers* (New York: Facts on File Inc., 1987) p. 207.
13. E.H. Wilson 'Low-Growing Conifers,' *House and Garden* 49 (Feb. 1926), p. 150. (Wilson 'Conifers')
14. Wilson 'Conifers,' p. 150.
15. *Flora of the U.S.S.R.* ed. V.L. Komarov (Leningrad: Izdatel'stvo Akademii Nauk SSSR, 1934) trans. (Jerusalem: Israel Program for Scientific Translations, '68), p. 103.
16. E. H. Wilson *The Conifers and Taxads of Japan* (Cambridge: Cambridge University Press, '16), p. 12,
17. Mark Silber 'Yews In Fiction and Fact' *Arnoldia* 30, no. 4, (July 15, 1970) p. 145.
18. Wilson *Trees*, p. 111.
19. James Duke 'Medicinal Plants of China' *Medicinal Plants of the World* no. 4 (Algonac: Reference Publications Inc., 1985), p. 619.
20. Edward Roark 'Yew for You' *Better Homes and Gardens* 15 (April 1937), p. 68-9.
21. Hui-Lin Li *Woody Flora of Taiwan* (Narberth: Livingston Publishing Company, 1963), pp. 499-500.
22. John Silba *Phytologia Memoirs VIII: Encyclopaedia Coniferae* (Corvallis: Harold Moldenke, 1986), p. 207.
23. Silba, p. 207.
24. H. A. Rose 'Yew' *Folklore* vol. XIII (London: David Nutt, '02), p. 201
25. Lowe, p. 109.
26. As cited in Lowe, p. 98.
27. Rose in *Folklore*, p. 201.
28. Bugala, p. 26.
29. Czartoryski, p. 116.
30. S. Bialobak 'Possibilities of Yew Cultivation in an Environment Modified by Man' in *Cis Pospolity*, p. 148.

31. Czartoryski pp. 116-7 and Stanley Scher and Thomas Jimerson 'Does Fire Regime Determine the Distribution of Pacific Yew in Forested Watersheds?' *USDA Forest Service General Technical Report PSW-109*, 1989.
32. 'The Yew' *House and Garden* (Jan. 1923), p. 102. ('The Yew')
33. Wilson *Romance of Our Trees*, pp. 111-2.
34. Wilson 'Conifers,' p. 150.

CHAPTER FIVE

1. Bugala, p. 23.
2. Krol, p.75.
3. 'Die Eibe,' p. 152.
4. Partsch, pp. 7-9
5. Czartoryski, p. 113.
6. Krol, p. 75 & see Czartoryski's list of yew trees in Poland, pp. 123-36.
7. Bugala, p. 26.
8. *Mountain Flora of Greece* vol. 1 ed. Arne Strid (Cambridge: Cambridge University Press, 1986), p. 49.
9. Voliotis, p. 50
10. Lowe, pp. 22-3.
11. Bean, p. 561.
12. *The Concise Oxford Dictionary of English Place-Names* 4th edition, ed. Eilert Ekwall (Oxford: Clarendon Press, 1965), pp. 169-70, 267-8, 544-5 and Ruth Tittensor 'Ecological History of Yew Taxus Baccata L. in southern England' *Biological Conservation* no. 17 (1980), p. 252.
13. Ekwall, p. 545.
14. As cited in *Folklore* vol. XIII, p. 96.
15. Adrian Room *A Dictionary of Irish Place Names* (Belfast: n.p., 1986), pp. 14, 74-5, 86, 90, 93, 97, 119, 123-5, 127-8.
16. Henri Hubert *The History of Civilization: The Greatness and Decline of the Celts* (London: Constable, 1987), p. 125.
17. Gerald Wilkinson *Trees in the Wild: and Other Trees and Shrubs* (London: Stephen Hope Books Ltd., 1973), p. 71.

18. Miles Hadfield *Topiary and Ornamental Hedges: Their History and Cultivation* (London: Adam and Charles Black, 1971), p. 16.
19. Czartoryski, p. 112.
20. 'The Yew,' p, 102.
21. John Selby *A History of British Forest-Trees, Indigenous and Introduced* (London: John Van Voorst, 1942), pp. 370-1.
22. 'Yew Wood' *Folklore* XIII, p. 96.
23. Withering *British Plants*, Selby *Forest Trees*, p. 71 and John Evelyn *Sylva* vol. I, p. 258. As cited in Lowe, p. 23.
24. Czartoryski, p. 112.
25. Voliotis, p. 47.
26. Lowe, p. 151.
27. Taylor *Medical Jurisprudence* 10th ed.. As cited in Lowe, p. 139.
28. *Medical and Philosophical Essays* 1774. As cited in Lowe, p. 142.
29. Phillip Miller *Gardener's Dictionary* 1807. Cited in Silber, p. 144.
30. As cited in Dallimore, p. 174.
31. *Cancer Treatment Reports* 60, no. 8, ed. Bruce Chabner (Washington: U.S. Department of Agriculture, Aug. 1976), p. 980.
32. John Evelyn, *Sylva*. As cited by Bean, p. 561.
33. Selby, pp. 363-4.
34. Dallimore, pp. 154-5.
35. W.H. Hudson *Nature in Downland* (London: J.M. Dent and Sons Ltd., 1923), p. 211.
36. Wilks, pp. 65-6.
37. Wilks, pp. 65-6.
38. Lowe, p. 83.
39. Williamson, p. 33.
40. Wilks, p. 65.
41. Wilks, p. 242.
42. Collinson, p. 79.
43. Walter Johnson *Folk-Memory: or, the Continuity of British Archaeology* (Oxford: Clarendon Press, 1908), n.p.
44. Hadfield, p. 17.
45. See Appendix no. 1.
46. Evelyn Cecil *A History of Garden-ing in England* (London: John Murray, 1910), pp. 105-6.
47. Wilson *Trees*, pp. 104-6.
48. Blomberg *The Formal Gardens of England* 1892. Cited in *Yew*, p. 106.
49. Blomberg. As cited in Yew, p. 106.
50. William Lawson. As cited in *Yew*, p.104.
51. Letter received from Mrs. J. Curry, Feb. 14, 1990.
52. Julia Berrall *The Garden: An Illustrated History* (New York: Viking Press, 1966), p. 250.
53. From *Remarks on Forest Scenery* 1791. As cited in Lowe p. 5.

CHAPTER SIX

1. Graves *Goddess*, p. 254.
2. Selby, p. 369.
3. As cited in Selby, p. 369.
4. As cited in Lowe, p. 98.
5. Dallimore, pp. 161-2.
6. W.H. Hudson. As cited in John Rodgers *The English Woodland* (London: B.T. Batsford Ltd., 1941), pp. 58-9 & *The Churchyard Yew and Immortality* (London: Frederick Muller Ltd., 1946), p. 14. (Cornish)
8. Wilks, p. 97.
9. Cornish, pp. 94-5.
10. Lowe, p. 95.
11. See Appendix no. 1.
12. Lowe, p. 43.
13. Letter received from A. R. Yarwood, March 7, 1990.
14. Wilks, p. 103.
15. As cited in Yarwood Letter.
16. As cited in Yarwood Letter.
17. As cited in Yarwood Letter.
18. Williamson, p. 36.
19. See Durley, Tisbury, Hope Bagot and Crowhurst (Surrey) yews.
20. Cornish, p. 19.
21. Lowe p. 85.
22. Bean, p. 562.
23. F.G.S. Thomas as cited in a letter received from Vicar George Royle, Nov. 8, 1990.

24. Cornish, p. 88.
25. Bean, p. 562.
26. As cited in Lowe, p. 251.
27. Letter received from Jill and Peter Drury, April 23, 1990.
28. Drury Letter.
29. As cited in Selby, p. 369.
30. *The Pattern of the Past* (Old Woking: Pitman Publishing, 1969), pp. 68-9. (Underwood)
31. Wilks, p. 243-4.
32. As cited in a letter received from R. MacDonnell, July 10, 1990.
33. Wilks, p. 244.
34. Underwood, pp. 68-9.
35. Letter received from Com. John Elgar, April 21, 1990.
36. Cornish, p. 52.
37. Letter received from E.A. Bateson, June 9, 1990.
38. Estyn Evans, *Prehistoric and Early Christian Ireland; A Guide* (London: B .T. Backsford, 1966), p.32
39. Dallimore, pp. 161-2.
40. Cornish, p. 31.
41. As cited in Lowe, p. 105.
42. Lowe, p. 212.
43. Graves, p. 56.
44. As cited in Graves, p. 43.

CHAPTER SEVEN

1. *Direction for Keeping Feasts All the Year*. As cited in Lowe, p. 100.
2. *Silva*. As cited in Charles Coltman Rogers *Conifers and Their Characteristics* (London: John Murray, 1920), p. 258.
3. V. i, pp. 276-80. As cited in Lowe, p. 99.
4. Selby, 369.
5. As cited in L.J.F. Brimble *Trees in Britain: Wild, Ornamental and Economic and Some Relatives in Other Lands* (London: MacMillan and Co. Ltd., 1948), p. 111.
6. As cited in Cornish, p. 42.
7. As cited in Dallimore, p. 163.
8. Dallimore, p. 163.
9. 'Yew Trees' *Atlantic Monthly* Jan.-June 1928, p. 715.
10. As cited in Lowe, pp. 109-10.
11. *The Magic Garden* (New York: Harper and Row, 1976), p. 70.
12. Cavendish, p. 3069.
13. Enid Porter *Cambridgeshire Customs and Folklore* (London: Routledge and Kegan Paul, 1969), p. 62.
14. Rowling, p. 96.
15. Cavendish, p. 3070.
16. Palmer, p. 56.
17. MacCulloch, p. 202.
18. From *Plant Lore*. As cited in Dallimore, p. 170.
19. Paul Sebillot *Le Folk-Lore De France: La Faune et La Flore* vol. 3 (Paris: Editions G.P. Maisonneuve et Larose, 1968), pp. 385-6.
20. Johnson, n.p.
21. Scott Cunningham *Encyclopedia of Magical Herbs* (St Paul: Llewellyn Publications, 1985), p. 228.
22. Cornish, p. 35.
23. Letter received from Mr. Ron George, March 29, 1990.
24. Wilks, p. 114.
25. Norton Letter.
26. Letter received from Canon Blake, March 5, 1990.
27. Letter recieved from E.H.T. Ridger, May 10, 1990.
28. As cited in Wilks, pp. 45-6.
29. Letter received from Rev. James Anderson, Aug. 14, 1990.
30. Anderson Letter.
31. Bean, p. 562.
32. Letter received from Pamela Cook, Aug. 22, 1990.
33. Lowe, pp. 11-12.
34. As cited in Waghorn Letter.
35. Bean, p. 562.
36. Letter received from Rev. C.W. Blissard-Barnes, March 12, 1990.
37. E.R.Yarham 'Churchyard Yews' *This England*, 1975, pp. 40.
38. Letter received from Rev. Hugh Pruen, March 24, 1990.
39. Letter received from Rev. G.C.H. Watson, April 6, 1990.
40. Roark, p. 68.

41. See Appendix no. 1.

CHAPTER EIGHT

1. As cited in Joseph Campbell *The Power of Myth* (New York: Doubleday, 1988), p. 34.
2. Ella Clark *Indians Legends of the Pacific Northwest* (Berkeley: University of California Press, 1969), pp. 146-7.
3. As cited in *Columbia University Contributions to Anthropology* vol. xxvi, p. 125.
4. Nancy Turner *Plants in British Columbia Indian Technology* (Victoria: British Columbia Provincial Museum, 1979), p. 118. (Turner *Plants*)
5. As cited in *Memoirs of American Museum of Natural History* v. iii, 1905, pp. 214-5.
6. Turner *Plants*, p. 120.
7. *Ethnobotany of the Hesquiat Indians of Vancouver Island* (Victoria: British Columbia Provincial Museum, 1982), p. 48. (Turner *Ethnobotany*).
8. Private communication.
9. Erna Gunther *Ethnobotany of Western Washington* revised (Seattle: University of Washington, 1973), p. 16 and Turner *Plants*, p. 120.
10. Duke *Northeast Indian Medicinal Plants*, p. 156.
11. Bolsinger, p. 14.
12. Gunther, p. 16.
13. Bolsinger, p. 14.
14. Gunther, p. 7.
15. Turner *Plants, p. 118* and Turner *Ethnobotany, p. 48*.
16. Turner *Plants*, p. 118.
17. Allen P. Slickpoo, Sr. *Noon Nee-Me-Poo (We, The Nez Perces) In All Ages and In All Climes* vol. 1 (Boulder: University of Colorado Press, 1973), p. 35.
18. Gunther, n.p.
19. Elizabeth Derr Jacobs *Nehalem*

Tilamook Tales (Eugene: Universtiy of Oregon Press, 1959), p. 149.
20. Bill Burwell interviewed by David Heine, Jan. 1991.
21. Charles Wilkes *Narrative of the United States Exploring Expeditions During the Years 1838–1842*, (Philadelphia: C. Sherman, 1894), Vol. 5 p 219.
22. Burwell Interview.
23. *History of Early Days in Oregon* (Riddle: The Riddle Enterprise, 1920) reprint 1968, p. 44.
24. See arrow with yew wood tip on cedar shaft at University of Oregon Museum of Natural History.
25. Riddle, p. 44-5.
26. R.F. Heizer and M.A. Whipple *The California Indians: A Source Book* (Berkeley: University of California Press, 1962), p. 16.
27. Kroeber, Theodora. *Ishi In Two Worlds; A Biography of the last Wild Indian in North America.* Berkeley: University of California Press, 1968. n.p.
28. Saxton T. Pope 'Yahi Archery' *University of California Publications in American Archaeology and Ethnology* vol. XIII (1917-23) ed. A.L. Kroeber (Berkeley: University of California Press, reprint 1965), p. 106.
29. Pope, pp. 105-8.
30. Pope, p. 110.
31. Gunther, p. 7.

CHAPTER NINE

1. *A Natural History of Western Trees* (Boston: Houghton Mifflin, 1953), p. 286.
2. Peattie, p. 285, Bolsinger, pp. 2-3 and George Sudworth *Forest Trees of the Pacific Slope* (Washington: Government Printing Office, 1908), p. 196-7.
3. Bolsinger, p. 3.
4. Bolsinger, p. 34.
5. Peattie, p. 286.

6. Peattie, p. 286.
7. Letter received from Brian O'Brian, Dec. 26, 1990.
8. Photo and Document from University of Idaho School of Forestry.
9. In 'Contributor's Comments' *Oregon Historical Journal* vol. 59 (Portland: Oregon Historical Society, 1958), p. 280.
10. Bolsinger, pp. 2-3.
11. O'Brian letter.
12. Don Adams interviewed by David Heine, April 1991.
13. Roark, p. 68.
14. Turner *Plants*, p. 120.
15. Chuck Edson *Oregon Reconnaissance Report: Taxus Brevifolia* (Corvallis: Chuck Edson, 1977), p. 6.
16. Ray Eller as cited in Lisa Strycker 'Cutting Trees to Cut Down Cancer' Eugene *The Register-Guard* June 3, 1987, pp. 1A, 4A. (Strycker 1987)
17. Lundberg Interview.
18. Don Adams as cited in Mike Thoele 'A Skill of Centuries Past Lives On' Eugene *The Register-Guard* Feb. 9, 1987, pp. 1A, 4A.
19. Adams in *The Register-Guard* Feb. 9, 1987, p. 4A.
20. Adams Interview.
21. Mike Heffley 'Wood of War and Music' *Northwest Magazine* Feb. 5, 1984, p. 13.
22. Bolsinger, p. 4.

CHAPTER TEN

1. *Cancer Treatment Reports* 60, no. 8, ed. Bruce Chabner (Washington: USDA, August, 1976), p. 3.
2. Bolsinger, p. 14.
3. Duke *China*, p. 619.
4. Dr. Matthew Suffness in Letter to Taxol Conference, June 1990.
5. Dr. Robert Holton in Letter to Commissioner Jerry Rust, May 11, 1987. (Holton 1987)
6. Suffness Letter.

7. Robert Holton in letter to Commissioner Jerry Rust, March 4, 1990. (Holton, 1990)
8. Dr. Robert Holton interviewed by David Heine, Oct. 1990. (Holton Interview)
9. Gina Kolata 'Tree Yields A Cancer Treatment, But Ecological Costs May Be High' *The New York Times* May 13, 1991, pp. A1. (Kolata *NYT*)
10. As cited in Kolata *NYT*, p. A9.
11. Marilyn Chase 'Cancer Drug Taxol May Work Better With Radiation' Washington *The Wall Street Journal* April 12, 1991, p. 43
12. Dr. Sterling Ainsworth, interviewed by David Heine, April 1991.
13. Marilyn Chase 'Cancer Drug May Save Many Human Lives - At Cost of Rare Trees' *The Wall Street Journal* April 9, 1991, p. A1. (Chase)
14. Jim Stiak 'Can Yew Be Saved' Eugene *What's Happening* Aug. 30, 1990, p. 25.
15. Stiak, p. 25.
16. Dr. Kenneth Snader in a Letter to Taxol Conference, June 1990.
17. Dr. Gordon Cragg as cited in Lisa Strycker 'Cancer Cure May Be in Common Yew' Eugene *The Register-Guard* April 1990, p. 1B. (Strycker 1987)
18. Kolata NYT, p. A1.
19. Tad Shannon 'Harvesting of Yew Forges Ahead' Eugene *The Register-Guard* Mar. 26, 1991, p. 2C. (Shannon 'Harvesting')
20. Dr. David Carver in Address to Native Yew Conservation Council (NYCC), Jan. 1991.
21. Pat Connolly as cited in Bolsinger, p. 16.
22. Data supplied by Oakridge Ranger District June 13, 1991 Yew Field Trip.
23. National Cancer Institute sources: Dr. Saul Shepartz in an interview

with David Heine, Jan. 1991 and Dr. Kenneth Snader in an Address to the NYCC April 1991.

24. Ray Eller as cited in Strycker 1987, p4A.

25. As cited in Paul Fattig 'Yew Tree's Bark Could Provide an Alternative to Chemotherapy' *The Seattle Times* Aug. 30, 1987, p. B10.

26. Patrick Connolly interviewed by Hal Hartzell, July 1990.

27. Shannon 'Harvesting' p. 2C.

28. Leverett Richards 'Attempts Under Way to Push Growth of Pacific Yew Tree' Portland *The Oregonian* May 30, 1991, p. E2. (Richards)

29. Snader Address and Shepartz Interview.

30. Strycker 1990, p. 1B. n.d.

31. As cited in Strycker 1990, p. 1B.

32. As cited in Shannon 'Harvesting', p. 2C.

33. Dr. Bruce Mannheim interviewed by David Heine, April 1991.

34. As cited in Harry Esteve 'Are Loggers Destroying A Lifesaver?' Eugene *The Register-Guard*, Aug. 22, 1990, p. 4A.

35. Dr. Charles Bolsinger interviewed by David Heine, Dec. 1990.

36. Bialobak, in *Cis Pospolity*, p. 3.

37. Krol, in *Cis Pospolity*, p. 75, 80-1.

38. Bolsinger Interview.

39. Stanley Scher and Thomas Jimerson 'Does Fire Regime Determine the Distribution of Pacific yew in Forested Watersheds?' *USDA Forest Service General Technical Report* PSW-109, n.p. (Scher)

40. Bolsinger, p. 15-6.

41. Dr. Koppaka Rao in an Address to the NYCC April 1991.

CHAPTER ELEVEN

1. As cited by Heffley, p. 13.

2. John Lowe (Deputy Forester for Region Six USFS) interviewed by David Heine, Jan. 1991.

3. As cited in Robert Sterling 'Timber Thieves Prey on Yew Trees' Medford *Mail Tribune* Sept. 5, 1990, p. 4A.

4. As cited in Shannon 'Harvesting,' p. 2C.

5. Lowe Interview.

6. Sherri Richardson 'Pacific Yew: A Miracle Cancer Cure?' in *Pacific Northwest Station Report* (Portland: Pacific Northwest Station, 1991), p. 12.

7. Jim Weir in an Address to the NYCC April 1991.

8. Chase *WSJ* April 12, 1991, p. 1.

9. Mannheim Interview.

10. Willamette N.F. Press Release June 13, 1991 Yew Field Trip.

11. David Barton interviewed by Hal Hartzell, June 1991.

12. Lowe Interview.

13. Commissioner Jerry Rust interviewed by Hal Hartzell, June '91.

14. As cited in 'Combing the Earth for Cures to Cancer, AIDS' *Science* vol. 237, (Aug. 1987), p. 28.

15. Weir Address.

16. Shepartz Interview.

17. Dr. Kenneth Snader in Ammendments to Report of NYCC June 14, 1991, pp. 10-11.

18. Holton Interview.

20. Mannheim Interview.

21. Tad Shannon 'Commissioner Battling to Restrict Yew Harvests' Eugene *The Register-Guard* Mar. 26, 1991, p. 2C.

22. Adams Interview.

23. 'Yew Group Statement' from first meeting of NYCC July 1990.

24. Rust Interview.

25. Dale Robertson (Forest Service Chief) in a letter to the NYCC October 1990.

26. Lowe Interview.

27. Lowe Interview.

28. Bristol-Myers Squibb Handout at Portland Press Conference, June 19, 1991.

29. Mannheim Interview.

30. Barton Interview.
31. Nancy Tarascio 'Federal Yew Bark Contract Chops Out County Jobs' Roseburg *The News Review* April 26, 1991, pp. 1, 8.
32. Information provided by Forest Service on Yew Field Trip June 13, 1991.
33. Rust Interview.
34. Kathleen Monje 'Yew Deal Spurs Call for Probe' Portland *The Oregonian* March 12, 1991, p. C1
35. As cited in Lance Robertson 'Harvest of Yew Trees Causing Forest Furor' Eugene *The Register-Guard* May 12, 1991, p. 4A.
36. Chase *WSJ* April 12, 1991, p. 1.
37. Rust Interview.

CHAPTER TWELVE

1. Ainsworth Interview.
2. Rust Interview.
3. Selby, pp. 367-8.
4. Steven W. Deitemeyer in letter to Commissioner Rust, Feb. 9, 1990.
5. As cited in Gina Kolata 'Demand Growing for Drug from Yew' Portland *The Oregonian* May 30, 1991, p. 1E.
6. Dr. John Noel-Denis 'A Highly Efficient, Practical Approach to Natural Taxol' *Journal of the American Chemical Society* Aug. 1988, p. 5917. (Denis 1988)
7. Holton Letter 1990.
8. Dr. J.C. Linden in a letter to Commissioner Rust, Jan. 9, 1990.
9. 'Yew Tree's Bark May Hold Cure for Ovarian Cancer', n.d., AP New Orleans.
10. Dr. G. Kingston 'The Chemistry of Taxol, A Clinically Useful anticancer Agent' *Journal of Natural Products* Jan.-Feb. 1990, p. 2.
11. Dr. John Noel-Denis 'An Efficient Enantioselective Synthesis of the Taxol Side Chain' *The Journal of American Chemistry* Ja.1986, p46.
12. Denis 1988, p. 5917.

13. Compiled from various papers, letters and interviews including: Holton, Chabner, and Keith Witherup 'Taxus SPP. Needles Contain Amounts of Taxol Comparable to the Bark of Taxus Brevifolia: Analysis and Isolation' *Journal of Natural Products* vol. 53, no. 5, pp. 1249-55.
14. Holton Letter 1990.
15. Holton Interview.
16. Holton Letter.
17. Kingston, p. 3 and Holton Interview.
18. Neil Jans in an Address to the NYCC April 1991.
19. Dr. David Carver interviewed by David Heine, April 1991.
20. Richards, p. E2.
21. James Wheeler in letter to Taxol Conference June 1990.
22. As quoted in *Pacific Northwest Station Report*, p. 13.
23. Richards, p. E2.
24. Bristol-Myers Squibb Press Release, June 19, 1991.
25. Rust Interview.
26. Ainsworth Interview.
27. Allen Lacy 'Despite All the Pruning, Yews Remain Popular' *New York Times* Mar. 5, 1987, p. 21.
28. As cited in Chase, p. 1.
29. Dr. Ed Croom in letter to Taxol Conference June 1990.

CHAPTER THIRTEEN

1. *Knight's Tale* 2920-3.
2. *Romaunt of the Rose* lines 1383-87.
3. *The Complaint.*
4. *Solomon* I. 61-4.
5. *Yew Trees.*
6. Lowe p. 187.
7. *Lines: (Left Upon a Seat In a Yew-Tree...).*
8. *Lines: Composed While Climbing the Left Ascent of Brockley Coomb, Somersetshire, May 1795.*
9. *Rokeby.*

10. *In Memoriam* 2, 9-13.
11. *Endymion* IV. 670-4.
12. Untitled.
13. *Holy Grail* 13-15.
14. *In Memoriam* 39, 1-12.
15. *In Memoriam* 29, 13-6.
16. *Scholar Gypsy.*
17. *Love in the Valley.*
18. *Parliament of Fowles* 180.
19. *Faerie Queene* I. i. 76.
20. *Prosopopoia: or Mother Hubbard's Tale* 747
21. *Richard II* III. ii. 117-20.
22. *Hamlet* I. v. 61-70.
23. *To the Cambro Britains and Their Harp.*
24. No title. As cited in Lowe, p. 167.
25. *Endymion* Bk. I, 481-2.
26. No title. As cited in Lowe, dedication page.
27. *Maid's Tragedy.*
28. *Twelfth Night* II. iv. 55-6.
29. *Palomon and Arcite.*
30. *Epistle to Burlington.*
31. *IX Song* in *Poetical Sketches.*
32. *Ceremonies for Candlemass Eve.*
33. *To the Reverand Shade of His Religious Father.*
34. *Ode to Melancholy.*
35. *Ave Atque Vale: In Memory of Charles Baudelaire.*
36. *Macbeth* IV. i. 28-9.
37. *Romeo and Juliet* V. iii. 3-7.
38. *Nymphadia, The Court of the Fairy.*
39. *Similes for Two Political Characters - 1819.*
40. *Endymion* I. 731-3.
41. *Romeo and Juliet* V. iii. 137-9.
42. *Titus Andronicus* II. iii. 106-7.
43. *Elegy Written in a Country Churchyard.*
44. *The Grave.*
45. *Europe.*
46. *Reflections.*
47. *The White Devil.*
48. Anderson Letter.
49. R. Szaniawski 'An Outline of Yew Physiology' *Cis Pospolity*, p. 59.

CHAPTER FOURTEEN

1. *Baucis and Philomon.*
2. Wilks 242 and *Transformations.*
3. *Voices from Things Growing in a Churchyard.*
4. *Elegy to the Lady Jane Pawlett.*
5. *Night Piece on Death.*
6. *Yew-Trees.*
7. *Naturalist's Poetical Companion.*
8. *In Memoriam* 2, 1-16.
9. *Ode: Autumn.*
10. *Baile and Aillinn.*
11. MacCulloch, p. 198.
12. *Ribh at the Tomb of Baile and Aillinn.*
13. *Ash Wednesday* section IV.
14. *Ash Wednesday* section V.
15. Peter Ackroyd *T.S. Eliot: A Life* (New York: Simon and Schuster, 1984) p. 180.
16. *Ash Wednesday* section VI.
17. Ackroyd, p. 262.
18. *Burnt Norton* section II.
19. *Animula.*
20. *Burnt Norton* section IV.
21. *Wasteland* section I.
22. *Wasteland* section III.
23. *Burnt Norton* section V.
24. *East Coker* section I.
25. Ackroyd, pp. 239, 335.
26. *Dry Salvages* section V.
27. *Idle Verses.*
28. *New Sirens.*
29. *Requiescat.*
30. Ackroyd, p. 239.
31. *Little Gidding* section V.
32. *The Force That Through the Green Fuse Drives the Flower.*
33. *The Moon and the Yew Tree.*
34. *Little Fugue.*
35. Graves *Goddess*, p. 194-5.

BIBLIOGRAPHY

Bialobak, Stefan, ed. *Cis Pospolity.* vol. 3. Trans. H. Markiewicz. Kornik: Polish Academy of Sciences Institute of Dendrology, 1975.

Bolsinger, Charles L. and Annabelle E. Jaramillo. 'Taxus Brevifolia Nutt. Pacific Yew.' In *Silvics of Forest Trees of North America* (revised). Portland: Pacific Northwest Research Station, 1990.

_____ 'Distribution, Abundance and Stand Characteristics of Taxus Brevifolia. Presented at the Workshop on Taxol and Taxus: Current and Future Perspectives. Bethesda: National Cancer Institute, 1990.

Cornish, Vaughan. *The Churchyard Yew and Immortality.* London: Frederick Muller Ltd., 1946.

Dallimore, W. *Holly, Yew and Box.* London: John Lane, The Bodley Head, 1908.

_____ and A. Bruce Jackson. *A Handbook of Coniferae: Including Ginkoaceae.* 2nd ed. London: Edward Arnold and Co., 1931.

Davidson, John. *Conifers, Junipers and Yew: Gymnospems of British Columbia.* London: Bouverie House, 1927.

Den Ouden, P and Boom, B. K. *Manual of Cultivated Conifers.* The Hague: Martinus Nighoff, 1965.

Edson, Chuck. *Oregon Reconnaissance Report: Taxus Brevifolia.* Corvallis: Chuck Edson, 1977.

Graves, Robert. *The White Goddess.* New York: Farrar, Straus and Giroux, 1948.

Gunther, Erna. *Ethnobotany of Western Washington.* Seattle: University of Washington, 1939.

Hadfield, Miles. *Topiary and Ornamental Hedges: Their History and Cultivation.* London: Adam and Charles Black, 1971.

_____ 'Tree of War and Worship.' In *Country Life,* (November 21, 1957), 1086-87.

Hartzell Jr., Harold R. and Jerry Rust. *Yew.* Eugene: Hartzell and Rust, 1983.

Kingston, D. G. I and G. Samaranayahe, C. A. Ivey. 'The Chemistry of Taxol, A Clinically Useful Anticancer Agent.' *Journal of Natural Products,* Jan. Feb. 1990, p. 1-12.

Kroeber, A. L. ed. *University of California Publications in American Archaeology And Ethnology.* vol. 13. Berkeley: University of California Press, 1965.

Kroeber, Theodora. *Ishi In Two Worlds; A Biography of the last Wild Indian in North America.* Berkeley: University of California Press, 1968.

Little Jr., Elbert L. *Atlas of United States Trees: Conifers and Important Hardwoods.* Vol. 1. Washington: Government Printing Office, 1971.

Lowe, John. *The Yew-Trees of Great Britain and Ireland.* London: MacMillan and Company Ltd., 1897.

Manfredi, J.J. and S.B. Horwitz. 'Taxol: An Antimitotic Agent With a New Mechanism of Action.' *Pharmacology and Therapy*, vol. 25, pp. 83-125.

Miller, R.W. 'A Brief Survey of Taxus Alkaloids and Other Taxane Derivatives.' *Journal of Natural Products*, 34, (July-Aug.) 1980, pp. 425-37.

National Cancer Institute Workshop on Taxol and Taxus. *Current and Future Perspectives.* Bethesda: National Cancer Institute, 1990.

Peattie, Donald Culross. *A Natural History of Western Trees.* Boston: Houghton Mifflin, 1953.

Richardson, Sherri. *Pacific Yew: A Miracle Cancer Cure?* Portland: Pacific Northwest Station, 1991.

Scher, Stanley and Thomas M. Jimerson. 'Does Fire Regime Determine the Distribution of Pacific Yew in Forested Watersheds?' In *USDA Forest Service Gen. Tech. Rep.* PSW-109, 1989. n.p.

Schiff, P. B. and J. Fand and S. B. Horwitz. Promotion of Microtubule Assembly in vitro By Taxol.' *Nature*, 22 Feb. 1979, pp. 665-67.

Selby, John Prideaux. *A History of British Forest-Trees, Indigenous and Introduced.* London: John Van Voorst, 1842.

Silba, John. *Phytologia Memoirs VIII: Encyclopaedia Coniferae.* Corvallis: Harold N. Moldenke, et. al., 1986.

Silber, Mark. 'Yews in Fiction and Fact.' In *Arnoldia*, Vol. 30, No. 4, July 15, 1970, pp. 139-147.

Sudworth, George B. *Forest Trees of the Pacific Slope.* Washington: Government Printing Office, 1908.

Tittensor, Ruth M. 'Ecological History of Yew Taxus Baccata L. in Southern England.' In *Biological Conservation* No. 17. Barking: Applied Science Publishers Ltd., 1980, pp. 243-65.

Turner, Nancy J. *Plants in British Columbia Indian Technology.* Victoria: British Columbia Provincial Museum, 1979.

Voliotis, D. 'Historical and Environmental Significance of the Yew (Taxus Baccata L.). In *Israel Journal of Botany*, 35, 1986, pp. 47-52.

Wilson, Ernest Henry. *The Conifers and Taxads of Japan.* Cambridge: Cambridge University Press, 1916.

_____*The Romance of Our Trees.* Garden City: Doubleday, Page and Company, 1920.

Wilks, J. H. *Trees of the British Isles in History and Legend.* London: Frederick Muller Ltd., 1972.

Williamson, Richard. *The Great Yew Forest.* London: MacMillan London Ltd., 1978.

Witherup, Keith, et. al. 'Taxus Spp. Needles Contain Amounts of Taxol Comparable To the Bark of Taxus Brevifolia: Analysis and Isolation.' *Journal of Natural Products*, 53 (Sept.-Oct. 1990) no. 5, pp. 1249-55.

INDEX

TYPESET IN GAILLARD ROMAN AND GARAMOND ITALIC
PRINTED BY KOKE PRINTING COMPANY, EUGENE, OREGON